D1572413

Mathematical Models for Surface Water Hydrology

Proceedings of the Workshop held at the IBM Scientific Center, Pisa, Italy

Workshop on Mathematical Models in " Hydrology, Pisa, 1974.

Edited by

Tito A. Ciriani

IBM Scientific Center,
Pisa, Italy

Ugo Maione

Hydraulics Institute of the University of Pavia,
Italy

James R. Wallis

IBM Research Center,
Yorktown Heights, New York
USA

A Wiley—Interscience Publication

JOHN WILEY & SONS

London · New York · Sydney · Toronto

Library of Congress Cataloging in Publication Data:

Workshop on Mathematical Models in Hydrology, Pisa, 1974.
 Mathematical models for surface water hydrology.

 Workshop co-sponsored by the IBM Scientific Center,
Pisa, and the Hydraulics Institute of the University of Pavia.
 'A Wiley–Interscience publication.'
 1. Hydrology – Mathematical models – Congresses.
2. Hydrology – Computer programs – Congresses. 3. Floods –
Mathematical models – Congresses. I. Ciriani, Tito A.
II. Maione, Ugo. III. Wallis, James R. IV. Centri di ricerca
scientifica I.B.M. Centro di Pisa. V. Pavia. Università.
Instituto di idraulica. VI. Title.
GB656.2.M33W67 1974   551.4'8'0184   76-13457

ISBN 0 471 99400 6

Typeset in IBM Journal by Preface Ltd, Salisbury, Wilts
and printed in Great Britain by Unwin Brothers Ltd.,
The Gresham Press, Old Woking, Surrey

Contributing Authors

ROBIN T. CLARKE   *Institute of Hydrology, Wallingford, Oxon. UK*

JAMES C. I. DOOGE   *Department of Civil Engineering, University College, Dublin, Ireland*

GIOVANNA FINZI   *Electrotechnics and Electronics Institute, Milan Polytechnic, Italy*

MARIO GALLATI   *Hydraulics Institute, University of Pavia, Italy*

FRANCESCO GRECO   *IBM Scientific Center, Pisa, Italy*

UGO MAIONE   *Hydraulics Institute, University of Pavia, Italy*

SERGIO MARTELLI   *IBM Scientific Center, Pisa, Italy*

NICHOLAS C. MATALAS   *US Geological Survey, National Center, Reston, Va., USA*

CRISTINA MUGNAI   *Computer Science Institute, University of Pisa, Italy*

LUIGI NATALE   *Hydraulics Institute, University of Pavia, Italy*

PATRICK E. O'CONNELL   *Department of Civil Engineering, Imperial College, University of London, UK*

J. P. J. O'KANE   *Department of Civil Engineering, University College, Dublin, Ireland*

LORENZO PANATTONI   *IBM Scientific Center, Pisa, Italy*

EZIO TODINI   *IBM Scientific Center, Pisa, Italy*

JAMES R. WALLIS   *IBM Scientific Center, Pisa, while on leave from IBM Research Center, Yorktown Heights, New York, USA*

DAVID A. WOOLHISER   *US Department of Agriculture, Agricultural Research Service, CSU Foothills Campus, Fort Collins, Colorado, USA*

Preface

The contributions to this book were presented at the Workshop organized by the Scientific Center of IBM Italy, at Pisa, December 9–12, 1974.

Problems relative to synthetic hydrology and flood modelling are dealt with in Parts 1 and 2 to give the theoretical basis for the applications covered in Part 3 on computer programs.

Most of the material and applications presented in detail at the Workshop was based upon the current research being conducted by the IBM Scientific Center and the Hydraulics Institute of the University of Pavia.

Contents

PART 3. COMPUTER PROGRAMS

Introduction

The planning and management of water resource systems are dependent upon information relating to the spatial and temporal distributions of hydrologic phenomena. Hydrologic data bases are seldom large enough to provide for the extraction of precise information and, as a result, planning and management decisions are subject to hydrologic uncertainty in addition to uncertainties of a non-hydrologic nature. What information is relevant and how precise the information must be depends upon the specific objectives and purposes of water resource systems and upon the sensitivities of the planning and management decisions to the uncertainties in the hydrologic information.

More precise information can be extracted from more extensive data bases; however, it is often difficult to justify delays in decision making pending the acquisition of additional data because resulting benefits would have to be forgone. A more feasible course of action is to develop and use mathematical models of hydrologic processes in order to extrapolate and interpolate information over time and space. The models themselves do not assure that information generated at specific points in time and space is sufficiently precise. However, the models allow information to be generated instantaneously and objectively, and the models provide a quantitative measure of the quality of the generated information, as well as efficiency in the information generating process via the use of digital computers.

Although stimulated in large part by problems encountered in planning and management of water resource systems, model building at universities and research institutes has been to a large extent pursued independently of any specific planning or management activity. As a consequence, hydrologic models have in general not been judged in terms of their data, computer or expertise requirements, or whether or not their use leads to better management decisions. The technical evaluation of models has mostly been in terms of how well the models fit historic hydrologic data and thereby measure, or so it is hoped, the degree of our understanding of hydrologic processes. For example, the notion of using synthetic flows to facilitate planning of water resources development was formulated by the Harvard University Water Resources Program in the late 1950s and early 1960s. In the following years, synthetic hydrology has come to be recognized as a very useful and powerful planning tool, at least in the research community, yet its application has been sparse. And in the meantime, the models for generating synthetic flows have grown more and more complex as the modellers have attempted to match their output ever closer to hydrologic reality.

In addition, the last few decades have witnessed great increases in the scope and scale of the planning and management of water resource systems by government agencies, and this has led to a proliferation of mathematical models of hydrologic processes. For all hydrologic processes more than one model has been constructed as agencies have attempted to take advantage of the expanding national hydrologic data bases and advances in hydrologic research and computer technology.

Although the mathematical construct of an operational model is conditioned on the modellers' conceptual view as to the dynamics of a hydrologic process, the model's complexity is always limited by the size of the available data base, and frequently by computer and economic constraints. Regional data bases are of unequal spatial and temporal extent and quality and, as a result, difficulties are often encountered in estimating model parameters and in transferring the use of a model from one region to another or even from project to project within a region.

In summary, the building of models has outpaced their use in specific water resource planning and management activities. The lag in the use of specific models may be attributed to many factors, among them being that planners and managers are unaware of recent developments in mathematical models, reluctant to use more sophisticated models when simpler ones seemingly suffice, or lack understanding of and competence in the use of advanced models. On the other hand, model builders have not always understood the problems faced by planners and managers, and have not in general constructed their models in ways that facilitate decision making.

Whether the burden of determining if the use of more complex models is warranted should be shouldered by planners and managers or by model builders is an open question. To the extent that the burden belongs to model builders and hydrologic researchers, the IBM Scientific Center, Pisa, and the Hydraulics Institute of the University of Pavia co-sponsored a Workshop on Mathematical Models in Hydrology held in Pisa, December 9—12, 1974, to discuss and demonstrate the use of specific mathematical models. The Workshop afforded an opportunity for model builders and hydrologic researchers to interact with a broad spectrum of individuals currently engaged in planning and management of Italy's water resources. It was not the intent of the Workshop to claim the superiority of one model over another, but rather to emphasize the importance of mathematical models of hydrologic processes to water resources planning and management, to illustrate the state-of-the-art of specific modelling activities, and to demonstrate the role of digital computers in the use of models. Both stochastic and deterministic models were considered, but limited to the case of surface water phenomena.

The role of stochastic models was discussed in the context of water resource systems planning. In this context, the purpose of the models is not to provide predictions of future flows, but rather to generate sequences of synthetic flows such that any sequence can be regarded as an equally likely realization of future flow sequence. Currently, synthetic flow generating models are designed to provide for resemblance between historic and synthetic flow sequences in terms of specific statistical parameters used to characterize historic flow sequences. The extent to which available models do provide resemblance was noted. Particular emphasis was given to the description of hydrologic persistence and the contrasting structures of Markovian and discrete fractional noise models for dealing with short- and long-term hydrologic persistence. The properties of autoregressive-integrated-moving average processes were discussed as well as the use of these processes to approximate discrete fractional noise processes.

The deterministic models were discussed in terms of their online predictive capabilities in the case of flood routing. Attention was drawn to the analytical and computer techniques for solving the St Venant equations that describe surface flow.

Also deterministic models for predicting runoff on a daily or longer period basis from rainfall were discussed. It was noted that rainfall—runoff models have grown in complexity in recent years in terms of their numbers of parameters. Problems associated with the use of these models and the extent to which physical interpretation of the parameters can be given were noted. That the predictive capability of the models has not increased in proportion to the increase in the numbers of their parameters was a subject of much discussion. That simple black-box models remain competitive with supposedly physical-based, large-number-parameter models was noted.

The papers given at the Workshop, as well as descriptions of computer programs used to demonstrate the application of specific stochastic and deterministic models, are presented in this volume.

Acknowledgement

Support for this workshop was provided by the Centro Nazionale Universitario di Calcolo Elettronico (CNUCE) at Pisa, an Institute of the National Research Council of Italy, who provided access to their computer and outstanding cooperation prior to and during the workshop.

Acknowledgement

Part 1

SYNTHETIC HYDROLOGY MODELS

Problems and Methods of Univariate Synthetic Hydrology

ROBIN T. CLARKE

Institute of Hydrology, Wallingford, Oxon, UK

1. Introduction

We are concerned with the generation of artificial sequences of a single hydrological variable, for use in (mainly) two contexts:

(1) where precipitation sequences are to be generated for routing through a rainfall—runoff model. One example is the following: in a small urban catchment, synthetic sequences of mean areal storm precipitation at, say, ten-minute intervals are required for routing through a proposed design for a storm sewer system to determine the frequency of urban flooding. As a second example, Sariahmed and Kisiel (1968) generated rainfall sequences for input to a watershed model for flood-forecasting, 'motivated not only by a desire to simulate summer floods on urban and rural watersheds, but also out of a need (a) to model the precipitation inputs to management models of the groundwater system and treated surface systems for capture of storm waters in isolated areas, and (b) to determine the efficiency of the hydrologic data collection system for prediction and control'.

(2) where streamflow at a single gauging site is to be generated to estimate the frequency with which an extreme event occurs. The generated streamflow sequence may be used as input to a storage, and the event may be that this storage — designed to meet target drafts — runs dry during its economic life; alternatively, the event may be that an already-constructed storage, with releases determined by a proposed set of operating rules, fails to meet the demands made on it. For such applications, sequences of monthly streamflow are commonly generated; for others, as in the study of the frequency with which peak flows exceed some level, the time-interval between successive values in the generated sequence is much shorter (days, or even hours).

Applications rarely arise for which synthetic sequences of variables other than precipitation and streamflow are generated; Erikson (1970) considered the statistical representation of 30 years of groundwater level observations in an esker south of Uppsala, but the relations obtained were not used for the generation of synthetic sequences. This paper therefore considers problems and methods in the generation of precipitation and streamflow sequences only; furthermore, it does not consider either the generation of one hydrological variable (such as streamflow) at several sites, or the generation of several variables at one site; the single-site simulation of sequences of water quality variables, a problem considered by a number of writers, is therefore beyond the scope of this paper, as is the generation of parallel sequences of monthly rainfall and temperature at a single site, for the purposes of estimating irrigation demand (FAO Report, 1970).

2. Why synthetic hydrology?

Synthetic hydrology may be defined as the application of Monte Carlo methods to estimation problems in hydrology. The use of such methods, known by such terms as streamflow synthesis or data generation, is now well established as a means of deriving numerical answers to problems concerned with estimating the frequency of occurrence of events of hydrological significance, where these problems cannot readily be solved by analytical means. Their use has been fostered by the continually-growing availability of modern computing power, which is a blessing insofar as it enables hydrologists to attempt solutions to problems of far greater complexity than those studied previously, but which brings danger with it also: so easy is it now to generate a thousand pseudo-random deviates at the touch of a console key that the hydrologist may be tempted to dispense with the short records of intractable data commonly at his disposal and to resort to theoretical exercises of the type described by one percipient Irish hydrologist as numerology.

It is useful by recording the basis for the of Monte Carlo methods in hydrology. Every Monte Carlo computation leading to quantitative results may be regarded as estimating the value of a multiple integral (Hammersley and Handscomb, 1964). For suppose that no computation requires more than N $(=10^{10}$, say) random numbers from a distribution rectangular over $(0, 1)$; then the computed results will form a vector-valued function:

$$R(\xi_1, \xi_2, \ldots, \xi_N)$$

of the sequence of random numbers $\xi_1, \xi_2, \ldots$, and $R(.)$ will be an unbiased estimator of the integral

$$\int_0^1 \int_0^1 \cdots \int_0^1 R(x_1, x_2, \ldots, x_N) \, dx_1, dx_2, \ldots, dx_N \tag{1}$$

Formally, therefore, any Monte Carlo estimation procedure — and hence any synthetic hydrological calculation — can be shown to be equivalent to the evaluation of the multiple integral, (equation 1); however, this result is of little practical value in the solution of specific problems.

2.1 Monte Carlo methods used in hydrology

In general, the following two Monte Carlo methods are those finding greatest application in synthetic hydrology.

(1) Crude Monte Carlo. Consider the simplest form of equation 1 in which it is required to evaluate the integral

$$G = \int_0^1 f(x) dx \tag{2}$$

Given a sequence of N values $\eta_1, \eta_2, \ldots, \eta_N$ each drawn independently from a distribution rectangular over the interval $(0, 1)$, then each of the quantities $f(\eta_1)$, $f(\eta_2), \ldots, f(\eta_N)$ estimates G, and so does their mean value:

$$\hat{G} = \{f(\eta_1) + f(\eta_2) + \ldots + f(\eta_N)\}/N \tag{3}$$

with standard error given by

$$\sqrt{\sum_i \{f(\eta_i) - \hat{G}\}^2 / \{N(N-1)\}} \tag{4}$$

The quantity $\hat{G}$ is then the crude Monte Carlo estimate of G. Particular hydrological applications (for which the equivalent integrals have many more dimensions that in the simple case, equation 2) occur where the small-sample properties are studied of estimators for the parameters in a hydrological model, such as the estimators H and K of the Hurst coefficient h (Wallis and Matalas, 1970).

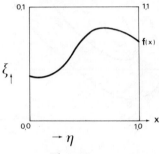

Figure 1

(2) *Hit-or-miss Monte Carlo.* Suppose that the function $f(x)$ in equation (2) lies entirely within the unit square bounded by the points $(0, 0)$, $(0, 1)$, $(1, 0)$ and $(1, 1)$, as shown in Figure 1. In this example, hit-or-miss Monte Carlo consists of taking N points (η, ξ) within the unit square (by means of sampling $2N$ values from a distribution uniform over the interval $(0, 1)$) and observing the number of points n which lie below the curve $f(x)$; the integral G is then estimated as

$$\hat{G} = n/N \tag{5}$$

with standard error

$$\sqrt{\{\hat{G}(1 - \hat{G})/N\}} \tag{6}$$

Particular hydrological applications of the use of hit-or-miss Monte Carlo occur where M sequences of monthly streamflow are generated for input to a reservoir designed to meet target drafts; if, for the particular design considered, the number m of such sequences is counted for which the target is not always met, then m/M is the hit-or-miss Monte Carlo estimate of the probability that the reservoir fails to meet demand.

2.2 Examples: trivial and less trivial

The following hydrological example illustrates further the equivalence between a Monte Carlo calculation and the evaluation of a multiple integral. It is of such triviality that its inclusion here could not be justified if it were not for the fact that it facilitates the presentation of three important points: first, that alternative Monte Carlo estimates of the same quantity are possible; second, that some Monte Carlo estimation procedures are much more efficient than others; third, that it pays the hydrologist to consider carefully which Monte Carlo estimation procedure he should use.

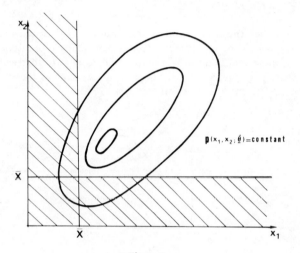

Figure 2

Let x_1, x_2 denote streamflow in months 1 and 2 respectively, and let $p(x_1, x_2, \theta)$ be the joint probability density function of x_1, x_2; here, θ is a set of parameters that must be estimated at some stage from the historic record of flows; these estimates will be denoted by $\hat{\theta}$. Suppose that the question be asked: 'What is the probability that streamflow fall below some critical level $\bar{X}$ in either month, or both?'. The required probability is obtained by integrating the function $p(x_1, x_2, \hat{\theta})$ over the shaded area in Figure 2, and is equal to

$$\int_{x_1=0}^{\infty} \int_{x_2=0}^{\bar{X}} p(x_1, x_2, \hat{\theta})\, dx_1, dx_2 + \int_{x_1=0}^{\bar{X}} \int_{x_2=0}^{\infty} p(x_1, x_2, \hat{\theta})\, dx_1\, dx_2$$

$$-\int_{x_1=0}^{\bar{X}} \int_{x_2=0}^{\bar{X}} p(x_1, x_2, \hat{\theta})\, dx_1\, dx_2$$

$$= I_1 + I_2 + I_3, \text{ say.}$$

For the integral I_1, change variables by the transformation $y_1 = \exp(-x_1)$, $y_2 = x_2/\bar{X}$; for I_2, $y_1 = x_1/\bar{X}$, $y_2 = \exp(-x_2)$; and for I_3, $y_1 = x_1/\bar{X}$, $y_2 = x_2/\bar{X}$. The sum of the three integrals is thereby transformed into an integral of the form

$$\int_{y_1=0}^{1} \int_{y_2=0}^{1} f(y_1, y_2, \hat{\theta})\, dy_1\, dy_2 \qquad (7)$$

This is precisely of the form of equation 1, and its value could be determined either by crude Monte Carlo or by hit-or-miss Monte Carlo; with the former procedure, N pairs of uniformly-distributed variates η_{1i}, η_{2i} would be generated, and the value of the integral estimated as

$$\sum_{i=1}^{N} f(\eta_{1i}, \eta_{2i}, \hat{\theta})/N \tag{8}$$

With the latter procedure, one approach would be to generate N pairs of values x_1, x_2 from the distribution $p(x_1, x_2, \hat{\theta})$, each pair constituting a sample 'trace'; if n of the traces were such that x_1, or x_2, or both, were less than $\bar{X}$, then n/N would be the hit-or-miss Monte Carlo estimate of the required probability. Alternative Monte Carlo procedures are therefore available for the solution of the problem; which should be used?

In general, crude Monte Carlo estimation is about three times more efficient than hit-or-miss Monte Carlo in the sense that the former requires the generation of only about a third of the number of uniformly distributed random variables required by the latter to achieve an estimate of comparable precision. If a problem to be solved by hit-or-miss Monte Carlo can be converted instead into one solvable by crude Monte Carlo, there will clearly be a saving of effort; furthermore, for particular problems, procedures can be found that are many times more efficient even than crude Monte Carlo. There has been little investigation of the applicability of such methods to hydrological problems, although Moran (1959) expressed doubts concerning their usefulness for the particular simulation problems that he then considered.

An example less trivial than that considered above is the following. Let the sequence of total annual flows at a gauging station be denoted by

$$\{\ldots, x_{-2}, x_{-1}, x_0, x_1, x_2, \ldots, x_t \ldots\}$$

and suppose that values up to and including x_0 have been observed. Suppose also that this sequence exhibits 'persistence' in the sense that x_i and x_j $(i \neq j)$ are not independently distributed random variables, and that the question to be answered is: 'What is the probability that one or more annual flows in the next 50 years will be less than some critical value $\bar{X}$?'. The present state of the system is dependent on the observed sequence $\{\ldots, x_{-2}, x_{-1}, x_0\} \equiv x_P$, so that we need to consider the conditional probability density

$$p(x_1, x_2, \ldots, x_{50}; \theta_1, \theta_2, \ldots \mid x_0, x_{-1}, x_{-2}, \ldots) = p(x_F; \theta \mid x_P) \tag{9}$$

where θ is the vector of parameters defining the probability density function of x_F. Denote by P_i, P_{ij}, etc. the probabilities

$$\int_{x_i < \bar{X}} \int_0^\infty \ldots \int_0^\infty P(x_F; \theta \mid x_P) \, dx_F \tag{10}$$

$$\int_{x_i < \bar{X}} \int_{x_j < \bar{X}} \ldots \int_0^\infty p(x_F; \theta \mid x_P) \, dx_F \tag{11}$$

Then the probability that flow fails to exceed $\bar{X}$ in one or more years of the fifty is

$$S(\overline{X}) = \sum_i P_i - \sum_{i,j} P_{ij} + \sum_{i,j,k} P_{ijk} - \ldots \pm P_{ijk} \ldots \tag{12}$$

which is a linear combination of multidimensional integrals. We note in passing that $S(\overline{X})$ is the probability conditional on the observed sequence x_P; if we were to consider the probability that any series of 50 annual flows contained one value or more that was less than $\overline{X}$, the expression $p(x_F; \theta \mid x_P)$ in equations 10 and 11 above must be replaced by

$$p(x_F; \theta) = \int_{x_0 = 0}^{\infty} \int_{x_{-1} = 0}^{\infty} \ldots p(x_F, x_P; \theta) \, dx_P$$

with the result that the dimensionality of the integrals to be evaluated in equations 10 and 11 is increased greatly. The suggestion by Garcia *et al.* (1972) that synthetic sequences should preserve a 'memory' of the historic sequence (i.e. that simulated projections over an economic time horizon should all be conditional on a common past) clearly makes good computational sense, by virtue of the resultant decrease in dimensionality of the integrals to be evaluated.

Direct numerical integration of the terms in equation 12 is a task of such magnitude as to be impossible in practice, even with present-day computing facilities. To evaluate it by (relatively inefficient) hit-or-miss Monte Carlo, N sequences x_F, each of 50 years length, would be generated with some appropriate correlational structure 'similar' to that of the unknown probability density function $p(x_F; \theta \mid x_P)$; if n is the number of sequences for which at least one element of the vector x_F is less than $\overline{X}$, then n/N estimates $S(\overline{X})$ in equation 12.

Apart from the computational difficulties associated with expressions such as that for $S(\overline{X})$, other difficulties arise because (a) the algebraic form of the distribution $p(x_F; \theta \mid x_P)$ is not known, but must be approximated by a manageable distribution having certain features in common with it; (b) the choice of which features are to be 'preserved' by the approximation is not straightforward; (c) the approximating distribution will contain parameters θ^* which must be estimated from the historic record. These difficulties are discussed further in the next section.

3. Problems and methods

It is instructive to compare the procedures for computing the probability that one or more annual flows in the next 50 years will fail to exceed a critical value $\overline{X}$ (a) when all persistence is absent, so that flows in any two years can be assumed independently and identically distributed; (b) when persistence is present and the probability is calculated by Monte Carlo. Table 1 illustrates the comparison.

When flows are not independently distributed, the use of simulation procedures for estimation at stage 4 (see Table 1) is often unavoidable. However, 'data' generation should be regarded as a method to be adopted only if there is none better; as Hammersley and Handscomb state, 'it should almost go without saying, if it were not so important to stress it, that whenever in the Monte Carlo estimation of a multiple integral we are able to perform part of the integration by analytical means, that part should be so performed. As in some other kinds of gambling, it pays to make use of one's knowledge of form'.

Having satisfied himself that analytical methods have made their full contri-

Table 1. Comparison of computational procedures for problem described in text: (a) with no persistence amongst annual flows; (b) with annual flows not independently distributed (in both cases, annual flow is assumed to be a stationary sequence)

Stage	(a) All persistence absent	(b) Annual flows are not independently distributed
1	Collect record of annual flows $\{x_i\}$	Collect record of annual flows $\{x_i\}$
2	Choose a probability density function $p(x, \theta)$	Choose a probability density function $p(x_F; \theta \mid x_P)$
3	Estimate parameters θ from historic record $(\hat{\theta})$	Estimate parameters θ from historic record $(\hat{\theta})$
4	Calculate the required probability $$S(\bar{X}) = 1 - \left\{ \int_{\bar{X}}^{\infty} p(x, \hat{\theta}) dx \right\}^{50}$$ with the integral evaluated by for example, Simpson's rule	Calculate the required probability $S(\bar{X})$, e.g. by hit-or-miss Monte Carlo (generate N sequences x_F with 50 elements; observe n/N, as in text)
5	Test the sensitivity of $S(\bar{X})$ to sampling variation in $\hat{\theta}$	Test the sensitivity of $S(\bar{X})$ to sampling variation in $\hat{\theta}$
6	Test the sensitivity of $S(\bar{X})$ to choice of distribution $p(x, \theta)$	Test the sensitivity of $S(\bar{X})$ to choice of 'model' $p(x_F; \theta \mid x_P)$

bution to the solution of his problem, the hydrologist who is about to embark on the use of data generation methods is confronted by the following problems:

(1) The problem of what probability density function is to be used to describe the joint distribution of the elements in the simulated sequences. (For the estimation of $S(\bar{X})$ in the last section, can some transformation of the elements x_i of x_F be assumed to have multivariate normal distribution? If so, will the transformation affect the conclusions significantly? If x_F cannot be so represented, what multivariate distribution should be used?)

(2) The problem of how the correlational structure amongst the elements in the simulated sequences is to be represented in terms of a small number of parameters with relevance to the problem in hand. (Can the elements x_i be represented by a lag-one autoregression of the form

$$x_i - \mu = \rho(x_{i-1} - \mu) + \epsilon_i \quad (\epsilon_i \sim N(0, \sigma_\epsilon^2)) \tag{13}$$

for which the variance–covariance matrix amongst the elements of x_F is determined by two parameters only, ϵ_ϵ^2 and ρ? If not, can they be represented by a lag-k autoregression, for which $k + 1$ parameters are required? Or is the correlational structure such that the Type II approximation to fractional Gaussian noise:

$$x_i - \mu = (H - \tfrac{1}{2}) \sum_{u=i-M}^{i-1} (i - u)^{H - 2/3} \epsilon_u \quad (\epsilon_u \sim N(0, 1)) \tag{14}$$

should be used instead?)

(3) The problem of how the parameters in the model are to be estimated.

(4) The problem of the choice of method by which synthetic sequences will be derived in the computer. A synthetic sequence such as x_F is obtained by first

generating a sequence of 'pseudo-random' variables each of which has a uniform distribution, and then transforming these to sample traces: the choice of pseudo-random number generator, and the choice of transformation, are of the greatest importance.

(5) The problem of determining how many sample traces are to be generated, and how these are to be distributed between the estimation procedure and the sensitivity analysis.

The remaining sections present an outline of some methods for the generation of synthetic precipitation and streamflow sequences, of problems of the above type encountered when using them, and of some attempts to resolve them.

4. The generation of sequences of mean areal rainfall

4.1 Statistical models

When sequences of precipitation depths, accumulated over short time-intervals, are generated, they must exhibit the alternation of sequences of wet and dry 'spells'. We use the term 'time-unit' or 'unit' to denote the interval over which precipitation is accumulated: where sequences of the areal precipitation are generated for the purpose of urban storm-sewer network design, the length of the time-unit must usually be measured in minutes, a ten-minute unit being used by several writers (Raudkivi and Lawgun, 1970; Grace and Eagleson, 1966). A dry spell is then defined as a series of consecutive precipitation-free units, and a wet spell is a series of consecutive units in each of which measurable precipitation occurs.

A common procedure whereby alternating wet and dry spells are introduced into a generated precipitation sequence is to assume probability distributions for the length of wet and dry spells and to draw values from these distributions by means of the simulation procedure; thus, Grace and Eagleson fitted one Weibull distribution to the histogram of wet spell durations and another to that of dry spell durations, having first ascertained that the correlation of length of dry spell with length of wet spell preceding (or following) it was small (0.03 and 0.06 respectively, with 130 degrees of freedom). This absence of appreciable correlation was taken by Grace and Eagleson to justify the simplification of the probabilistic relation

$$P(W_1 = n_1, D_2 = n_2, W_3 = n_3 \ldots) = P(W_1 = n_1) \, P(D_2 = n_2 \mid W_1 = n_1)$$

$$P(W_3 = n_3 \mid D_2 = n_2, W_1 = n_1) \ldots (15)$$

where $P(W_1 = n_1)$ is the probability that the first (wet) spell is of duration n_1 units, and similarly for $D_2, n_2, \ldots$, to the relation

$$P(W_1 = n_1, D_2 = n_2, W_3 = n_3, \ldots) = P(W_1 = n_1) \, P(D_2 = n_2) \, P(W_3 = n_3) \, \cdots$$

$$(16)$$

The generating mechanism thereby becomes an alternating renewal process. Strictly, however, it is not obvious that lack of correlation necessarily implies statistical independence in this case.

The distribution of precipitation within a wet spell was achieved by Grace and Eagleson using a two-stage procedure. First, a total storm depth was generated by means of a linear regression of depth on duration of wet spell, calculated using the historic record. To the depth so estimated, a 'depth residual' was added, calculated using a beta distribution with integral parameters. Second, the resultant precipitation depth was distributed amongst the time-units of the wet spell, using the following 'urn model'.

Suppose that N precipitation points (e.g. N x 0.01 inches) are to be distributed amongst T time-units. The N points are regarded as black balls to be distributed amongst T boxes arranged in sequence, with the serial correlation structure introduced by means of balls of a different colour (green, say). A box is chosen at the outset from an initial probability distribution $p_1, p_2, \ldots, p_T$; if box i is selected, it then receives a black ball and, in addition, N_0 green balls, whilst the $(i-1)$th and $(i+1)$th boxes each receive N_1 green balls, the $(i-2)$th and $(i+2)$th boxes receive N_2 green balls, and so on. The relative probability that the next black ball lands in box j, containing n_j green balls, as compared to box k containing n_k green balls, is

$$(n_j/N_0 + 1)/(n_k/N_0 + 1) \tag{17}$$

This procedure is repeated until all N precipitation points (black balls) have been exhausted. Near the end of their distribution, it must be ascertained that both the first and last boxes contain at least one black ball, for only then is the storm of the duration actually specified.

This procedure requires knowledge of the following parameters: (a) the initial probabilities $p_1, p_2, \ldots, p_T$; (b) the numbers $N_0, N_1 \ldots$ of green balls to be allocated to the box to which a black ball is allocated, and to those neighbouring it. Grace and Eagleson estimated these quantities by trial and error.

A different approach was used by Raudkivi and Lawgun (1970). Lengths of dry periods were represented by a Weibull distribution, as before, but the distribution of precipitation depths within a wet spell was obtained by simulation using a matrix of transition probabilities given by

$$\mathbf{P} = \begin{bmatrix} 0 & p_{01} & p_{02} & \cdots \\ p_{10} & p_{11} & p_{12} & \cdots \\ \cdots & \cdots & \cdots & \end{bmatrix} \cdots \tag{18}$$

Denoting by n_{ij} the number of transitions from state i to state j (i.e. the number of times in the historic record that i hundredth of an inch of precipitation in one time-unit was followed by j hundredths in the next) and by n_i the number of times that state i was entered, then the P_{ij} of the matrix (equation 18) were computed as

$$P_{ij} = \Sigma n_{ij}/\Sigma n_i; \quad i, j = 0, 1, 2, 3, \ldots$$
$$(i, j \neq 0 \text{ together})$$

Generation then proceeds by the following steps. First, the length of a dry spell is found by sampling from the Weibull distribution fitted to those observed in the historic record. Second, a precipitation depth in the first time-unit is obtained by effecting the transition from state 0 to state i, say, using the first row of the transition matrix in equation (18). Third, row i of the matrix is entered to give the depth of precipitation for the second time-unit; let this be j. This procedure is followed until a transition to zero occurs, which is taken to mark the end of the wet spell. There are two principal difficulties in such a procedure: first, if a transition between two states has not occurred in the past, it will never occur in the generated sequence either; and second, the number of possible states must be limited for computational purposes. Raudkivi and Lawgun used 25 states, so that a maximum of 0.25 inches could occur in any one time-unit of the generated sequence, despite the fact that the ten-minute fall with 50-year return period was estimated as 0.99 inches. To increase the number of possible states affords a partial solution only, because the number of transition probabilities to be estimated from the historic record increases approximately as the square of the number of states.

Much work has elucidated the probabilistic models that are suitable for the representation of *daily* precipitation. The earliest work, concerned with runs of wet and dry days during the rainy season at Tel Aviv, is the classic study by Gabriel and Neumann (1957). They used a two-state Markov chain to describe the transitions from a wet (or dry) day i to a wet (or dry) day $i + 1$, and their method was adopted by some workers (Hopkins and Robillard, 1964; Feyerherm and Bark, 1965) and extended by others (Cole and Sherriff, 1972). Other workers have sought probability distributions for daily rainfall depths (Mielke, 1973; Smith and Schreiber, 1974) although these were not used to generate synthetic data sequences.

4.2 Physically-based models of storm rainfall

The approaches of Section 4.1 are purely statistical in that they make no attempt to include, in the model formulation, any knowledge of the physical characteristics of storm development in time and space. In recent years, attempts have been made (for example, by Osborn *et al.* (1972)) to model thunderstorm rainfall by consideration of the occurrence, growth and movement of storm cells. Such models commonly require assumptions concerning the probability of development of a thunderstorm at any point in a region; concerning the probability that the storm consist of N cells; concerning the 'depth' of the storm precipitation at the centre of each cell, and in the manner in which it decreases towards the cell 'boundary'; concerning the change in time of the depth at the centre of each cell; and concerning the rate and direction of movement of cell centres, relative to one another.

Much further development is required before these models can be regarded as providing practical tools for the solution of hydrological problems, and they are more likely, in any case, to have application where sequences of short time-interval precipitation are to be generated at several sites; because this paper is concerned with problems and methods of univariate generation, and because the data available for the estimation of the many parameters are usually limited, they are not considered further in this paper.

5. The generation of synthetic streamflow sequences

The methods used to generate synthetic sequences of streamflow depend greatly on the time-interval (yearly, monthly, daily, hourly) for which sequences of synthetic streamflow are required. For the generation of annual flow sequences, the lag-one autoregressive process

$$x_{t+1} - \mu = \rho(x_t - \mu) + \epsilon_t; \quad E(\epsilon_t) = 0; \quad E(\epsilon_t^2) = \sigma_\epsilon^2$$

fails in general to account for the well-documented 'Hurst law' that is a feature of hydrological and geophysical sequences; and as is now well-known, Mandelbrot and Wallis (1968, 1969a, b, c, d, e) have presented a model accounting for the Hurst law with properties that have been subsequently studied in depth by Wallis and Matalas (1970, 1972). A conceptually simpler model the (1, 0, 1) ARIMA process, has been used successfully to model Hurst's law by O'Connell (1971, 1974), and a quasi-physical justification for its use has been given by Moss (1972); a further model, the broken-line process (Rodriguez-Iturbe *et al.*, 1972; Mejia *et al.*, 1972) has been proposed which also accounts for Hurst's law, and which, the authors claim, had advantages over both the Markov (autoregressive) process and the fractional Gaussian noise model of Mandelbrot and Wallis, a claim that is a matter for some dispute.

It is not possible, within the confines of the present paper, to give a full account of these methods, which have been the subject of so much intensive study, in the last six years, by many research hydrologists. It is sufficient to say that the undisputed reality of the Hurst law is a phenomenon which requires physical explanation of the type attempted recently by Klemes (1974).

The question of synthetic sequences of monthly streamflow, beginning with the Thomas–Fiering (1962) model in which each month's flow is regressed on that in the month preceding, is arguably the field of stochastic streamflow generation that has had greatest application by engineering hydrologists. The disaggregation problem — namely, that of generating a sequence of monthly streamflows which simultaneously preserves statistical properties of both the sequence of annual totals and the sequence of monthly flows — has been solved by Valencia and Schaake (1973), who suggest the generation of the annual totals x_t by a process such as the Type II approximation to fractional Gaussian noise or a Markov process, followed by the application of a sub-model of the form

$$\mathbf{y}_t = \mathbf{A}\mathbf{x}_t + \mathbf{B}\mathbf{z}_t$$

to obtain the disaggregated monthly flows $\mathbf{y}_t$. Singh and Lonnquist (1974) used an alternative method to generate monthly flows such that the annual totals retained desirable characteristics; their method was based on the assumption that monthly flows could be described by a mixture of two normal distributions.

Where streamflow sequences are generated to assist with planning the operation of dual-purpose reservoirs built for flood control and water supply, the time-unit of the generated sequence may need to be as small as one day; both the Thomas–Fiering model and autoregressive models based on the Gaussian distribution, are then likely to be less satisfactory than one which preserves the hydrograph characteristics of rapidly rising limb followed by more gradually decreasing recession. No model based on the Gaussian distribution can reproduce these recessions, no matter what transformation or what order of autoregression is used, whilst the Thomas–Fiering model has the further disadvantage that the number of parameters to be estimated is then large (although the number may be made manageable by judicious harmonic fitting: Quimpo (1968)). A generating model

14

which preserves the characteristic hydrograph shape and which has been applied to the stochastic generation of daily flows, is the 'shot-noise' model. This was described by Parzen (1962) and applied to the daily streamflow generating problem by Weiss (1973a). Its algebraic expression is

$$X(t) = \sum_{m=-\infty}^{\infty} w(t - \tau_m, Y_m) \tag{19}$$

representing the superposition of impulse shapes $w(.)$ occurring at random times $\ldots \tau_{-1}, \tau_0, \tau_1 \ldots$ according to a Poisson process with intensity ν; $\{Y_m\}$ is assumed to be a sequence of independently-distributed random variables which indexes the sequence of impulses. Weiss took the $\{Y_m\}$ to be sampled from an exponential distribution with mean θ, and the form of the recession to be exponential with parameter b, so that equation 19 became

$$X(t) = \sum_{m=-0}^{N(t)} Y_m e^{-b(t-\tau_m)} \tag{20}$$

the model can be shown to be equivalent to a lag-one autoregressive model in continuous time, expressible in the form

$$X(t + s) = e^{-bs} X(t) + \epsilon(t + s)$$

but differs from the Gaussian first-order autoregression by virtue of the distribution of $\epsilon(t + s)$ which is skew, with positive probability of being exactly zero. The model parameters are estimated by the method of moments, and the generation of synthetic sequences of daily flows requires only the calculation of pseudo-random numbers for an exponential distribution, which are easily found by logarithmic transformation of pseudo-random numbers from a uniform distribution.

The shot-noise model described above, applied to mean daily flows of some British streams, preserved the mean, variance and lag-one serial correlation coefficient of daily data; however, the monthly totals derived from the shot-noise process had much smaller variances and serial correlation coefficients than those observed in the historic data. Moreover, the recessions decayed too quickly and there were too many rises and recessions. Weiss ascribed this failure to the inability of shot-noise to model streams having a pronounced base-flow component, and generalized it to form the sum of two independent shot-noise processes: $X_1(t)$ with parameters ν_1, θ_1, b_1 and $X_2(t)$ with parameters ν_2, θ_2, b_2, the former parameters being larger than the latter. The process $X_1(t)$ then had more recessions, higher jumps and a faster decay rate than $X_2(t)$, and the sum of the two processes then preserved the historic mean, variance and lag-one correlation of daily flows together with the variance and lag-one serial correlation of monthly flows.

A particular problem lies in the formulation of models for the generation of synthetic streamflow sequences in arid climates. Features of hydrographs from such streams are that recessions are more rapid than exponential and that alternating sequences of time-units occur in which there is flow or no flow. The latter characteristic may be modelled by the methods described in Section (4.1); thus Yakowitz (1973) used a Markov chain to derive a sequence of wet and dry months, with a further matrix of transition probabilities giving the alternating sequences of days with or without flow. The streamflow on the first day of a flow period was sampled from the empirical distribution function for daily flows, and flow thereafter was generated by expressing the flow X_{n+1} on day $n + 1$ as proportional to X_n times a ratio of linear combinations of $X_n, X_{n-1}, X_{n-2}, X_{n-3}, X_{n-4}$.

6. Problems of parameter estimation

When the model parameters are to be estimated from data, difficulties arise from the limited length of historic record usually available; although the difficulties in the univariate case are formidable, there is some comfort in the fact that the difficulties in the multivariate case (not considered here) are even greater.

Slack (1973) discussed problems arising when parameters are to be estimated from what he terms a conditional model: that is, one in which feasible values for parameters are restricted to lie in certain regions (for example, if a stationary sequence has lag-k correlation ρ_k, the ρ_k must satisfy the inequalities $\rho_1^2 \leqslant 1$; $\rho_2 \geqslant 2\rho_1^2 - 1; \ldots$ obtained from the condition that all minors on the leading diagonal of the Laurent matrix must be positive). If the model used were an 'exact' representation of reality, and if its parameters lay near the boundary of a feasible region, then sequences derived from it may give estimates of the parameters which will fail to satisfy the constraints satisfied by the true parameter values; a sequence may therefore 'deny' that it came from a particular generating mechanism. Slack conjectures that, the more complex the model used, the more likely is it that unfeasible estimates of model parameters will be obtained.

The problem of denial appears to be analogous to that sometimes encountered elsewhere in applied statistics when pathological samples arise: for example, where estimated components of variance in a Type II ANOVA analysis are negative. More common is the difficulty of small-sample bias in parameter estimates, which draws attention to the question of how the statistical resemblance is to be maintained between the historic record and the synthetic sequences. Thus, the estimates of variance and lag-one serial correlation obtained from a sequence of length n derived from a lag-one autoregression are both biased; correction of the estimate $\hat{\rho}$ for bias increases its variance whilst the expectation of the estimate s^2 (of σ^2) is a complex function of ρ, the true value of which is unknown Wallis and O'Connell (1972)). The problem of statistical bias arises with other models also: for discrete fractional Gaussian noise, the small-sample biases in estimates of ρ_1, σ^2 and h are acute (Wallis and Matalas (1971)), whilst for the ARIMA (1, 0, 1) process, O'Connell (1974) has shown that the reliable estimation of parameters from annual streamflow sequences of moderate length is a very difficult undertaking.

Even if procedures could be found for removing bias from estimates, there remains the fact, that, because of sampling variation, they would differ from the true (unknown) parameter values $\{\theta\}$, *even if the model were an exact description of the generating process*, which will not be the case. If synthetic sequences are generated from the assumed model, using the parameter estimates $\{\hat{\theta}\}$ obtained from the historic sequence, the expected values of the statistics $\{\hat{\theta}\}$ calculated from the synthetic sequences, even after adjustment for possible bias, would be $\{\hat{\theta}\}$, and not $\{\theta\}$. It is for this reason that sensitivity analysis is necessary, to investigate the possible effect on the conclusions of the fact that $\{\hat{\theta}\}$ has a probability distribution about $\{\theta\}$.

7. Problems of pseudo-random number generation

The generation of synthetic sequences of hydrological 'data' has as its starting point the generation of sequences of pseudo-random numbers from a distribution uniform over the interval (0, 1). Commonly used as the multiplicative congruence methods:

$$x_{i+1} = ax_i \text{ (modulo } m) \tag{21}$$

or

$$x_{i+1} = (ax_i + c) \text{ (modulo } m) \tag{22}$$

where $m = 2^n$ for an n-bit binary machine; given a starting value x_0 and values a and c fulfilling certain criteria, values x_i can be generated either by equation 21 or equation 22. Whichever method is used, the generated sequence will inevitably reproduce itself after generation of at most m numbers; for machines with words of between 30 and 40 bits, the period (beyond which the sequence is repeated) is $m/4$ if equation 21 is used, provided that a differs by 3 from the nearest multiple of 8 and that x_0 is odd. For equation 22, the period is m, provided that c is odd and that a is one greater than a multiple of 4 (Hammersley and Handscomb (1964)).

Whether or not maximum period is achieved, the warning has been given by Lewis et al. (1969): 'It has been our experience that many generators (of type equation 21) put forward without documentation turn out to be defective. This is because inadequate test statistics have been used, or because the test statistic has been misused, or because the series tested have not been long enough to detect subtle departures from randomness'. Maclaren and Marsaglia (1965), dissatisfied with the performance of a congruential method, found much improvement if two congruential generators were used, one of which 'shuffled' the sequence produced by the other. Thus, the sequence

$$U_{k+1} = (2^{17} + 3)U_k \text{ (modulo } 2^{35})$$

was used to generate values for allocation to 128 storage locations; to generate the required sequence x_k, they took the first 7-bits of V_k, generated by:

$$V_{k+1} = (2^7 + 1)V_k + 1 \text{ (modulo } 2^{35})$$

as an index to get x_k from the table. Location of x_k was then followed by its replacement, in the store, by the next number generated from $\{U_k\}$. Further problems arise when the uniformly distributed variances are to be transformed to those having the required distribution. For the generation of random normal deviates $N(0, 1)$ a commonly used method is the Box–Müller (1958) transform

$$\begin{bmatrix} y_1 \\ y_2 \end{bmatrix} = (-2 \ln x_1)^{\frac{1}{2}} \begin{bmatrix} \sin \\ \cos \end{bmatrix} (2\pi x_2) \tag{23}$$

where x_1 and x_2 are rectangular over (0, 1). Using the multiplicative congruence generator, equation 21, to give these values x_i, with $m = 2^{35}$, $a = 131$, $x_0 = 1234567$, Neave (1973) found that the values y_i had a distribution which departed significantly from the expected Gaussian and, indeed, found that it possessed (a) a limited range (from -3.3 to $+3.6$); (b) infinite discontinuities in the tails. The fault lies not in the Box–Müller generator, but in its use with a particular form of the multiplicative congruence generator, and Neave recommends instead that the values x_i in equation 23 be generated by the shuffling method of Maclaren and Marsaglia. To some extent, also, Neave's result is due to the small value of a constant ($a = 131$) (Swick, 1974).

In research on Monte Carlo methods, a great deal of effort has been put into the study of methods for the reduction of variance by the use of techniques such as antithetic variates and conditional Monte Carlo; the saving of effort (relative to 'crude' Monte Carlo, or direct simulation) that results from their use is often enormous. At present, however, there appear to be no published accounts of attempts to utilize such methods in synthetic hydrology and it may well be that the application of research in this direction would be worthwhile. Furthermore, good Monte Carlo practice uses each random number, or each combination of random numbers, several times over whenever it is safe to do so, and it seems likely that hydrologists could do much to improve the efficiency of their simulation techniques.

8. Conclusions

The above discussion shows that the application of synthetic hydrological methods must be preceded by difficult decisions concerning the assumed model structure, concerning the parameter estimation procedures to be adopted, concerning the computer methods to be used for pseudo-random number generation, and concerning the strategy to be adopted for testing the sensitivity of the conclusions to the assumptions; the uncritical usage of stochastic generation methods, applied without regard to the individual characteristics of the problem, should therefore be avoided at all costs.

Because of the very nature of the systems being studied, it is an unfortunate fact that the conclusions reached by synthetic hydrological methods can rarely be subjected to scientific test against observation. This, together with the mystique and the technical jargon which all too frequently accompanies computer applications, is the biggest problem of all: namely, that apparently firm conclusions can be reached by methods that are slipshod and unprofessional – and no one need ever know.

Shot Noise Models in Synthetic Hydrology

PATRICK E. O'CONNELL
Department of Civil Engineering, Imperial College, University of London, UK

1. Introduction

In the literature on synthetic hydrology, considerable attention has been paid to models for the generation of monthly and annual flows with relatively little attention being paid to the generation of daily flows. This may be attributed partly to the belief that available monthly models can be readily applied to daily flows if necessary and partly to the fact that most water resource system simulations do not require the level of refinement given by a daily time-unit. However, in England and Wales, at least, a daily time-unit is frequently required for simulation, owing to the fact that recent water resources development had involved the design of a number of pumped storage reservoirs, the behaviour of which cannot be accurately simulated unless a daily time-unit is adopted (Harris, 1964). The belief that monthly flow models, which frequently employ a logarithmic transformation so that a linear Gaussian process can be applied to model the transformed process, can be readily applied to model daily flows is generally incorrect. Recession effects, which are frequently evident in daily flows but which tend to be averaged out in monthly and annual flows, cannot be reproduced by any linear model based on a Gaussian distribution (Weiss, 1973a,b).

A class of models, referred to as filtered Poisson processes (Parzen, 1962), has been adapted by Weiss (1973b) for generating synthetic daily flows. These processes are particularly suited to reproducing recession effects in addition to other required properties in synthetic daily flows. Some of the models, called shot noise models and developed by Weiss (1973b) under a contract between Imperial College and the former Water Resources Board of England and Wales are described in the following sections. A brief description of some of these models and their properties has been given by Clarke (herein).

2. Properties of mean daily flow

A study was made initially of daily streamflow data from some gauging sites situated in the catchment areas of the Rivers Nene and Great Ouse in East Anglia, UK. The following properties were noted:

(1) The daily data were derived by averaging several discrete measurements of continuous streamflow over a period of one day.
(2) The daily data exhibited significant skewness.

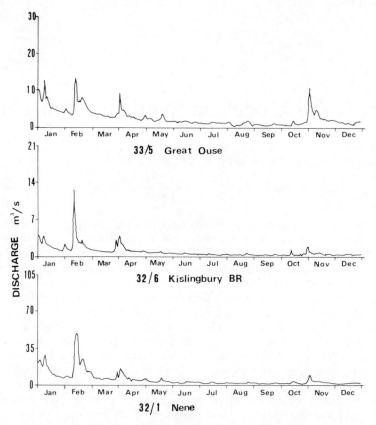

Figure 1. Daily streamflows, East Anglia, 1953

(3) A prominent feature in the data was the existence of rapid rises followed by slow recessions.

(4) Seasonality was pronounced.

(5) A 'baseflow' component in the flows was evident.

Some of these properties are illustrated in figure 1 which is a plot of one year of daily flows for three sites in the river basins of the Nene and Great Ouse, UK.

3. The single shot noise model

The existence of rapid rises followed by slow recessions in the flows suggested a model in which a sequence of random disturbances occur at random times, each causing a rise followed by a recession in the flow. This contrasts with Gaussian based models where random disturbances occur at all time points. In addition, linear Gaussian processes are time reversible, i.e. the statistical properties of the process are the same regardless of the direction in which time is measured, in contrast to observed daily flows which have been found to be time irreversible owing to the classic asymmetric shapes of hydrographs.

A class of models with basic properties well suited to the modelling of daily flows are filtered Poisson processes (Parzen, 1962) which have been adapted for generating synthetic daily flows by Weiss (1973b). A filtered Poisson process is defined as

$$X(t) = \sum_{m=N(-\infty)}^{m=N(+\infty)} w(t - \tau_m, y_m) \tag{1}$$

where $N(t)$ is a Poisson process and the random value y_m associated with the random time τ_m produces a pulse in the flow given by $w(t - \tau_m, y_m)$. One of the simplest filtered Poisson processes is obtained when $w(t - \tau_m, y_m)$ is linear and defined as

$$w(t - \tau_m, y_m) = y_m e^{-b(t-\tau_m)} \tag{2}$$

The resulting process is referred to as a single shot noise process, which can be synthesized through the following series of steps

(1) Random event times ..., $\tau_{m-1}, \tau_m, \tau_{m+1}$ ... are generated according to

$$P(N(t) = n) = \frac{e^{-\nu t}(\nu t)^n}{n!} \tag{3}$$

which means that the time between events is exponentially distributed with mean $(1/\nu)$ (Figure 2(a)).

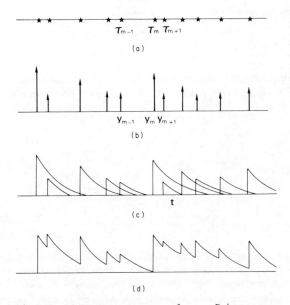

(a)

(b)

(c)

(d)

Figure 2. (a) Events ..., τ_m, ... from a Poisson process with rate ν. (b) Jumps ..., y_m, ... from an exponential distribution with mean θ. (c) Pulses with values ..., $y_m e^{-b(t-\tau_m)}$, ..., at time t. (d) Schematic plot of continuous single shot noise process

(2) Associated with the random times $\ldots, \tau_{m-1}, \tau_m, \tau_{m+1}, \ldots$, random jumps $\ldots, y_{m-1}, y_m, y_{m+1}, \ldots$ are generated from an exponential distribution with mean θ (Figure 2(b)).

(3) Associated with the random times $\ldots, \tau_{m-1}, \tau_m, \tau_{m+1}, \ldots$ and random jumps $\ldots, y_{m-1}, y_m, y_{m+1}, \ldots$ are pulses with values $\ldots, y_{m-1}e^{-b(t-\tau_{m-1})}$, $y_m \ e^{-b(t-\tau_m)}, y_{m+1} \ e^{-b(t-\tau_{m+1})}, \ldots$ at time t (Figure 2(c)).

(4) The continuous single shot noise process is defined as the sum of all contributing pulses at time t (Figure 2(d)).

$$X(t) = \sum_{m=N(-\infty)}^{N(t)} y_m e^{-b(t-\tau_m)} \tag{4}$$

The continuous single shot noise process with parameters ν, θ and b can be regarded as a model of continuous daily streamflow. The marginal distribution of the process is gamma with density function

$$f(X) = \frac{(1/\theta)^{\nu/b} X^{(\nu-b)/b} e^{-X/\theta}}{\Gamma(\nu/b)} \tag{5}$$

It can be suggested that the pulse function employed does not yield a very realistic model of continuous daily streamflow. However, more realistic pulse functions increase the number of parameters and make the resulting process more mathematically intractable.

For application to daily flows, the single shot noise process must be defined as an averaged process over a period of one day, i.e.

$$X_t = \int_{t-1}^{t} X(s)ds \tag{6}$$

As a result, the averaged process will not exhibit vertical jumps in the flow. The properties of X_t have been studied by Weiss (1973b) who has suggested that the parameters ν, θ, and b can be defined from the following equations

$$\mu = \frac{\nu\theta}{b} \tag{7}$$

$$\sigma^2 = \frac{2\nu\theta^2}{b^3} \ [b(1 - e^{-b})] \tag{8}$$

$$\rho_1 = \frac{(1 - e^{-b})^2}{2[b - (1 - e^{-b})]} \tag{9}$$

In applying the single shot noise model to daily flows, the parameters ν, θ and b were estimated separately for each month, thus ensuring that seasonality was accounted for. A multisite single shot noise process was developed (Weiss, 1973b) to ensure that cross-correlations between sites were modelled. Computer algorithms for generating synthetic shot noise data have also been developed by Weiss (1973a,b).

In Figure 3 a graphical plot of one year of synthetic flow data from a single shot noise model for the sites represented in Figure 1 is presented, from which some of

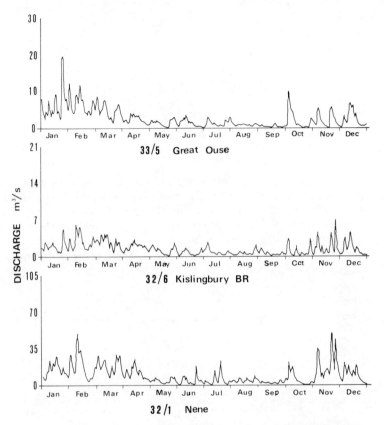

Figure 3. Single shot noise model, synthetic daily data

the deficiencies of the model can be deduced. The synthetic flows were found to have too many peaks and the recessions were found to approach zero flow too quickly. While the model did preserve the mean, standard deviation and lag-one serial correlation of the daily flows within each month, the standard deviations and lag-one serial correlations of monthly synthetic data obtained by aggregating synthetic daily data were found to be much smaller than the corresponding quantities for the historic monthly data.

4. The double shot noise model

In an attempt to improve the monthly properties and the rather poor representation of a baseflow mechanism given by the single shot noise model, a double shot noise process was formulated as the sum of two independent single shot noise processes $X_1(t)$ with parameters ν_1, θ_1 and b_1 and $X_2(t)$ with parameters ν_2, θ_2, and b_2:

$$X(t) = X_1(t) + X_2(t) \tag{10}$$

24

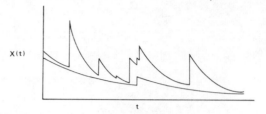

Figure 4. Schematic plot of continuous double shot
noise process

The parameters ν_1, θ_1 and b_1 are assumed to be larger than the parameters ν_2, θ_2 and b_2, thus ensuring that $X_1(t)$ has more events, higher jumps and a faster decay rate than $X_2(t)$. Thus, $X_1(t)$ may be thought of as representing a surface runoff mechanism, and $X_2(t)$ as representing a 'baseflow' mechanism. A schematic representation of the process is given in Figure 4.

The properties of the averaged double shot noise process X_t obtained by

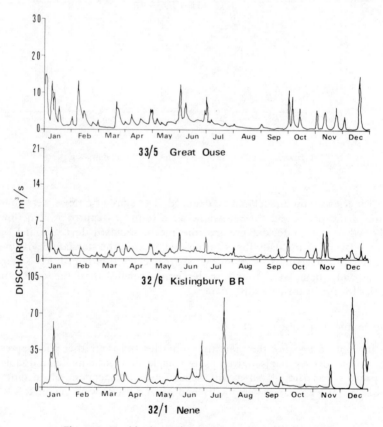

Figure 5. Double shot noise model, synthetic daily data

applying equation 6 to $X(t)$ in equation 10 have been studied by Weiss (1973b) who has also developed a multisite version of the process. As in the case of the single shot noise model, the double shot noise model was applied separately to the daily data for each calendar month, requiring the estimation of the six parameters ν_1, θ_1, b_1, ν_2, θ_2 and b_2 for each of twelve months. The mean, standard deviation and lag-one autocorrelation of daily flows for each month, and of monthly flows defined as the average daily flow for a month, were related to the parameters ν_1, θ_1, b_1, ν_2, θ_2 and b_2 by Weiss (1973b), effectively providing five equations in six unknowns, as the mean of daily flows for a month, and daily flows averaged over the length of that month, are the same. The parameter ν_1 was chosen for estimation separately and was defined for each calendar month by counting the number of peaks within that month over the total number of years of record.

In Figure 5, a graphical plot of one year of synthetic daily flows from the double shot noise model for the sites represented in Figures 3 and 4 is presented, which illustrates an improvement over the single shot noise model in modelling the baseflow mechanism in the flows. However, a criticism of the model is that the 'slow' and 'fast' processes are independent which conflicts with physical reality. In a few instances, the slow process accounted for a large proportion of the variance in one month and a small proportion of the variance in the following month, resulting in excessive 'carryover' from the first month to the second. This was then reflected in biased estimates of the mean and variance in synthetic flows for the second month.

5. The second-order shot noise model

In response to criticism of the independence of the 'slow' and 'fast' processes in the double shot noise model, a shot noise model which overcomes this problem is currently being developed as a part of a contract between the Water Research, UK, and Imperial College, The model, initially considered by Weiss (1973b) is based on one event rate ν and one exponential distribution with mean θ for jump heights. However, a proportion of each jump magnitude y_m produces a pulse in the flow equal to $\alpha y_m e^{-b_1(t-\tau_m)}$ while the remainder of the jump produces a pulse equal to $(1-\alpha)y_m e^{-b_2(t-\tau_m)}$ where $b_1 > b_2$. Thus, the parameter b_1 governs the 'fast' response while the parameter b_2 governs the 'slow' response to the jump y_m. A schematic representation of the 'slow' and 'fast' components of the process is given in Figure 6.

The process can be described by a second-order linear differential equation. Relations between the parameters ν, θ, b_1, b_2, α and the mean, standard deviation

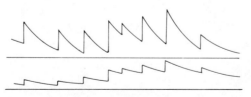

Figure 6. Schematic plot of components of continuous second-order shot noise process

and lag-one serial correlation coefficient of daily and averaged monthly flows have been established by Weiss (1973b). Thus, the problem of the 'extra' parameter in the double shot noise model is eliminated, and the model is in closer accord with physical reality.

6. Summary

The development of models for generating synthetic daily flows with hydrograph properties close to those of the historic flows is a rather difficult task. Models which are based on linear Gaussian processes or their transformations are usually adequate for modelling monthly or annual flows but are generally unsuitable for application to daily flows owing to the inherent property of time irreversibility in the flows. Time irreversibility is attributed to rapid rises and slow responses in the flow, features which can be reproduced by shot noise models in addition to the usual standard properties required for simulation purposes. Shot noise models are also open to physical interpretation, but the tendency to introduce more physical reality into these models invariably leads to more formidable mathematical difficulties in relating flow properties to the parameters of the models, so that the parameters can be estimated in a proper statistical manner. However, the formulation of models for generating synthetic flows without consideration of the physical nature of stream flow should be discouraged. Such considerations, allied to Clarke's warning against 'the uncritical usage of stochastic generation methods, applied without regard to the individual characteristics of the problem' should lead to the successful use of synthetic hydrology in planning water resource systems.

Generation of Multivariate Synthetic Flows

NICHOLAS C. MATALAS
US Geological Survey, National Center, Reston, Va., USA

1. Introduction

In general, water resource systems planning is concerned with determining the size and operation of not one but several reservoirs. Moreover, the seasonal variability of flows is likely to be of interest. In such cases, the use of a univariate (single-site, single-season) model for generating synthetic flows at each site of interest is limited because the flows at various sites tend to be interdependent, and at a given site the flows for various seasons also tend to be interdependent. Thus the multivariate (multisite, multiseason) properties of the flows must be considered in generating synthetic flows at all the sites.

In principle, the generation of multivariate synthetic flows is the same as the generation of univariate synthetic flows. A set of flow characteristics to be preserved is specified and a model, constructed to preserve the flow characteristics, is used to generate at each site several synthetic flow sequences each of length equal to the economic time horizon of the system under consideration. In the multivariate case, the set of flow characteristics includes those that describe the flows at each site and season of interest, as well as the structure of temporal and spatial interdependence.

The mathematical structure of a multivariate synthetic flow generator is of course more complex than that of a univariate generator. The complexity of a multivariate generator leads to some mathematical problems in the construction of the generator and some operational problems in the generator's use. In the following sections some of these problems are discussed for multisite, single-season synthetic flow generation.

2. Markov models

Synthetic flow sequences are generated such that they resemble the corresponding historic flow sequences in terms of certain statistics which characterize the historic flow sequences. If the basic statistics of interest are the observed mean, standard deviation, and coefficient of skewness of the annual flows at each of N sites, as well as the observed lag $k = 1$ covariance structure among the flows, then, under the assumption that streamflow is a stationary stochastic process, a lag-one model may be used to generate synthetic flow sequences at each of N sites.

The mathematical structure of the general Markov model is defined as

$$X(t) = AX(t-1) + B\epsilon(t) \tag{1}$$

where $X(t)$, $X(t-1)$ and $\epsilon(t)$ are ($N \times 1$) matrices of random variables and A and B are ($N \times N$) matrices of coefficients. The ith elements of $X(t)$ and $X(t-1)$ are defined as $X_i(t) - \mu_i$ and $X_i(t-1) - \mu_i$, where $X_i(t)$ and $X_i(t-1)$ are random variables (flow) at times t and $t-1$ pertaining to the ith site, $i = 1, \ldots, N$, and $\mu_i = E[X_i(t)] \; \forall \; t$ denotes the mean flow at the ith site.

Let

$$M(0) = E[X(t)] [X(t)]^T \tag{2}$$

$$M(1) = E[X(t)] [X(t-1)]^T \tag{3}$$

denote ($N \times N$) matrices whose (i, j)th elements are

$$m_{i,j}(0) = E[X_i(t) - \mu_i] [X_j(t) - \mu_j] \; \forall \; t \tag{4}$$

$$m_{i,j}(1) = E[X_i(t) - \mu_i] [X_j(t-1) - \mu_j] \; \forall \; t \tag{5}$$

The superscript T denotes the operation of matrix transposition. The matrix $M(0)$ is the lag $k = 0$ variance–covariance matrix of the flows. For $i = j$, $m_{i,j}(0) = \sigma_i^2$, the variance of the flows at site i. $m_{i,j}(0)$ denotes the lag $k = 0$ covariance between the flows at sites i and j. $M(1)$ denotes the lag $k = 1$ covariance matrix of the flows, where the (i,j)th element, $m_{i,j}(1)$, denotes the lag $k = 1$ cross-covariance between the flows at sites i and j. For $i = j$, $m_{i,i}(1)$ denotes the lag $k = 1$ autocovariance of the flows at site i.

The ith element of $\epsilon(t)$, denoted as $\epsilon_i(t)$, is a random variable distributed with $E[\epsilon_i(t)] = 0 \; \forall \; t$. Also it is assumed that $\epsilon_i(t)$ is independent of $\epsilon_j(t) \; \forall \; i \neq j$ and that $\epsilon_i(t)$ is independent of $X_j(t-k) \; \forall \; i, j$ and $\forall \; k > 0$. Whereby the following relations hold

$$E[\epsilon(t)] [\epsilon(t)]^T = I \tag{6}$$

$$E[\epsilon(t)] [X(t-1)]^T = E[X(t-1)] [\epsilon(t)]^T = 0 \tag{7}$$

where I is an ($N \times N$) identity matrix and 0 is an ($N \times N$) null matrix. The (i,i)th element of I denotes the variance of $\epsilon_i(t) \; \forall \; t$.

If both sides of equation 1 are postmultiplied by $[X(t-1)]^T$, then the expectations of the various matrix products, defined above, lead to

$$A = M(1)M^{-1}(0) \tag{8}$$

where $M^{-1}(0)$ denotes the inverse of $M(0)$. Similarly, the postmultiplication of both sides of equation 1 by $[X(t)]^T$ leads to

$$BB^T = M(0) - M(1)M^{-1}(0)M^T(1) \tag{9}$$

(Matalas, 1967). As there is no physical significance attached to the elements of B, it is convenient to define B as a lower triangular matrix. Note, if θ is an ($N \times N$) matrix, such that $\theta\theta^T = I$, then $B^*B^{*T} = BB^T$, where $B^* = B\theta$. A matrix θ may be defined such that B^* is lower triangular.

The model expressed by equation 1 defines the entire lag $k = 1$ covariance structure among the flows at the N sites. If $a_{i,j}$ and $b_{i,j}$ denote the (i,j)th elements of A and B, where B is lower triangular, then the ith element of $X(t)$ may be expressed as

$$X_i(t) - \mu_i = \sum_{j=1}^{N} a_{i,j}[X_j(t-1) - \mu_j] + \sum_{j=1}^{i} b_{i,j}\epsilon_j(t) \tag{10}$$

Note, the flow at time t at site i is related to the flows lagged by one unit of time at all the sites, including the ith site.

For the general Markov model, the coefficient of skewness of $\epsilon_i(t)$, denoted as $\gamma_i(\epsilon) \ \forall \ t$, is defined as

$$\gamma_i(\epsilon) = [b_{ii}^3]^{-1} \left\{ \gamma_i(X)\sigma_i^3 - \sum_{j=1}^{N} a_{ij}^3 \gamma_j(X)\sigma_j^3 \right.$$

$$- 3\left[\sum_{j=1}^{N-1} \sum_{u=j+1}^{N} a_{ij}a_{iu}^2 \lambda(X_j, X_u^2) + \sum_{j=1}^{N-1} \sum_{u=j+1}^{N} a_{ij}^2 a_{iu} \lambda(X_j^2, X_u) \right]$$

$$- 6 \sum_{j=1}^{N-2} \sum_{u=j+1}^{N-1} \sum_{v=u+1}^{N} a_{ij}a_{iu}a_{iv} \lambda(X_j, X_u, X_v)$$

$$\left. - \sum_{j=0}^{i-1} b_{ij}^3 \gamma_j(\epsilon) \right\} \tag{11}$$

where $\gamma_i(X)$ denotes the coefficient of skewness of X_i and

$$\lambda(X_j, X_u^2) = E[X_j(t) - \mu_j][X_u(t) - \mu_u]^2 \tag{12}$$

$$\lambda(X_j^2, X_u) = E[X_j(t) - \mu_j]^2 [X_u(t) - \mu_u] \tag{13}$$

$$\lambda(X_j, X_u, X_v) = E[X_j(t) - \mu_j][X_u(t) - \mu_u][X_v(t) - \mu_v] \tag{14}$$

$\forall \ t$. Equation 11 may be solved recursively to obtain $\gamma_i(\epsilon)$, $i = 1, \ldots, N$ (Matalas and Wallis, 1976).

If the lag-one autocovariance structure, but not the lag-one cross-covariance structure, is of interest, then equation 1 may be expressed as

$$X(t) = \tilde{A}X(t-1) + \tilde{B}\epsilon(t) \tag{15}$$

$\tilde{A}$ is an $(N \times N)$ diagonal matrix whose (i,i)th element is

$$\tilde{a}_{i,i} = m_{i,i}(1)/\sigma_i^2 = \rho_i(1) \tag{16}$$

where $\rho_i(1)$ denotes the first-oder autocorrelation coefficient of the flows at the ith site. $\tilde{B}$ is an $(N \times N)$ lower triangular matrix whose (i,j)th element, $\tilde{b}_{i,j}$, is given by the solution of

$$\tilde{B}\tilde{B}^T = M(0) - \tilde{A}M(0)\tilde{A}^T \tag{17}$$

The ith element of $X(t)$, defined by equation 15 is

$$X_i(t) - \mu_i = \rho_i(1)[X_i(t-1) - \mu_i] + \sum_{j=1}^{i} \tilde{b}_{i,j}\epsilon_j(t) \tag{18}$$

Note, equation 18 defines a Markov process for the flows at each site and therefore equation 15 is referred to as a local Markov process.

For a Markov process, equation 11 reduces to

$$\gamma_i(\epsilon) = [\tilde{b}_{i,i}^3]^{-1} \left\{ [1 - \rho_i^3(1)]\gamma_i(X)\sigma_i^3 - \sum_{j=0}^{i-1} \tilde{b}_{i,j}^3 \gamma_j(\epsilon) \right\} \tag{19}$$

where $\tilde{b}_{i,0} = 0 \; \forall \; i$.

The general Markov model may be used to generate synthetic flow sequences that resemble the corresponding historical flow sequences in terms of estimates of μ_i, σ_i, $\gamma_i(X)$, and $R_{ij}(1) = m_{ij}(1)/\sigma_i\sigma_j$, where $R_{ii}(1) \equiv \rho_i(1)$. In the case of the Markov model, resemblance is limited to estimates of μ_i, σ_i, $\gamma_i(X)$, and $\rho_i(1)$. Moreover, estimates of $m_{ij}(1) \; \forall \; i \neq j$, $\lambda(X_j, X_u^2)$, $\lambda(X_j, X_u)$, and $\lambda(X_j, X_u, X_v)$ do not have to be calculated.

3. Fractional noise model

For a time series of length n, the ratio of the range, R, of the cumulative departures from the mean to the standard deviation, σ, is proportional to n raised to a power, denoted as h

$$R/\sigma \sim n^h \tag{20}$$

(Hurst, 1951, 1956). Streamflow sequences tend to yield estimates of $h \neq 1/2$. Mandelbrot and Wallis (1968) noted that short (finite) memory processes, such as the lag-one and Markov processes, are characterized by values of $h = 1/2$, at least asymptotically, and thus to consider values of $h \neq 1/2$, streamflow would need to be modelled as a long (infinite) memory process.

Mandelbrot and Wallis (1968, 1969) suggested the use of discrete fractional noise processes, characterized by infinite memories, in order to consider $h \neq 1/2$. To define a discrete fractional noise process, let $B(t)$ denote a Brownian motion process. If a portion of $B(t)$ in the interval 0 to T is expressed as $B(\alpha T)$, where $0 < \alpha < 1$, then $\alpha^{-\frac{1}{2}} B(\alpha T)$ has the same distribution function for every value of T and therefore $B(t)$ is said to be self-similar. A fractional noise process is defined as the derivative of fractional Brownian motion, $B_h(t)$, where

$$B_h(t) - B_h(0) = \int_{-\infty}^{0} [(t - v)^{h - \frac{1}{2}} - (- v)^{h - \frac{1}{2}}] \, dB(v)$$

$$+ \int_{0}^{t} (t - v)^{h - \frac{1}{2}} dB(v) \tag{21}$$

If $h = 1/2$, then $B_{0.5}(t) - B_{0.5}(0) = B(t) - B(0)$ and thus fractional noise is a generalization of Brownian motion. Discrete fractional noise, where t is integer valued, is defined as $B_h(t) - B_h(t-1)$. For a discrete fractional noise process, the kth order autocorrelation coefficient, $\rho^*(k)$, is given by

$$\rho^*(k) = \frac{1}{2}[|k + 1|^{2h} - 2|k|^{2h} + |k - 1|^{2h}] \tag{22}$$

For $h = 1/2$, $\rho^*(k) = s0 \; \forall |k| > 0$.

Because a discrete fractional noise process has infinite memory, the process must be approximated by a process having large but finite memory for purposes of computer simulation. One approximation, referred to as Type 2 (Mandelbrot and Wallis, 1969), is defined as

$$X(t) = \mu + [W(h,M)]^{-1} \sigma \sum_{\delta=pt-M}^{pt-1} [pt - \delta]^{h-3/2} \epsilon(\delta) \tag{23}$$

where μ and σ denote the mean and standard deviation of $X(t) \ \forall \ t$ and where $\epsilon(\delta)$s are independently distributed with zero mean and unit variance $\forall \ \delta$. The three parameters, h, M and p are defined as follows: h is the Hurst coefficeint, $p \geqslant 1$ is an integer introduced to reduce the dominance of low frequency components (Matalas and Wallis, 1971), and M is an integer, such that M/p is the memory of the process. The term $W(h,M)$ is defined as

$$W(h, M) = \left[\sum_{l=1}^{M} l^{2h-3} \right]^{1/2} \tag{24}$$

As defined by equation 23, the Type 2 process is applicable for $h > \frac{1}{2}$. A more general form given by Mandelbrot and Wallis (1969) may be used for values of $h < \frac{1}{2}$. Because historic flow sequences tend to yield estimates of $h > \frac{1}{2}$, the following discussions are limited to the use of equation 23 to generate synthetic flow sequences.

Type 2 processes may be used to generate synthetic flows at a single site such that the synthetic flows resemble the corresponding historic flows in terms of estimates of μ, σ, $\gamma(x)$ and h. Some difficulty is encountered with respect to resemblance in terms of the estimate of $\rho(1)$. For the Type 2 process, $\rho(1)$ is defined as

$$\rho(1) = \sum_{l=1+p}^{M} [l(l-p)]^{h-3/2} \bigg/ \sum_{l=1}^{M} l^{2h-3} \tag{25}$$

For the discrete fractional noise process, $\rho(1)$ is a function only of h; whereas, for the Type 2 process, $\rho(1)$ is a function of M and p as well as h. It is possible to choose M and p such that for a given value of h, the two values of $\rho(1)$ are equal. However, estimates of $\rho(1)$ and h are not likely to satisfy equation 22, although values of M and p may be chosen such that the estimates very nearly satisfy equation 25. Values of $\rho(1)$ as a function of M, p and h, where $M/p = 1000$ are given in Table 1. The values of $\rho(1)$ in the last row of Table 1 are given by equation 22.

To generate Type 2 synthetic flows at each of N sites, the flow at the ith site is expressed as

$$x_i(t) = \mu_i + \sum_{\delta=pt-M_i}^{pt-1} [pt - \delta]^{h_i-3/2} \sum_{q=1}^{i} b_{iq} \epsilon_q(\delta) \tag{26}$$

where $i = 1, \ldots, N$ and p is a constant $\forall \ i$. The variance of $x_i(t)$ is given by

$$\sigma_i^2 = \sum_{l=1}^{M_i} l^{2h_i-3} \sum_{q=1}^{i} b_{iq}^2 \tag{27}$$

32

Table 1. $\rho(1)$ v. b and p for Type 2
process: $M/p = 1000$

p \ b	0.6	0.7	0.8	0.9
1	0.67	0.73	0.80	0.87
5	0.35	0.45	0.57	0.71
10	0.24	0.34	0.47	0.63
20	0.16	0.25	0.38	0.56
DFN	0.15	0.32	0.52	0.74

Note, for

$$i = 1, \quad b_{11} = \sigma_1 \Bigg/ \left[\sum_{l=1}^{M_i} l^{2h_i-3} \right]^{1/2} = \sigma_1/W(b_i, M_i),$$

where $W(b_i, M_i)$ is defined by equation 24. The lag-zero covariance between the flows at sites i and j, $m_{i,j}(0)$, is given by

$$m_{i,j}(0) = \sum_{l=0}^{L} \left[(M_i - l)^{h_i-3/2} (M_j - l)^{h_j-3/2} \right] \sum_{u=1}^{U} b_{iu} b_{ju} \qquad (28)$$

where L is equal to the smaller of the two values $(M_i - 1)$ and $(M_j - 1)$ and U is equal to the smaller of the values i and j. For the ith site, given the values of $\rho_i(1)$ and b_i, the values of M_i and p are chosen such that equation 25 is satisfied. Thus given the values of σ_i, $m_{i,j}(0)$, b_i M_i and p, the values of b_{iq} can be determined by the solutions of equations 27 and 28.

For the Type 2 multivariate process, equation 26, the coefficient of skewness of $\epsilon_i(\delta)$, denoted as $\gamma_i(\epsilon) \ \forall \ \delta$, is defined as

$$\gamma_i(\epsilon) = b_{ii}^{-3} \left\{ \gamma_i(x)\sigma_i^3 \left[\sum_{l=1}^{M_i} l^{3h_i-9/2} \right]^{-1} - \sum_{u=0}^{i-1} b_{iu} \gamma_u(\epsilon) \right\} \qquad (29)$$

where $b_{i,0} = 0 \ \forall \ i$. Given the values of $\gamma_i(x)$, $i = 1, \ldots, N$, equation 29 may be solved recursively to obtain $\gamma_i(\epsilon)$ for $i = 1, \ldots, N$.

The Type 2 model may be used to generate synthetic flow sequences that resemble the corresponding historical flow sequences in terms of estimates of μ_i, σ_i, $\gamma_i(x)$, $\rho_i(1)$ and b_i.

4. Alternative models

Alternative processes for approximating discrete fractional noise processes have been sought and at present two have been developed. One is the broken-line process developed by Ditlevsen (1971) in his investigations of extreme values and adapted to synthetic flow generation by Mejia (1971) and by Garcia et al. (1972). The other is the ARIMA process (Box and Jenkins, 1970) which has been used to describe streamflow sequences (Carlson et al., 1970) and adapted to synthetic flow generation by O'Connell (1971, 1974).

A broken-line process consists of a summation of a finite number of simple broken-line processes, which are defined as follows. A simple broken-line process is a sequence of intersecting line segments, where the projections of the line segments on the time axis are of equal length and where the magnitude of the intersections are randomly distributed. The projection length is allowed to vary in a prescribed manner from one simple broken-line process to another. By selecting appropriate values for the broken-line parameters, which include a basic projection length and the number of simple broken-lines to be summed, statistical resemblance can be achieved in terms of h, as well as in terms of the other parameters handled by the Type 2 process.

The term ARIMA is used to denote an autoregressive-integrated-moving average process. Such a process is similar to a lag-p autoregressive process, but with two basic differences. First, the random component for the ARIMA process is a moving average of length q of independent random components. Second, the random variable at time t denotes a dth order difference of random variables at other time points defined by the $(d - 1)$th difference. Such a process is said to be of order (p,d,q). For $d = 0$, the random variable at time t is the random variable (flow) at time t. Note, a $(p,0,0)$ ARIMA process is a pth order autoregressive process, a $(1,0,0)$ ARIMA process is a Markov process, and a $(0,0,0)$ ARIMA process is a purely independent process.

O'Connell (herein) has considered ARIMA processes of order $(p,0,q)$ and noted that with small values of p and q values of $h > 1/2$ can be preserved in long generated synthetic flow sequences. In particular, he has adapted a $(1,0,1)$ ARIMA process for the generation of synthetic flows and for the process he investigated the small sample properties of estimates of $\sigma, \rho(1)$ and h.

5. Statistical resemblance

Let Ω denote a parameter used to characterize streamflow and let ω denote the value of Ω. Although ω is unknown, an estimate of ω, denoted as $\hat{\omega}$, may be derived from the historic flows and used to derive the parameter values of a particular synthetic flow generator. Relative to the generated synthetic flows, $\hat{\omega}$ is in effect a population value. Given a synthetic flow sequence of length $\tilde{n}$, an estimate of $\hat{\omega}$, denoted as $\tilde{\omega}$, may be obtained. If $\tilde{\omega} \rightarrow \omega$ as $\tilde{n} \rightarrow \infty$, then the synthetic flows are said to resemble the historic flows in the long run with respect to $\hat{\omega}$.

For finite values of $\tilde{n}$, statistical resemblance is defined as follows. At each site of interest, L synthetic flow sequences, each of length $\tilde{n}$, are generated. For the lth sequence, the estimate of $\hat{\omega}$ is denoted as $\hat{\omega}_l$, $l = 1, \ldots, L$, and the mean of the $\tilde{\omega}_l$s is denoted as $\tilde{\omega}^* = \Sigma_{l=1}^{L} \tilde{\omega}_l / L$. If $E[\tilde{\omega}] = \lim_{L \rightarrow \infty} \tilde{\omega}^* = \tilde{\omega}$ then the synthetic flows are said to resemble the historic flows in the short run with respect to $\hat{\omega}$. Short run resemblance implies long run resemblance, by the converse is not necessarily so. In general, $\tilde{\omega}$ is a biased estimate of $\hat{\omega}$, that is $E(\tilde{\omega}) \neq R \omega$, and therefore short run resemblance does not hold. To obtain short run resemblance, the values of $\hat{\omega}_l$ must be corrected for bias.

In the generation of synthetic flows, more than one parameter characterizing streamflow is of interest. Short and long run resemblance is defined with respect to the estimate values for each of the parameters. In the above discussions of the lag-one, Markov and Type 2 models, various parameters characterizing streamflow were considered. One of the parameters was μ. The estimate of μ, denoted by $\bar{x}$, the average of the historic flows, is an unbiased estimate of the value of μ. However, for the other parameters, the moment estimates of the parameter values are biased and therefore the estimated values must be corrected for bias in order to obtain short run resemblance.

In general, the correction of bias depends upon (a) the length of synthetic sequences, $\tilde{n}$, to be generated, (b) the mathematical structure of the synthetic flow generator and (c) the assumed underlying distribution function of the random inputs, ϵ, to the synthetic flow generator. Given the complexity of the mathematical structure of synthetic flow generators, it would be very difficult to derive the analytical expressions for the bias corrections. However, Monte Carlo procedures can be used to obtain bias corrections.

Apart from the matter of bias, a distribution function for ϵ must be chosen in order to generate random numbers to be transformed into synthetic flows. If a specific distribution function for the synthetic flows is not sought, then any distribution may be chosen for ϵ such that it has finite moments up to an order equal to the highest-order moment which defines the streamflow parameters of interest. In the above discussions of the general Markov, local Markov and Type 2 models, the highest-order moment of the flows was the third to define the coefficient of skewness, in which case the distribution of ϵ must have finite moments of orders one, two and three.

Only recently has the matter of bias been considered, and to date no exact procedures have been developed for making bias corrections. A few results are available. Matalas and Wallis (1974) used Monte Carlo procedures to obtain bias corrections for moment estimates of the standard deviation, the lag-one auto-correlation coefficient, and the Hurst coefficient for the Markov and the Type 2 models on a single site basis under the assumption that ϵ is normally distributed and $\tilde{n} = 100$. The results are as follows. Let $\hat{\sigma}$, $\hat{\rho}(1)$, and $\hat{h}$ denote the estimates derived from a historic flow sequence of length n of the standard deviation, σ, the lag-one autocorrelation coefficient, ρ (1), and the Hurst coefficient, h, and let the corresponding estimates derived from a synthetic flow sequence of length $\tilde{n}$ be denoted as $\tilde{\sigma}$, $\tilde{\rho}(1)$ and $\tilde{h}$. An unbiased estimate of σ is given by $\tilde{\sigma}/\alpha$, where α

Table 2. α — Markov model: $\tilde{n}= 100$

$\hat{\rho}(1)$	0	0.1	0.2	0.3	0.4	0.5	0.6	0.7	0.8	0.9
α	1	0.99	0.99	0.99	0.98	0.98	0.97	0.95	0.94	0.90

Table 3. α—Type 2 model: $\tilde{n} = 100$, $M/P = 1000$

p \ $\hat{h}$	0.6	0.7	0.8	0.9
1	0.90	0.88	0.80	0.70
5	0.96	0.94	0.90	0.80
10	0.98	0.96	0.92	0.84
20	0.98	0.96	0.92	0.84

Table 4. $\hat{\rho}(1)$ v. $E[\tilde{\rho}]$ — Markov model: $\tilde{n} = 100$

$\hat{\rho}(1)$	0.1	0.2	0.3	0.4	0.5	0.6	0.7	0.8	0.9
$E[\tilde{\rho}]$	0.09	0.18	0.28	0.38	0.48	0.57	0.66	0.76	0.86

Table 5. $\hat{\rho}(1)$ v. $E[\tilde{\rho}]$ — Type 2 model: $\tilde{n} = 100$, $M/P = 1000$

p \\ $\hat{h}$	0.6		0.7		0.8		0.9	
	$\hat{\rho}(1)$	$E[\tilde{\rho}]$	$\hat{\rho}(1)$	$E[\tilde{\rho}]$	$\hat{\rho}(1)$	$E[\tilde{\rho}]$	$\hat{\rho}(1)$	$E[\tilde{\rho}]$
1	0.66	0.58	0.73	0.62	0.80	0.66	0.87	0.71
5	0.35	0.29	0.44	0.36	0.57	0.45	0.68	0.52
10	0.24	0.19	0.33	0.26	0.45	0.34	0.59	0.45
20	0.17	0.13	0.25	0.19	0.36	0.27	0.50	0.37

Table 6. $E[\tilde{h}]$ v. $\hat{h}$ — Type 2 model: $\tilde{n} = 100$, $M/P = 1000$

p \\ $\hat{h}$	0.6	0.7	0.8	0.9
1	0.81	0.82	0.83	0.85
5	0.74	0.76	0.78	0.81
10	0.71	0.73	0.75	0.79
20	0.68	0.71	0.74	0.78

depends upon $\hat{\rho}(1)$ for a Markov model, Table 2, and upon M, p and $\hat{h}$ for a Type 2 model, Table 3.

The expected values of $\tilde{\rho}(1)$, $E[\tilde{\rho}]$, given $\hat{\rho}(1)$ for a Markov model are given in Table 4, and the expected values of $\tilde{\rho}(1)$, $E[\tilde{\rho}]$, given $\hat{\rho}(1)$, M, $\hat{h}$ and p for a Type 2 model are given in Table 5.

For a historic flow sequence of length n, the Hurst coefficient h is estimated by

$$\hat{h} = \log(R/\hat{\sigma})/\log(n/2) \tag{30}$$

where R denotes the range of cumulative departures from $\bar{x}$. For a Type 2 model, the expected values of $\tilde{h} = \log(\tilde{R}/\tilde{\sigma})/\log(n/2)$, $E[\tilde{h}]$, given M, p and $\hat{h}$, are given in Table 6.

Wallis and O'Connell (1972) have investigated various algorithms for extimating $\rho(1)$ from small samples. Based on an algorithm suggested by Jenkins and Watts (1968) and Box and Jenkins (1970), Wallis and O'Connell suggested that $\hat{\rho}(1)$ be replaced by

$$\rho^*(1) = [\bar{\rho}(1) + (1/\tilde{n})]/[1 - 4/\tilde{n}] \tag{31}$$

where

$$\bar{\rho}(1) = \sum_{t=1}^{n-1} [X(t) - \hat{\mu}] \ [X(t+1) - \mu]/n\hat{\sigma}^2 \tag{32}$$

In doing so,

$$E[\tilde{\rho}] \approx \rho^*(1) \qquad\qquad (33)$$

6. Incomplete data sets

In practice, the historic flow sequences at each site of interest are unlikely to be concurrent and of equal length and consequently problems are likely to be encountered in generating synthetic flows. The nature of the problems is illustrated for the general Markov model. With incomplete historic data sets, the lag-zero variance—covariance matrix, $M(0)$, may be inconsistent, that is, not positive semi-definite. The solution for the elements of the matrix A, equation 8, requires the inverse of $M(0)$. If $M(0)$ is inconsistent, its eigenvalues will not all be positive, in which case some elements of A will be complex numbers and, in turn, the synthetic flows will be complex numbers. Beard (1967) and Fiering (1968) have suggested techniques for transforming an inconsistent matrix $M(0)$ into a consistent one.

Crosby and Maddock (1970) noted that for the lag-one model, even if $M(0)$ and $M(1)$ are both consistent, the matrix BB^T, defined by equation 9, may not be consistent. For a monotone sample, Crosby and Maddock (1970) have developed a technique for obtaining a consistent BB^T matrix. A monotone sample is defined as a set of sequences, each of which may have originated at different points in time and which are all continuous up to the present. The technique can be applied to the Markov model. At present, no investigations have been made as to whether or not incomplete data sets will yield complex values for the b_{iq} in the Type 2 model.

In some situations, historic flow sequences may not exist at some sites of interest. At sites where historic flow sequences do not exist, estimates of the values of parameters of interest may be obtained via regression analysis. For a particular parameter, the estimates of its values at sites for which historic flow sequences exist may be regressed on physiographic and meteorologic factors that characterize the sites (Benson and Matalas, 1967). Via the regression relation and the physiographic and meteorologic factors that characterize the sites at which historic flow sequences do not exist, estimates of the parameter values for each of the sites can be obtained.

Apart from the mean and standard deviation, it may be difficult to define an acceptable regression relation for the streamflow parameters of interest. If for a particular parameter an acceptable regression relation cannot be developed, then one might interpret the variations in the estimated values of the parameter as being entirely due to chance, whereby, the average of the estimated values might be taken as the estimate at each site where historic records do not exist and, perhaps, at those sites where historic records exist as well.

However the estimates are derived, there is no assurance that synthetic flows can be generated for those sites at which historic records do not exist. Moreover, it may not be possible to generate synthetic flows at any of the sites. For example, with the general Markov model, some elements of $M(0)$ and $M(1)$ will be estimates for sites where historic records do not exist. The matrices $M(0)$ and $M(1)$ and perhaps BB^T may not be consistent. If this is the case, then the estimates for the sites where historic records do not exist will need to be modified or the matrices adjusted to achieve consistency.

7. Summary

Three models, namely the general Markov, local Markov and Type 2, were discussed in detail as to their use in generating synthetic flow sequences, and brief mention was made of broken-line and ARIMA models as alternatives to the Type 2 model. Basically, the lag-one and Markov processes are short-memory processes characterized, at least asymptotically, by $h = 1/2$. If values of $h > 1/2$ are of interest, then a Type 2 process or some other process for approximating discrete fractional noise would have to be used to generate synthetic flows.

To be useful, synthetic flows should bear some resemblance to the corresponding historic flows. For the the most part, statistical resemblance has been defined in terms of a specified set of parameters to characterize streamflow. The choice of synthetic flow generator is determined in part by what specific set of parameters is of interest. Two types of statistical resemblance were defined — long run and short run. Long run resemblance implies a matching of the estimated values of the parameters between finite historic sequences and infinite synthetic sequences. Short run resemblance implies a matching with respect to finite synthetic sequences, Because for finite sequences the estimated values are in general biased, short run resemblance cannot be achieved without taking into account the biases. As yet, exact procedures to account for bias have not been developed.

If the historic sequences are not concurrent and of equal length, it may not be possible to generate synthetic flow sequences. It was noted that in such situations, the generated synthetic flows may be in effect complex numbers. Techniques have been developed to overcome this problem for the lag-one and Markov models. If historic flow sequences do not exist at some sites of interest, it is necessary to use some technique, such as regression analysis, in order to provide estimates of the values of parameters of interest at the sites. The estimates, however, may lead to problems similar to those encountered when the historic sequences are not concurrent and of equal length.

Comment upon Multivariate Synthetic Hydrology

GIOVANNA FINZI
Electrotechnics and Electronics Institute, Milan Polytechnic, Italy

EZIO TODINI
IBM Scientific Center, Pisa, Italy

JAMES R. WALLIS
IBM Scientific Center, Pisa (while on leave from IBM Research Center, Yorktown Heights, New York, USA)

'Secondary worlds of the imagination must possess not only internal consistency, but also strangeness and wonder arising from their freedom from the domination of observed fact . . . they should combine the ordinary with the extraordinary, the fictitious with the actual' (from *Master of Middle Earth* by Paul H. Kocher, 1972).

1. Introduction

In a recent paper O'Connell (1973) has suggested that the computer program Numerical Multisite Package (Young and Pisano, 1968) has an error that can be and should be corrected, and that the change would be relatively simple to make. We concur that the specified error exists in the NMP coding, but we believe that the suggested correction is insufficient to make the program reproduce the Matalas (1967) algorithm.

In particular, the introduction of only the O'Connell correction is insufficient to prevent the program from generating sequences with spurious properties. Finally, even if a completely corrected coding is obtained (Finzi, Todini and Wallis, herein), we have reservations about the usefulness of the obtainable results, at least as far as the two Italian river systems which we have investigated are concerned.

2. Matalas algorithm

The Matalas algorithm is based upon a multivariate weakly stationary generating process:

$$X_t = AX_{t-1} + B \cdot \epsilon_t \tag{1}$$

where X_t and X_{t-1} are N length vectors of standardized flows at time t and time

Appeared in *Water Resources Research*, 11, (6), 844–850, 1975.

$t-1$, and N the number of sites. A and B are two $N \times N$ matrices which must be defined so as to preserve the first two moments of the generated sequences, together with the lag 0 and lag 1 auto- and cross-correlations between sequences. ϵ_t is an N length vector of standardized variables from an independent process. Imposing the above-mentioned conditions we obtain

$$A = M_1 M_0^{-1} \tag{2}$$

where

$$M_0 = E[X_t X_t^T] \tag{3}$$

and

$$M_1 = E[X_t X_{t-1}^T] \tag{4}$$

Furthermore from the assumption of weak stationarity

$$M_0 = E[X_t X_t^T] = E[X_{t-1} X_{t-1}^T] \tag{5}$$

we obtain

$$BB^T = M_0 - M_1 M_0^{-1} M_1^T \tag{6}$$

An infinite number of B exist that satisfy equation 6 such that BB^T is a positive definite matrix (Slack, 1973; Young, 1968).

To provide an easy-to-obtain unique solution, matrix B can be thought of as a lower triangular matrix (Young, 1968).

3. O'Connell correction

O'Connell (1973) pointed out a discrepancy between the NMP computer algorithm and the Matalas formulation, namely that the estimate of BB^T as given by Young and Pisano

$$(BB^T)^* = M_0 - \tfrac{1}{2}[M_1 M_0^1 M_1 + M_1^T M_0^{-1} M_1^T] \tag{7}$$

which is different from equation 6 and we concur with his suggestion that the NMP coding should be modified to reflect equation 6. However, a further major problem exists in the coding that nullifies the expected benefits of O'Connell's proposed correction.

A closer look at the computer coding reveals that the correlation matrix specified by equation 4 is not computed, but instead a matrix which is essentially a lag-one correlation matrix defined as

$$M_1^* = E[X_{t-1} X_t^T] = E[(X_t X_{t-1}^T)^T] = M_1^T \tag{8}$$

More precisely the program attempts to use the circular definition of correlation for which the generic element of M_1 would be

$$m_{pq} = \frac{1}{n} \left[\sum_{t=2}^{n} X_t^p X_{t-1}^q + X_1^p X_n^q \right] \tag{9}$$

with p and q being stations and n the length of the flow records.

Actually the coding leads to

$$m_{pq}^* = \frac{1}{n} \left[\sum_{t=2}^{n} X_{t-1}^p X_t^q + X_1^p X_n^q \right] \qquad (10)$$

which means that the elements of M_1^T are computed rather than those of M_1 except for the last term of the summation which is computed following equation 9.

Given the above-mentioned discrepancy in the estimate of M_1 it becomes evident that NMP package gives a different estimate of A and BB^T from that specified by Matalas.

$$A^* = M_1^* M_0^1 \cong M_1^T M_0^1 \qquad (11)$$

$$(BB^T)^* \simeq M_0 - \tfrac{1}{2}[M_1^T M_0^{-1} M_1^T + M_1 M_0^{-1} M_1] \qquad (12)$$

with equation 12 almost equal to equation 7.

However, the introduction of the O'Connell correction with M_1 defined as an approximation of M_1^T leads to yet another estimate of BB^T

$$(BB^T)^{**} \cong M_0 - M_1^T M_0^{-1} M_1 \qquad (13)$$

A consequence of using equation 11 with either equation 12 or equation 13 is that the elements of the variance—covariance matrices of the simulated sequences are not preserved by NMP with or without the O'Connell correction being applied.

In particular, a consequence of a generating mechanism based upon A^* is that the generated sequences will have a lag-one correlation structure that is the transpose of the desired one. Confirmation for the above statement is contained in Young and Pisano (1968) where it can be seen that the historic M_1 is the transpose of the simulated M_1, both of which have been calculated by the same NMP subroutine.

For the readers convenience we have reproduced in Table 1 the observed and simulated M_1 matrices given by Young and Pisano.

Table 1. The historical and simulated M_1 matrices presented by Young and Pisano

				Historical				
1	0.246	0.306	0.321	0.310	0.275	0.300	0.258	0.185
2	0.287	0.397	0.384	0.380	0.318	0.336	0.294	0.198
3	0.277	0.381	0.409	0.366	0.280	0.333	0.298	0.237
4	0.258	0.357	0.357	0.352	0.304	0.331	0.267	0.169
5	0.212	0.289	0.268	0.296	0.329	0.326	0.236	0.143
6	0.194	0.255	0.257	0.275	0.272	0.347	0.239	0.145
7	0.175	0.221	0.245	0.229	0.210	0.265	0.229	0.175
8	0.157	0.184	0.213	0.193	0.174	0.246	0.242	0.270

				Simulated				
1	0.233	0.265	0.262	0.242	0.204	0.188	0.165	0.155
2	0.277	0.356	0.343	0.321	0.266	0.238	0.193	0.166
3	0.297	0.346	0.378	0.325	0.249	0.252	0.228	0.211
4	0.289	0.344	0.339	0.323	0.276	0.263	0.210	0.183
5	0.240	0.272	0.251	0258	0.280	0.229	0.176	0.154
6	0.280	0.308	0.328	0.302	0.294	0.316	0.248	0.243
7	0.258	0.291	0.308	0.263	0.238	0.245	0.235	0.259
8	0.195	0.214	0.267	0.183	0.160	0.170	0.200	0.312

42

4. SPUMA: An altered and corrected version NMP

In addition to the errors in coding found in NMP we found that the program was too slow and not flexible enough for our needs. We prepared a corrected and altered coding (Finzi, Todini and Wallis, herein) that is operable under CP-CMS time sharing, and with this version of the program, called SPUMA, we have made extensive tests on two Italian river systems.

5. Simulation results obtained with SPUMA

For our tests of SPUMA we used driving parameters estimated from 29 years of monthly flow data for five Arno river sites (Figure 1), and 22 years of monthly flow data for five Tiber river sites (Figure 2).

For these two Italian river systems at least, we shall show below that the simple Markovian algorithm represented by equation 1 does not yield an accurate representation of the observed monthly flows. While we do not know the operational effect of using such biased simulated sequences we suggest that the magnitude of the biases observed for the Arno and Tiber river systems might be sufficient to disturb the results of any subsequent reservoir optimization study.

In the closing sections of this note we shall briefly present some of our simulation results and compare them with the observed correlation structure, means, standard

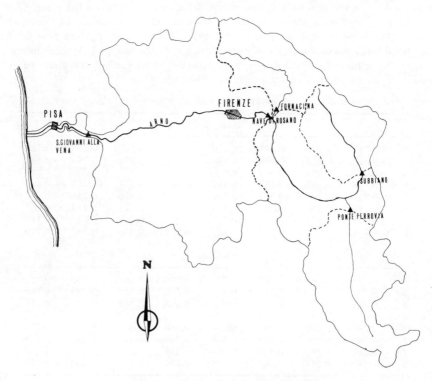

Figure 1. Map of the Arno river basin

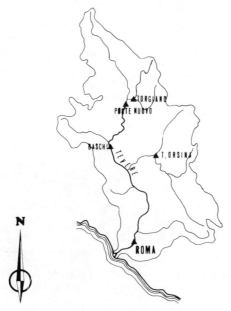

Figure 2. Map of the Tiber river basin

deviations, skewness and extreme values of the observed sequences. We shall conclude with a short look at the internal consistency of the generated sequences.

6. Correlation structure

The correlograms of the monthly standardized flows do not appear to be well represented by the simple Markovian hypothesis of equation 1. In Figures 3 and 4 we present two observed correlograms along with the average correlograms for simulated Markovian sequences of equal length and equal ρ_1.

It would appear that our observed sequences tend to be more persistent than is consistent with the use of the simple Markov model of equation 1. It should be possible to remove this bias in the synthetic flow correlation structure by using autoregressive-moving average models, ARMA processes, as adapted for synthetic hydrology by O'Connell (1974) and hence to estimate whether this bias is operationally important.

7. M_0 and M_1 correlation matrices

The Matalas algorithm preserves the observed M_0 and M_1 correlation structure in infinite samples. The small sample bias introduced by using monthly design sequences is not very large and appears unlikely to cause much distortion in subsequent reservoir design studies. The observed M_0 and M_1 matrices for the Arno river data are presented in Table 2.

Monthly river flow data are invariably positively skewed. Currently, SPUMA assumes a normal distribution for the term ϵ_t in equation 1, and therefore a

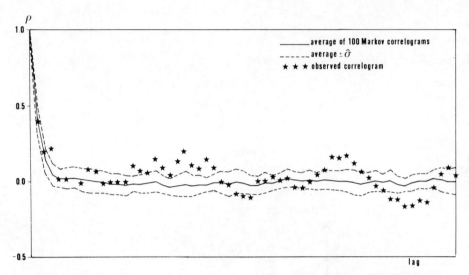

Figure 3. Observed correlogram for 29 years of standardized monthly flows for the Arno river at San Giovanni alla Vena. A least squares ARMA (1,1) fitted to this observed correlogram has $\varphi = 0.58920$ and $\theta = 0.24072$

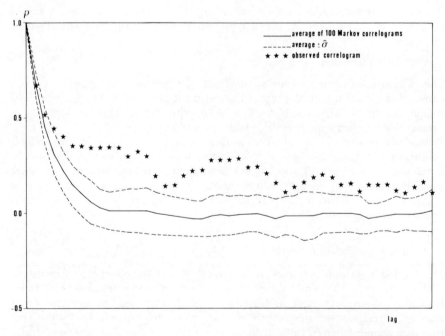

Figure 4. Observed correlogram for 22 years of standardized monthly flows for the Tiber river at Rome. A least squares ARMA (1,1) fitted to this observed correlogram has $\varphi = 0.94450$ and $\theta = 0.58489$

Table 2. M_0 and M_1 matrices for 29 years of standardized monthly Arno river data

M_0				
1.00				
0.93	1.00			
0.87	0.94	1.00		
0.83	0.90	0.91	1.00	
0.75	0.81	0.82	0.70	1.00

M_1				
0.26	0.25	0.26	0.24	0.23
0.28	0.30	0.31	0.30	0.26
0.32	0.34	0.39	0.37	0.31
0.32	0.33	0.35	0.38	0.27
0.21	0.22	0.27	0.24	0.24

transformation of the flows may be necessary to justify this assumption. Based upon the observed value of skewness a decision can be implemented under the CP-CMS monitor to apply either no transformation or a logarithmic or square root transformation. If no transformation is applied the synthetic flows will have a multivariate normal distribution and the algorithm will produce a percentage of negative synthetic flows. As will be discussed later both the quantity and magnitude of these negative synthetic flows can be quite large. For the Arno and Tiber river systems these negative simulated flows can be set to zero without appreciably influencing the resulting average M_0 and M_1 simulated correlation matrices. However, if a logarithmic transformation of the data is selected a small distortion is introduced into the M_0 and M_1 matrices. Table 3 shows the results for logarithmic

Table 3. Difference between average of 100 simulated and the observed M_0 and M_1 matrices for 29 years of Arno river data. Simulated sequences were of the same length as the observed sequences, logarithmic and subsequent exponentiation transformation used

$\bar{M}_0$ (simulated) $-$ M_0 (observed)				
0.00				
−0.01	0.00			
+0.01	−0.00	0.00		
+0.03	−0.01	−0.01	0.00	
−0.05	−0.05	−0.02	−0.01	0.00

$\bar{M}_1$ (simulated) $-$ M_1 (observed)				
+0.10	+0.07	+0.06	+0.07	+0.04
+0.07	+0.07	+0.05	+0.05	+0.05
+0.07	+0.07	+0.05	+0.04	+0.06
+0.06	+0.05	+0.04	+0.04	+0.05
+0.08	+0.08	+0.05	+0.04	+0.11

transformed sequences of length equal to the observed sequences (29 years), increasing the simulated sequence length to 50 or 100 years to slightly increase the magnitude of these biases.

8. The means

When no transformation is applied to the flows SPUMA does a good job of preserving the monthly means. The observed monthly mean flows for one site, the Tiber at Rome, are shown in Table 4, along with the average and standard deviation resulting from 100 simulated sequences of equal length (22 years).

The simulated sequences for the Rome site had few negative flows and therefore setting those that occurred to zero had only a negligible effect on the means for the simulated sequences; however, not all sites display this favourable characteristic. For instance, as shown in Table 5, the simulated sequences for the Arno river at San Giovanni had many negatives in the simulated sequences and setting these to zero or using a logarithmic transform introduces a bias in the expected value of the monthly means.

9. The standard deviations

As expected the standard deviation of simulated sequences of equal length to the observed sequences are less variable than the observed, but as pointed out by Matalas (herein) there is as yet no known analytic solution to this problem. Table 6 gives the standard deviations of the observed sequences and the average of 100 simulated runs and it can be seen that this bias is small unless the negative flows are set to zero or a logarithmic transformation is used. It is worth noting that the standard deviation is seriously underestimated if negative flows are set to 0.0, and that there is a tendency for the wet month synthetic flows to be more variable than the observed if the logarithmic transformation is invoked.

10. Extreme values

The computer algorithm has no explicit provision for preserving the seasonal coefficient of skewness, γ, and if the observed γs are much different from zero the

Table 4. Monthly mean flow for the Tiber river at Rome and the average and standard deviation for 100 simulated sequences of equal length (22 years)

Item	Jan.	Feb.	March	Apr.	May	June	July	Aug.	Sept.	Oct.	Nov.	Dec.
Observed	319	382	324	269	240	184	139	126	146	176	248	334
Average of simulated sequences	320	382	321	265	239	183	139	125	146	177	248	334
Standard deviation of simulated sequences	33	56	35	25	23	15	10	8	10	18	27	52

Table. 5. Average of 100 simulated sequences for the Arno river at San Giovanni compared to the observed monthly data. All sequences of equal length (29 years)

Item	Jan.	Feb.	March	Apr.	May	June	July	Aug.	Sept.	Oct.	Nov.	Dec.
% of monthly flows equal to 0.0 in the observed rec	0.0	0.0	0.0	0.0	0.0	0.0	0.0	0.0	0.0	0.0	0.0	0.0
% of monthly simulated flows less than or equal to 0.0	3.3	5.9	5.9	2.3	5.7	8.2	6.7	0.8	17.9	18.9	10.6	10.1
Observed monthly means	164	193	183	113	90	54	18	10	20	64	130	188
Simulated monthly means using no transformation	164	194	180	111	90	54	18	10	20	66	128	187
Simulated monthly means with negatives set to zero	165	197	183	112	91	55	18	10	23	73	133	193
Simulated monthly means using logarithmic transformation	168	203	187	114	89	55	18	10	19	66	132	198

Table 6. Observed monthly standard deviation and the average standard deviation for 100 simulated sequences of equal length to the observed (29 years)

Item	Jan.	Feb.	March	Apr.	May	June	July	Aug.	Sept.	Oct.	Nov.	Dec.
Observed	90.7	124.3	115.0	54.3	59.4	37.7	12.1	4.4	22.8	75.6	101.6	143.6
Average of synthetic sequences	89.7	123.8	114.8	54.2	57.6	37.8	11.7	4.3	22.5	73.6	99.6	142.0
Average of synthetic sequences with negatives set to zero	87.4	117.0	109.7	53.1	54.5	35.0	11.1	4.2	19.2	61.7	90.7	130.9
Average of synthetic sequences with logarithmic transformation	108.3	163.7	138.3	67.5	55.0	44.3	10.2	5.1	18.6	96.4	117.9	195.2

Table 7. Coefficient of skewness, γ, for the observed Arno river flow measurements at San Giovanni and the average γs for synthetic traces of varying lengths. Averages based upon 100 repetitions with logarithmic and subsequent exponentation transformation of the data

Item	Jan.	Feb.	March	Apr.	May	June	July	Aug.	Sept.	Oct.	Nov.	Dec.
Observed γs, 29 years	0.79	1.18	1.39	0.14	1.72	1.23	2.41	0.26	2.42	1.35	1.09	1.03
Simulated γs, 29 years	1.42	1.78	1.71	1.44	1.40	1.70	1.38	1.29	2.14	2.57	1.94	2.00
Simulated γs, 60 years	1.76	2.16	1.87	1.66	1.64	2.14	1.44	1.37	2.47	3.30	2.25	2.32
Simulated γs, 90 years	1.88	2.26	1.94	1.52	1.81	2.36	1.72	1.79	2.66	3.99	2.32	2.41

extreme values of the simulated sequences (highs and lows) will be biased. The simulated sequences are generated with zero seasonal skewness and the use of a simple logarithmic transformation could only be expected to give synthetic sequences with appropriate skewness under rather rare circumstances; some results for one river are shown in Table 7. The increase in the average value of skewness observed for the logarithmic transformed synthetic sequences as a function of sequence length usually accords with known expected values for an independent logarithmic normal distribution. As an example consider the last column of Table 7 which shows the average γs for 100 simulated samples of length 29, 60 and 90

Table 8. Observed monthly highs for the Tiber river gauge at Rome based upon 22 years of record, and the average simulated monthly highs for sequences of similar and different length

Item	Jan.	Feb.	March	Apr.	May	June	July	Aug.	Sept.	Oct.	Nov.	Dec.
Observed peak 22 years	604	990	597	501	534	360	228	197	224	341	459	1015
Average highest length 22 years	581	793	596	465	431	310	209	182	227	328	447	734
Average highest length 60 years	638	905	654	516	480	342	226	199	248	371	501	831
Average highest length 90 years	664	958	706	534	497	363	229	200	249	384	509	862
Logarithmic transformation												
Average highest length 22 years	690	916	708	530	496	335	221	193	247	573	512	824
Average highest length 60 years	820	1119	843	612	591	393	243	216	280	743	585	997
Average highest length 90 years	880	1205	911	662	636	423	254	222	294	823	609	1096

ranging from 2.00 to 2.32 to 2.41. The expected values for a three-parameter logarithmic normal with $\gamma = 5$ at lengths of 30, 60 and 90 are 2.04, 2.55 and 2.85 (Wallis *et al.*, 1974a).

Often in synthetic hydrology the algorithm is driven with parameters estimated from short sequences while the simulated sequences to be used in the reservoir design studies are considerably longer. Long synthetic sequences could be expected to yield higher peak values than short sequences, and this expectation is confirmed by the results presented in Table 8. However, it should be pointed out that if the logarithmic transformation is not used then the peak simulated values are too low for sequences of equal length to the observed length, and the peaks increase only slightly with increasing length. The increases in observed peak values shown in Table 8 for the logarithmically transformed data are more reasonable, but comparative values for sequences of equal length are unfortunately not very close.

11. Internal consistency

The flows of some rivers are consistently bigger than those of others, but the synthetic sequences generated by this algorithm are not constrained to have this property. For instance, from Figure 1 we could expect that the flow at Fornacina (catchment area 831 km^2) would be considerably less than the same monthly flow at Nave di Rosano (catchment area 4063 km^2), a prediction that is confirmed by the values to be found in Table 9. Without logarithmic transformation the

Table 9. Statistics of difference between monthly flows for Nave di Rosano minus Fornacina

Item	Jan.	Feb.	March	Apr.	May	June	July	Aug.	Sept.	Oct.	Nov.	Dec.
Observed values												
% negative	0.0	0.0	0.0	0.0	0.0	0.0	0.0	0.0	0.0	0.0	0.0	0.0
Mean difference	68	83	77	50	39	22	7	4	9	25	54	80
Standard deviation of difference	41	59	48	26	31	19	5	3	11	33	43	58
Simulated flow (sample of 500 years)												
% negative	2.6	5.0	2.4	1.4	5.0	5.6	2.2	2.2	6.8	8.6	5.0	4.6
Mean difference	69	84	77	49	40	25	7	4	10	30	55	83
Standard deviation of difference	40	54	47	25	28	17	4	3	9	27	39	56
Simulated flows logarithmic transformation (Sample of 500 years)												
% negative	0.0	0.0	0.0	0.0	0.0	0.0	0.0	0.0	0.0	0.0	0.0	0.0
Mean difference	70	84	78	50	39	23	7	4	8	25	54	85
Standard deviation of difference	51	75	61	29	31	21	5	3	9	40	52	85

simulated flows preserve the first two moments of the difference in monthly flow between these two stations, but not the third moment. Completely unreasonable combinations do occur a small percentage of the time. Logarithmic data transformation eliminates almost all of the pathological problem of the small tributary having a simulated flow greater than the main channel flow, but results in differences for the highflow months being more variable than the observed differences.

It is evident that internal consistency is not likely to be preserved by a simple Markov multisite multiseason generating model, and the user should consider whether or not internal consistency is an important enough property that it should be specified in the generating algorithm. While an explicit specification for consistency that would cover all situations might be difficult to obtain it is felt that an explicit attempt at preserving the observed skewness, and a better attempt at preserving the observed correlation structure, might go a long way towards removing the inconsistency problem.

12. Summary of simulation results

Multisite multiseason synthetic hydrology can be useful in the evaluation of proposed water reservoir systems. However, the authors concur with Clarke's statement (herein), 'the uncritical usage of stochastic generation methods, applied without regard to the individual characteristics of the problem, should therefore be avoided at all costs'.

It is evident, at least for the two Italian river systems studied, that a simple lag-one monthly Markov model produces population statistics for which many of the observed statistics would have to be considered as rare events. In particular, if persistence, that is, runs of high or low values is important, or if the magnitude and probability of extreme events are important, then there are grounds to question the validity of using such a simple algorithm for the generation of synthetic sequences.

ARIMA Models in Synthetic Hydrology

PATRICK E. O'CONNELL

Department of Civil Engineering, Imperial College, University of London, UK

1. Introduction

Among recent developments in synthetic hydrology, the phenomenon of persistence has received considerable attention. Persistence in streamflow is invariably defined as a tendency for low flows to follow low flows and high flows to follow high flows and, for the purpose of generating synthetic flows, is usually considered to be synonymous with autocorrelation which may in turn be attributed to storage effects. In the application of synthetic hydrology to the design of water resource systems, the modelling of persistence merits careful consideration, as it directly determines reservoir storage sizes.

Persistence in annual streamflow sequences was perhaps first comprehensively studied by Hurst (1951, 1956) who was primarily concerned with the design of storage reservoirs on the river Nile. Hurst quantified observed persistence in terms of a parameter *h*, the average value of which he found to be approximately 0.73 for a very large number of time series, and which he noted to be in distinct disagreement with the value of *h* equal to 0.5 synonymous with an independent random process. Early attempts at generating synthetic streamflows assumed that observed persistence was essentially short-term and could be represented by Markovian autocorrelation (Thomas and Fiering, 1962), an assumption which did not appear to accord with the findings of Hurst (Matalas and Huzzen, 1967). In a significant contribution to synthetic hydrology, Mandelbrot and Wallis (1969a,b,c,d,e) contended that Hurst's findings could not be explained by Markovian autocorrelation and proposed fractional Gaussian noise instead as a model with a suitable theoretical basis. The autocorrelation function of fractional Gaussian noise, governed by the parameter *h*, implies the existence of a long-term memory, giving rise to the phenomenon of long-term persistence, the intensity of which increases as the parameter *h* increases from 0.5 to 1. Markovian autocorrelation is synonymous with a value of *h* of 0.5.

Fractional Gaussian noise (fGn) being a process with an infinte memory, finite memory approximations to fGn are required for generating synthetic flows on a digital computer. Recent approximations to fGn include fast fractional Gaussian noise (Mandelbrot, 1971); ARIMA models (Box and Jenkins, 1970) as applied by O'Connell (1971, 1974); filtered fractional Gaussian noise (Matalas and Wallis, 1971) and the broken-line process (Mejia *et al.*, 1972). Of these approximations ARIMA processes are relatively easily applied in generating synthetic flows, and some of the small sample parameter estimation problems associated with generating sequences of annual flows may to some extent be overcome (O'Connell, 1974).

In Section 2, long-term persistence and fractional Gaussian noise are discussed. The application of one of the family of ARIMA models in modelling long-term persistence is illustrated in Section 3, while the application of the model in the generation of synthetic flows is dealt with in Section 4.

2. Long-term persistence and fractional Gaussian noise

2.1 Range of cumulative departures

In his study of the long-term storage capacity of reservoirs, Hurst (1951, 1956) employed a statistic referred to as the range of cumulative departures which is defined as follows. Let $X_1, X_2, \ldots, X_n$ be a sequence of annual inflows into a reservoir over n years. Let $\bar{X}$ denote the sample mean and define

$$D_n = \sum_{i=1}^{n} X_i$$

where D_n represents the total amount of water flowing into the reservoir in the n years. To maintain a constant outflow equal to the average inflow would require the removal of

$$\frac{1}{n} \sum_{l=1}^{n} X_i$$

each year. With such a rate of removal

$$\frac{k}{n} \sum_{i=1}^{n} X_i$$

is the amount removed over the first k years. Hence

$$D_k^* = \sum_{i=1}^{k} X_i - \frac{k}{n} \sum_{i=1}^{n} X_i$$
$$= D_k - kD_n/n$$

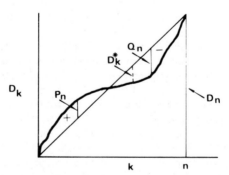

Figure 1. Schematic plot of range of cumulative departures

represents the excess or deficiency relative to the amount removed up to the kth year (Figure 1).

Defining

$$P_n = \max D_k^* \quad 1 \leqslant k \leqslant n$$

and

$$Q_n = \min D_k^* \quad 1 \leqslant k \leqslant n$$

as the largest excess and greatest deficiency respectively over the constant outflow during the n years the quantity

$$R_n = P_n - Q_n$$

is known as the range of cumulative departures from the sample mean or adjusted range. The 'ideal' reservoir represented by this concept becomes extremely large over a long time span and accordingly is never economically justifiable.

However, the variation of R_n with n provides insight into the yield that might be maintained from any given capacity of reservoir.

2.2 Hurst phenomenon

In his extensive analysis, Hurst (1951, 1956) computed the quantity R_n for some 800 times series of annual values of streamflow, precipitation, temperature, tree rings, mud varves etc. ranging in length from 40 to 2000 years. He then standardized each value of R_n by dividing R_n by S_n, the standard deviation of the time series of n values to yield the statistic R_n/S_n, referred to as the rescaled range, which he then found to vary with n as

$$\frac{R_n}{S_n} \sim n^h \tag{1}$$

with values of h lying in the range 0 to 1, implying that the relationship between $\ln(R_n/S_n)$ and $\ln(n)$ is linear with slope h (Figure 2). To determine h, Hurst defined

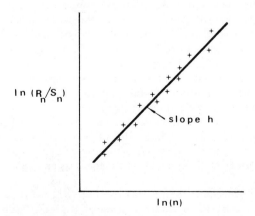

Figure 2. Schematic plot of Hurst's law

$$\frac{R_n}{S_n} = \left\{\frac{n}{2}\right\}^K \tag{2}$$

and computed K, which represents an estimate of h for each of the time series. Over all phenomena K was found to have an average value of 0.73 with a standard deviation of 0.08.

For a purely random normal process with n large, Hurst (1951) and Feller (1951) independently showed that

$$E\{R_n\} = \left(\frac{n\pi}{2}\right)^{1/2} \sigma \tag{3}$$

where σ denotes the population standard deviation of the process. Feller also indicated that this result was distribution free for an independent process. The failure of the exponent K in equation 2 to accord with theory based on random inflows (equation 3) ($h = 0.5$) has been labelled the Hurst phenomenon (Lloyd, 1967). In physical terms Hurst's findings suggest that for a given value of n, the size of the ideal reservoir would need to be larger than the capacity corresponding to a purely random series of inflows. Departures from Hurst's law would be represented by variation in h with n. An explanation of the Hurst phenomenon requires finding a statistical process for which Hurst's law, with $h > 0.5$, holds for values of n comparable with the longest geophysical records available.

In the literature, a number of possible explanations of the Hurst phenomenon have been offered:

    (i) skewness
   (ii) transience
  (iii) non-stationarity
  (iv) autocorrelation

The hypothesis (i) may be discarded on the basis of studies by Matalas and Huzzen (1967) and Mandelbrot and Wallis (1969e), who showed that the behaviour of the rescaled range R_n/S_n for a number of stochastic processes is unaffected by the marginal distribution of the process, confirming an earlier observation by Langbein (1956) on Hurst's data. However, some erroneous explanations of the Hurst phenomenon have been based on marginal distribution through considering the behaviour of the unscaled range R_n which is affected by marginal distribution, unlike the rescaled range R_n/S_n.

With regard to hypothesis (ii), the implication is that, if sufficiently long time series were available in nature, h would tend to a value of 0.5 corresponding to asymptotic independence. Rejection or acceptance of this hypothesis must await the availability of longer geophysical records. However, whether or not this hypothesis is true, an explanation of the observed transient behaviour with h greater than 0.5 must still be attempted. At this stage hypotheses (iii) and (iv) must be considered as either of these could be advanced as an explanation of the Hurst phenomenon.

In an attempt to account for his own findings, Hurst (1957) invoked a crude form of non-stationarity in the mean of simulated series, resulting in some very approximate agreement with the behaviour of the rescaled range observed in nature. Klemes (1974) generalized Hurst's approach and showed that good agreement could be obtained with Hurst's law with $0.5 < h < 1$ over long transients. However, non-stationarity is a rather intractable assumption if the ultimate aim is to generate synthetic flows; provided stationary stochastic processes which can reproduce the Hurst phenomenon are available, these would appear to be more desirable for application in the planning of water resource systems, provided strong physical grounds do not inhibit their use.

Early attempts at explaining the Hurst phenomenon through hypothesis (iv), autocorrelation, employed models of the autoregressive type, with the lag-one autoregressive or Markov process receiving particular attention (Matalas and Huzzen, 1967; Fiering, 1967). However, these attempts were largely unsuccessful. In the case of the lag-one Markov process, the autocorrelation function ρ_k is given as

$$\rho_k = (\rho_1)^k \tag{4}$$

A typical value of $\hat{\rho}_1$ for yearly streamflow data is 0.3; hence ρ_k approaches zero very quickly and the memory of such a process is extremely short. The behaviour of the rescaled range here is characterized by a short initial transient, where for small values of n, $h > 0.5$, followed by a break to the classical '$h = 0.5$' law. Such behaviour is not representative of geophysical time series where no convergence to the '$h = 0.5$' law has been observed. In applying multi-lag autoregressive models, Fiering (1967) found that he required a 20-lag model to ensure Hurst's law (equation 1), with $h > 0.5$ held for $n \leqslant 60$. Computational, not statistical grounds, prevented an extension of this approach.

2.3 Fractional Gaussian noise

In a series of papers, Mandelbrot and Wallis (1968, 1969a,b,c,d,e) proposed a stationary stochastic process called fractional Gaussian noise which had as a theoretical basis Hurst's law with h lying anywhere in the range 0 to 1, thus accounting for the Hurst phenomenon. The form of the autocorrelation function implies the existence of an infinite memory, which in turn gives rise to the phenomenon of long-term persistence or the tendency for periods of high (or low) flow to be extremely long. Some of the the relevant theoretical properties of fGn are as follows

$$\rho_k = \tfrac{1}{2}[|k + 1|^{2h} - 2|k|^{2h} + |k - 1|^{2h}] \tag{5}$$

which implies for large k that

$$\rho_k \sim k^{2h-2}$$

while the rescaled range obeys Hurst's law asymptotically:

$$\frac{R_n}{S_n} \sim n^h \qquad 0 < h < 1 \tag{6}$$

The structure of fGn places considerable emphasis on low frequencies, reflected

56

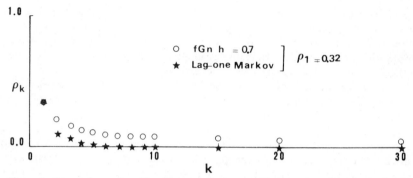

Figure 3. Comparison of ρ_k for fGn and the lag-one Markov process on the basis of equal values of ρ_1

in the variance of the sample mean $\bar{X}$ which obeys

$$\mathrm{Var}(\bar{X}) = \frac{\sigma^2}{n^2} - 2b \tag{7}$$

and reduces to the well known result for an independent process when $b = 0.5$.

The distinction between fGn and other stationary stochastic processes is perhaps best appreciated by considering the summation of the autocorrelation function $\Sigma_{k=0}^{\infty}\rho_k$ which for models of the autoregressive and moving average type is finite, allowing them to be classified with the 'Brownian domain of attraction' (Mandelbrot and Wallis, 1968). However, for fGn, $\Sigma_{k=0}^{\infty}\rho_k$ is divergent, thus placing it outside the 'Brownian domain'. A graphical comparison of ρ_k for fGn and the lag-one Markov process is presented in Figure 3 on the basis of equal values of ρ_1 for both processes which emphasizes the large disparity in the behaviour of the autocorrelation functions for large lags, which is why Markovian autocorrelation fails to account for the Hurst phenomenon. It is also perhaps pertinent to point out that a stationary linear Guassian process with equation 6 as a basis possesses a unique autocorrelation function, i.e. that of fGn which is given by equation 5.

For application in synthetic hydrology, fGn must be specified as a generating process which must have a finite memory and thus represents only an approximation to fGn. This in turn means that $\Sigma_{k=0}^{\infty}\rho_k$ now becomes finite, placing the generating process in the Brownian domain of attraction. However, provided the autocorrelation function of the approximation follows closely the theoretical form given by equation 5 with prespecified values of b, up to some finite value of the lag-k, referred to as the memory of the approximation, M, the behaviour of the rescaled range will follow equation 6 with the desired value of b up to some value of $n = M^*$ where $M^* \geqslant M$. For $n > M^*$, b then tends to 0.5. The virtue of fGN is that equation 6 is asymptotically valid and, consequently, values of M may be chosen as large as desired.

2.4 Approximations to fGn

Mandelbrot and Wallis (1969a) proposed approximations to fGn which they referred to as Type 1 and Type 2, both of which possessed some deficiencies. The

57

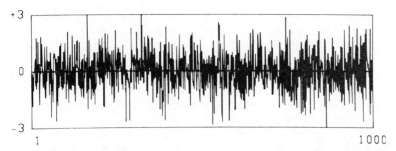

Figure 4. Plot of 1000 points of Gaussian white noise standardized to have zero mean and unit variance

Type 1 approximation proved expensive computationally, while the Type 2 approximation was notably lacking in high frequencies. Since then, better approximations have emerged, two of which are fast fractional Gaussian noise (Mandelbrot, 1971) and filtered fractional noise (Matalas and Wallis, 1971). Only the latter approximation will be considered here, which is expressed as

$$X_t = (b - 0.5) \sum_{i=pt-M}^{pt-1} (pt - i)^{h-1.5} \epsilon_i \quad 0.5 < b < 1 \quad (8)$$

where M is the memory of the process and $p > 1$ is an integer. Thus, values X_1, X_2, ... are generated by applying the set of weights $\{M^{h-1.5}, \ldots, i^{b-1.5}, \ldots, 1^{b-1.5}\}$ successively to the sequence of independent random variables

$$\{\epsilon_{p-M}, \epsilon_{p-M+1}, \ldots, \epsilon_{p-2}, \epsilon_{p-1}\}, \{\epsilon_{2p-M}, \epsilon_{2p-M+1}, \ldots, \epsilon_{2p-2}, \epsilon_{2p-1}\}, \ldots$$

respectively. Perhaps the best way to appreciate the difference between white Gaussian noise and fractional Gaussian noise is to compare sample functions: Figure 4 is a 1000-point realization from an independent $N(0, 1)$ process while Figure 5 is a 1000-point realization from a filtered fractional Gaussian noise process with $b = 0.8$. Figure 5 exhibits considerably more low frequency behaviour or long-term persistence than does Figure 4, where the spectral variance of the process is uniformly distributed with frequency.

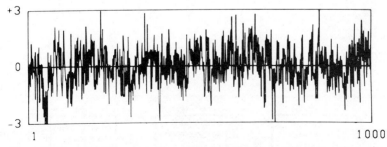

Figure 5. Plot of 1000 points generated by a filtered fractional Gaussian noise approximation with $b = 0.8$, $p = 20$ and $M = 20000$, standardized to have zero mean and unit variance

58

The mean, μ, variance, σ^2, skewness, γ, and lag-one autocorrelation ρ_1 of the filtered fGn approximation given by equation 8 have been derived by Matalas and Wallis (1971). Thus, estimates of these parameters, denoted as $\hat{\mu}$, $\hat{\sigma}^2$, $\hat{\gamma}$ and $\hat{\rho}_1$, and of h may be obtained from a historic sequence, and equation 8 can then be used to generate synthetic flows which resemble historic flows in terms of the estimated parameters. However, some consideration must be given to the type of resemblance to be maintained between historic and synthetic flows as pointed out by Matalas (herein). As estimates of σ^2, ρ_1 and h from small samples are biased in the presence of long-term persistence, bias corrections must be applied to estimates of these parameters in order to maintain short-run resemblance, i.e. resemblance between historic and synthetic sequence of equal length. Until such time as the effects of maintaining different types of resemblance between historic and synthetic flows is examined in terms of design losses, short-run resemblance would appear to be the appropriate resemblance to maintain. However, to maintain short-run resemblance, only limited results, derived by Monte Carlo methods, are available which could be used to apply bias corrections, and these exist only for the filtered fractional noise approximation (Matalas, herein).

Some further generating processes have been proposed which can be regarded as approximations to fGn, namely ARIMA processes (Box and Jenkins, 1970) as applied to O'Connell (1971, 1974) and the broken-line process (Mejia et al., 1972). Some of the properties of the broken-line process are discussed by Mandelbrot (1972) and O'Connell (1974). In the following sections the long-term properties of an ARIMA process, the ARIMA (1, 0, 1), are considered, and its adaptation to synthetic flow generation is illustrated.

3. ARIMA modelling of long-term persistence

3.1 The general ARIMA (p, d, q) process

Box and Jenkins (1970) have developed a model called an autoregressive-integrated-moving average (ARIMA) process which have shown to be capable of describing a wide range of behaviour in time series observed in business and industry. For a concise description of the general form of the model it is convenient to define the following simple operators. Let X_t represent a stochastic process in discrete time. Define a backward shift operator B as

$$BX_t = X_{t-1} \tag{9}$$

hence

$$B^m X_t = X_{t-m}$$

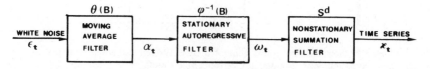

Figure 6. Block diagram representation of ARIMA $(p, d, q,)$ process

Define a backward difference operator:

$$\nabla X_t = X_t - X_{t-1} = (1 - B)X_t \tag{10}$$

The operator ∇ has for its inverse the summation operator S given by

$$\nabla^{-1} X_t = SX_t = \sum_{i=0}^{\infty} X_{t-i}$$

$$= X_t + X_{t-1} + X_{t-2} + \ldots$$

$$= (1 + B + B^2 + \ldots)X_t$$

$$= (1 - B)^{-1} X_t$$

Consider a mixed autoregressive-moving average process (ARMA (p, q)) as follows:

$$X_t = \varphi_1 X_{t-1} + \varphi_2 X_{t-2} + \ldots + \varphi_p X_{t-p} + \epsilon_t - \theta_1 \epsilon_{t-1}$$
$$- \theta_2 \epsilon_{t-2} - \ldots - \theta_q \epsilon_{t-q} \tag{11}$$

where ϵ_t, ϵ_{t-1}, ϵ_{t-2}, ... form a series of uncorrelated random variables (white noise), and p, q define the orders of the autoregression and moving average, respectively. In terms of the previously defined operators, equation 11 may be written as

$$(1 - \varphi_1 B - \varphi_2 B^2 - \ldots - \varphi_p B^p)X_t = (1 - \theta_1 B - \theta_2 B^2 - \ldots - \theta_q B^q)\epsilon_t$$

or

$$\varphi(B)X_t = \theta(B)\epsilon_t$$

where $\varphi(B)$ and $\theta(B)$ are polynomials of degree p and q in B respectively. Stationarity of X_t requires that the roots of the polynomial

$$\varphi(B) = 0$$

lie outside the unit circle, with no condition on $\theta(B)$. Similarly, for invertibility (the facility of expressing moving average behaviour in autoregressive terms with convergent weights), the roots of

$$\theta(B) = 0$$

must lie outside the unit circle, with no condition on $\varphi(B)$.

If X_t is not stationary, but the latter conditions on $\varphi(B)$ and $\theta(B)$ are maintained, the process may be written as follows:

$$\varphi(B)\nabla^d X_t = \theta(B)\epsilon_t \tag{13}$$

i.e. if

$$W_t = \nabla^d X_t$$

is stationary, where ∇^d represents the dth difference of the process X_t, then W_t may be described by a stationary ARMA process of order (p, q). Equation 13 is known as an ARIMA process of order (p, d, q) and may be represented in the block diagram form of figure 6.

Box and Jenkins (1970) have found that for most time series encountered in

60

business and industry, p, d and q are at most 2. While non-stationary ARIMA models with $d > 0$ may be used for forecasting, it would be inappropriate to employ such models for generating synthetic flows (Watts, 1972). In any case, for some ranges of parameter values, stationary ARIMA models with $d = 0$ possess autocorrelation functions which damp out rather slowly, thus implying they could be used to model long-term persistence.

3.2 The ARIMA (1, 0, 1) model of long-term persistence

By putting both p and q equal to unity in equation 11, the simple ARIMA (1, 0, 1) process is obtained, which, omitting the subscripts, is written as

$$X_t = \varphi X_{t-1} + \epsilon_t - \theta \epsilon_{t-1} \tag{14}$$

The stationarity and invertibility conditions for the process are $-1 < \varphi < +1$ and $-1 < \theta < +1$, respectively and are represented in Figure 7. The autocorrelation function of the process is defined as

$$\rho_1 = \frac{(\varphi - \theta)(1 - \varphi\theta)}{1 + \theta^2 - 2\varphi\theta} \tag{15a}$$

$$\rho_k = \varphi \rho_{k-1} \quad k \geqslant 2 \tag{15b}$$

which implies that ρ_k decays exponentially from ρ_1 onwards, the rate of decay being controlled by the value of φ. O'Connell (1971, 1974) has explored the parameter space of the process given in Figure 7 and has found that the sub-region defined by $0 < \theta < 1$, $0 < \varphi < 1$, $\varphi > \theta$ (shown hatched in Figure 7) is of particular interest in modelling long-term persistence.

The ARIMA (1, 0, 1) process reduces to the ARIMA (1, 0, 0) or lag-one Markov process for the case of $\theta = 0$; nevertheless, for similar short-term properties, measured, for example, by ρ_1, the processes can exhibit distinctly different long-term properties, as evidenced by the following comparison. A typical value of ρ_1 for annual streamflow is probably of the order of 0.4, allowing for bias in

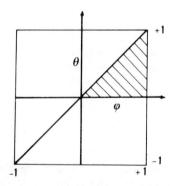

Figure 7. Parameter space for a stationary invertible ARIMA (1,0,1) process. The shaded sub-region is the area of the parameter space relevant in modelling long-term persistence

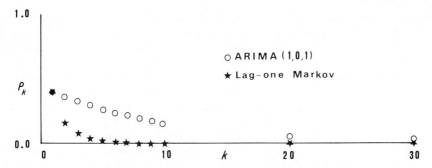

Figure 8. Comparison of ρ_k for the ARIMA (1,0,1) process with $\phi = 0.90$ and $\theta = 0.64$ and the lag-one Markov process in the basis of equal values of ρ_1

estimates of ρ_1. For the ARIMA (1, 0, 0) process ρ_k is then determined for higher lags by equation 4. In the case of the ARIMA (1, 0, 1) process, for any value of φ greater than $\rho_1 = 0.4$, a value of θ can be found such that the process has the required value of ρ_1, with large values of φ ensuring the autocorrelation function decays slowly. For the case of $\varphi = 0.90$ and $\theta = 0.64$, $\rho_1 \cong 0.4$, and a comparison of ρ_k can be made for the lag-one Markov process on the basis of equal values of ρ_1 (Figure 8), illustrating that the processes can have distinctly different long-run properties. The difference is reinforced visually by comparing sample functions presented in Figures 9 and 10 where the lack of low frequencies is evident for the

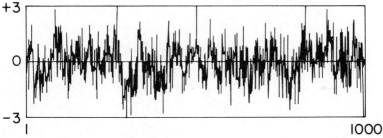

Figure 9. Plot of 1000 points generated by the ARIMA (1,0,1) process with $\varphi = 0.90$, $\theta = 0.64$ and $\rho_1 = 0.4$ standardized to have zero mean and unit variance

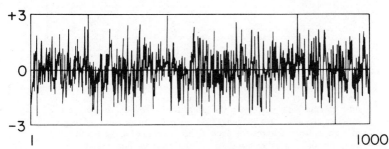

Figure 10. Plot of 1000 points generated by a lag-one Markov process standardized to have zero mean and unit variance, with $\rho_1 = 0.4$

lag-one Markov process. Hence, although b theoretically is equal to 0.5 for the ARIMA (1, 0, 1) process, long transients in the behaviour of R_n/S_n with estimates of b greater than 0.5 can be obtained, as in the case of filtered and fast fGn approximations. Although the form of ρ_k for fGn (equation 5) is not followed very closely by equation 15, the resultant behaviour of R_n/S_n is not adversely affected, showing good agreement with Hurst's law up to large values of n (O'Connell, 1971), 1974). An example of the agreement obtained is given in Figure 11. As φ and ρ_1 increase, larger observed values of b are obtained. Thus, the ARIMA (1, 0, 1) can be regarded as provinding a satisfactory explanation of the Hurst phenomenon. The question as to whether or not b ultimately assumes a value of 0.5 in nature must await the availability of longer geophysical records that are known to be stationary and non-cyclic.

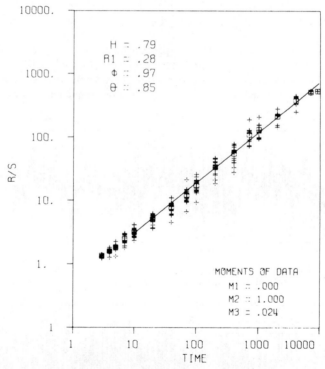

Figure 11. Plot of $\ln(R_n/S_n)$ against $\ln(n)$ for an ARIMA (1,0,1) Gaussian series of 9000 values standardized to have zero mean and unit variance. To construct the plot, the series was divided into a number of sub-series of length n, and the mean value of R_n/S_n plotted as little squares for each selected value of n. An estimate of b is obtained as the slope of a least squares line fitted to the logarithms of the mean values of (R_n/S_n). Note that ρ_1 is designated as R1

4. Generation of ARIMA (1, 0, 1) synthetic flows

4.1 Annual flows

The shortness of available historic sequences of annual streamflow presents problems in maintaining the required resemblance between historic and synthetic flows as discussed in Section 2.4. While the estimate of the mean μ, defined as the arithmetic mean of the available sequence of observations may be shown to be unbiased, estimates of the variance σ^2, the lag-one autocorrelation ρ_1 and the Hurst coefficient h have been shown to be biased for the ARIMA (1, 0, 1) process (O'Connell, 1974). In order to maintain short-run resemblance as defined by Matalas (herein), the small sample properties of these quantities have been obtained by O'Connell (1974). The small sample estimate of the variance, defines as

$$S^2 = \frac{1}{n-1} \sum_{i=1}^{n} (X_i - \bar{X})^2 \tag{16}$$

obeys

$$E\{S^2\}_n = \sigma^2 \left[1 - \frac{2\rho_1}{n(n-1)} \left\{ \frac{n(1-\varphi) - (1-\varphi^n)}{(1-\varphi)^2} \right\} \right] \tag{17}$$

The small sample expectations of ρ_1 and K (defined from equation 2) have been defined for sample sizes 25, 50 and 100 for selected values of φ and θ through Monte Carlo methods and have been presented in tabular form by O'Connell (1974); an extract from these results is given in Table 1.

For the purpose of generating synthetic flows, the ARIMA (1, 0, 1) process may be defined as

$$X_t = \mu + \varphi(X_{t-1} - \mu) + \sigma(\epsilon_t - \theta\epsilon_{t-1}) \tag{18}$$

where μ and σ are the mean and standard deviation of the process, and the variance

Table 1. Values of $E[K]_n$ and $E[\hat{\rho}_1]_n$ for selected values of φ and θ

| | | $\varphi = 0.92$ | | | | | |
| | | $E[K]_n$ | | | $E[\hat{\rho}_1]_n$ | | |
θ	ρ_1	25	50	100	25	50	100
0.88	0.049	0.657	0.664	0.654	0.001	0.012	0.028
0.84	0.114	0.687	0.680	0.686	0.005	0.046	0.079
0.80	0.189	0.686	0.705	0.709	0.072	0.093	0.123
0.76	0.269	0.699	0.735	0.745	0.082	0.160	0.208
0.72	0.349	0.725	0.751	0.756	0.116	0.199	0.240
0.68	0.426	0.740	0.782	0.783	0.169	0.269	0.332
0.64	0.496	0.772	0.783	0.800	0.218	0.309	0.390
0.60	0.560	0.773	0.796	0.803	0.273	0.364	0.437
0.56	0.616	0.774	0.820	0.825	0.285	0.432	0.516
0.52	0.665	0.794	0.825	0.828	0.335	0.467	0.532

of ϵ_t which, for annual streamflow, is usually sampled from a normal independent process, is defined by

$$\sigma_\epsilon^2 = \frac{(1 - \varphi^2)}{(1 + \theta^2 - 2\varphi\theta)} \tag{19}$$

Thus, estimates of μ, σ (or σ^2), φ and θ must be obtained from a historic sequence such that short-run resemblance between historic and synthetic flows in terms of these estimates is maintained. If estimates of φ and θ are defined through $\hat{\rho}_1$ and K, then short-run resemblance between historic and synthetic flows in terms of $\hat{\mu}$, $\hat{\sigma}^2$, $\hat{\rho}_1$ and K can now be achieved in the following manner:

(1) Derive estimates $\hat{\mu}$, $\hat{\sigma}^2$, $\hat{\rho}_1$ and K from a historic sequence of length n.
(2) From the tables prepared by O'Connell (1974), identify values of φ and θ such that

$$E(K)_n \approx K \tag{20}$$

and

$$E(\hat{\rho}_1)_n \approx \hat{\rho}_1 \tag{21}$$

where $E(K)_n$ and $E(\hat{\rho}_1)_n$ denote the small sample expectations of K and ρ_1 defined in the tables; some interpolation may be necessary.
(3) By re-writing equation 17 as

$$E(S^2)_n = \sigma^2 f(n, \rho_1, \varphi)$$

where ρ_1 and φ have been defined under (2) and equating $E(S^2)_n$ with $\hat{\sigma}^2$, an unbiased estimate of σ^2 may be defined as

$$\hat{\sigma}^{*2} = \hat{\sigma}^2 / f(n, \rho_1, \varphi) \tag{22}$$

(4) The quantities $\hat{\mu}$, $\hat{\sigma}^*$, φ and θ are then incorporated into equation 18 whence synthetic flows may be generated.

Alternative means of estimating the parameters φ and θ have been suggested by Box and Jenkins (1970) which do not take account of small sample biases. Nevertheless, such estimation procedures must be considered until it has been established which estimation procedure leads to minimum expected design losses. Essentially, Box and Jenkins (1970) derive initial moment estimates of the parameters of an ARIMA model and then use these as initial values in an iterative search for maximum likelihood (ML) estimates. Such procedures have been shown by Box and Jenkins to work quite well for longer time series, but for shorter series containing less than a hundred observations, for example, difficulties may be encountered (O'Connell, 1974). In order to evaluate the Box–Jenkins approach when applied to small sample, the following sampling experiments were conducted.

(1) For sample sizes $n = 25, 50, 100$ and $250, 500$ samples of size n were generated from the ARIMA $(1, 0, 1)$ model with specified values of φ and θ.
(2) The Box and Jenkins moment and ML estimation techniques were applied to each sample to estimate the parameters φ and θ. Moment estimates of φ and θ are derived from $\hat{\rho}_1$ and $\hat{\rho}_2$ via equations 15a and 15b.

(3) The mean, variance and mean square error (m.s.e.) of the total number of moment and ML estimates obtained were derived.

Table 2 presents the results of the sampling experiments for the case of $\varphi = 0.80$ and $\theta = 0.50$. The total number of moment and ML solutions obtained are presented, showing that in a large proportion of cases, estimates of φ and θ satisfying the stationarity and invertibility conditions are unobtainable. Moment estimates of φ and θ are defined from $\hat{\rho}_1$ and $\hat{\rho}_2$ which must lie within certain constraints in order to satisfy the conditions $-1 < \varphi < +1$ and $-1 < \theta < +1$ (Figure 12). In random sampling, these constraints can be violated frequently, particularly in small samples, which means that initial estimates for the ML search are unobtainable. Even when moment estimates are available, feasible ML estimates are not always obtained, as evidenced by Table 2.

The means and variances of the moment and ML estimates obtained are given in Table 2, illustrating that in small samples both moment and ML estimates have large biases and variances, with ML estimates tending to have somewhat better properties, although the results are not strictly comparable owing to the different number of estimates on which the ML and moment statistics are based.

Owing to the biases in estimates of φ and θ, short-run resemblance between historic and synthetic flows in terms of these parameters will not result, assuming

Table 2. Properties of moment and ML estimates for 500 samples of size n from an ARIMA (1,0,1) process with $\varphi = 0.80$, $\theta = 0.50$

n	25	50	100	250
No. of moment solutions	319	351	394	460
No. of ML solutions	266	333	381	452
Mean $\hat{\varphi}^{(m)}$	0.359	0.544	0.655	0.751
Variance $\hat{\varphi}^{(m)}$	0.186	0.105	0.058	0.018
M.s.e $\hat{\varphi}^{(m)}$	0.375	0.171	0.079	0.020
Mean $\hat{\varphi}^{(ml)}$	0.425	0.550	0.673	0.767
Variance $\hat{\varphi}^{(ml)}$	0.160	0.121	0.055	0.011
M.s.e. $\hat{\varphi}^{(ml)}$	0.301	0.184	0.071	0.012
Mean $\hat{\theta}^{(m)}$	0.057	0.227	0.357	0.455
Variance $\hat{\theta}^{(m)}$	0.174	0.116	0.075	0.030
M.s.e. $\hat{\theta}^{(m)}$	0.370	0.191	0.095	0.032
Mean $\hat{\theta}^{(ml)}$	0.063	0.199	0.362	0.465
Variance $\hat{\theta}^{(ml)}$	0.138	0.127	0.064	0.016
M.s.e. $\hat{\theta}^{(ml)}$	0.329	0.218	0.083	0.017
Mean $\hat{\rho}_1^{(m)}$	0.314	0.364	0.367	0.388
Variance $\hat{\rho}_1^{(m)}$	0.048	0.023	0.012	0.006
M.s.e. $\hat{\rho}_1^{(m)}$	0.055	0.024	0.013	0.006
Mean $\hat{\rho}_1^{(ml)}$	0.383	0.408	0.386	0.396
Variance $\hat{\rho}_1^{(ml)}$	0.060	0.027	0.013	0.006
M.s.e. $\hat{\rho}_1^{(ml)}$	0.060	0.027	0.013	0.006

66

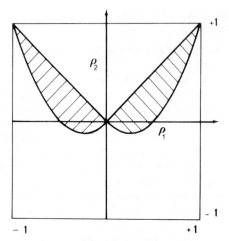

Figure 12. Feasible region (shown hatched) for ρ_1 and ρ_2 for the ARIMA (1,0,1) process with parameter, space
$$-1 < \phi < +1, \; -1 < \theta < +1$$

that the Box and Jenkins procedure does in fact provide feasible estimates. Taking into consideration also the computational effort involved in obtaining ML estimates, the estimation procedure which uses the small sample properties of $\hat{\rho}_1$ and K would appear to be more desirable, as a solution can always be obtained, even if both $\hat{\rho}_1$ and K are not always preserved exactly.

4.2 Monthly flows

The ARIMA (1, 0, 1) model has been applied to the generation of monthly flows by Finzi, Todini and Wallis (herein). Monthly flows invariably exhibit significant skewness, so a logarithmic or square root transformation was applied to the monthly flows which were then standardized to account for seasonality in the monthly means and standard deviations as

$$Z_t = \frac{Y_t - \mu_i'}{\sigma_i'} \quad i = 1,2,\ldots,12 \tag{23}$$

where μ_i' and σ_i' denote the monthly means and standard deviations of the transformed flows Y_t. Procedures for applying log-transformations to the ARIMA (1, 0, 1) model have been considered by O'Connell (1974), in addition to other procedures for preserving skewness.

The ARIMA (1, 0, 1) model was then fitted to the series Z_t. Owing to the fact that the series Z_t contains $12n$ values where n is the number of years of record, parameter estimation for the ARIMA (1, 0, 1) model can be expected to become more feasible and reliable than in the case of annual flows. An attractive approach to estimating the parameters θ and φ has been employed by Finzi, Todini and Wallis (herein) as follows. The parameter φ is estimated by minimizing the function

$$F = \sum_{k=2}^{L} (\hat{\rho}_k - \varphi^{k-1} \hat{\rho}_1)^2 \tag{24}$$

i.e. the sum of the squares of the deviations between the estimated and theoretical lag k autocorrelation coefficients, with the condition $\rho_1 = \hat{\rho}_1$ imposed. The parameter θ is then estimated by solving equation 15a in terms of ρ_1 and φ. This procedure overcomes problems created by $\hat{\rho}_2 > \hat{\rho}_1$ in applying the Box—Jenkins moment estimation procedure, and is computationally more convenient than the iterative ML approach.

4.3 Multisite ARIMA (1, 0, 1) models

In order to generate multisite ARIMA (1, 0, 1) synthetic flows, O'Connell (1974) has formulated a multivariate ARIMA (1, 0, 1) model as

$$\mathbf{x}_t = \mathbf{A}\mathbf{x}_{t-1} + \mathbf{B}\boldsymbol{\epsilon}_t - \mathbf{C}\boldsymbol{\epsilon}_{t-1} \tag{25}$$

where $\mathbf{x}_t$ and $\mathbf{x}_{t-1}$ are $(m \times l)$ vectors of standardized random variates at times t and $t - 1$, respectively, and $\mathbf{A}$, $\mathbf{B}$ and $\mathbf{C}$ are matrices of coefficients which must be defined from $\mathbf{M}_0$, $\mathbf{M}_1$ and $\mathbf{M}_2$, the lag-zero, lag-one and lag-two correlation matrices, respectively. The matrix $\mathbf{A}$ is solved for in a straightforward manner as

$$\mathbf{A} = \mathbf{M}_2 \mathbf{M}_1^{-1} \tag{26}$$

while, for the matrices $\mathbf{B}$ and $\mathbf{C}$, the equations which have to be solved are

$$\mathbf{B}\mathbf{B}^T + \mathbf{C}\mathbf{C}^T = \mathbf{S} \tag{27}$$

$$\mathbf{C}\mathbf{B}^T = \mathbf{T} \tag{28}$$

where the matrices $\mathbf{S}$ and $\mathbf{T}$ are the functions of $\mathbf{M}_0 \mathbf{M}_1$ and $\mathbf{M}_2$. Methods of solving equations 27 and 28 have been proposed by O'Connell (1974).

5. Summary

In recent years, considerable advances have been made in techniques for generating synthetic streamflows. In particular, the phenomenon of persistence has received particular attention because of its importance in the design of reservoir storage systems. Recent studies have led to the development of stochastic models whose properties adequately represent observed long-term persistence in nature. In applying some of these models to the generation of synthetic flows, small sample biases in estimates of model parameters adversely affect the statistical resemblance to be maintained between historic and synthetic flows. If, however, the small sample properties of model parameters are known, this difficulty can be overcome.

The ARIMA (1, 0, 1) model has been shown to be an adequate model of long-term persistence, as evidenced by good agreement with Hurst's law with $h > 0.5$ over long transients. The model has been suitably adapted for generating synthetic flows through establishing the small sample expectations of the model parameters, thus allowing short-run statistical resemblance between historic and synthetic flows to be maintained (Matalas, herein). Some difficulties encountered in applying the Box and Jenkins (1970) approach to parameter estimation have been discussed.

To facilitate the generation of multisite synthetic flows, a multivariate ARIMA (1, 0, 1) model has been developed which preserves cross-correlations between sites in addition to the required temporal properties at each site (O'Connell, 1974).

Until recently, application of synthetic flow generation in the planning of water resource systems has centred on the use of the lag-one Markov process mainly because of its ease of application and the availability of computer algorithms for multisite synthetic flow generation. However, as a model of observed long-term persistence, the lag-one Markov process has notable deficiencies. The justification for considering the use of a model which approximates fGn more closely has undoubtedly been established, and it is hoped that the ARIMA (1, 0, 1) process, which approximates fGn sufficiently closely and which is only slightly more complicated than the lag-one Markov process, will be applied in water resources planning where the deficiencies of the lag-one Markov process are evident.

Part 2

FLOOD MODELS

Problems and Methods of Rainfall—Runoff Modelling

JAMES C. I. DOOGE
Department of Civil Engineering, University College, Dublin, Ireland

1. Conceptual models of hydrologic processes

1.1 Approaches to modelling

A model involves similarity without identity. The model simulates some but not all the characteristics of the prototype. Consequently, any model cannot usefully be described or discussed without consideration of the definition of the objective of the modelling and of the standards of accuracy required. In any model of a physical system there is necessarily a compromise between the desire to keep the model as simple as possible and the need to achieve a prescribed degree of accuracy in predicting the prototype behaviour.

The particular characteristics of the behaviour of water that interest an individual will vary enormously with the field of inquiry of that individual. The mathematical models used by different scientists to describe the features of particular interest to them will be widely different and in many cases contradictory of one another. The theoretical physicist uses the mathematical models of his quantum mechanics to explore the movements in water particles on a sub-atomic scale. The physical chemist studies the behaviour of water on a molecular scale and may use either the mathematical models of statistical mechanics or simple conceptual models to study such problems as the diffusion of oxygen across an air—water interface or its diffusion through a body of water. The expert in fluid mechanics, who is interested in the motion of water on a somewhat larger scale, ignores the fine structure of water studied by the physicist and the physical chemist and applies the methods of continuum mechanics in order to obtain mathematical models of the types of fluid movement of interest to him.

The hydrologist is concerned with the behaviour of water on a still larger scale but may approach his problem in a number of different ways. These different approaches may be considered as an extension of the spectrum of approaches already described. If the hydrologist adopts a hydraulic viewpoint, he in fact uses the approach of continuum mechanics but usually does so in a simplified form as exemplified by the St Venant equations of unsteady flow dealt with in this Workshop (Gallati and Maione, herein). In the case of runoff from a natural catchment, conditions are so complex that the application of the hydraulic approach would involve: (1) a topographical survey of great magnitude and complexity; and (2) an extremely long series of computations of great complexity. Accordingly, two further types of response to the rainfall—runoff problem have arisen in hydrology. These are the use of conceptual models which is the subject of this paper and the use of black-box analysis dealt with in the Workshop by Natale and Todini (herein).

It is important to realize that the three approaches — hydraulics, conceptual models and black-box analysis — all have their place in applied hydrology. Each of them has its own particular area of effectiveness depending on the degree of complexity of the problem, the objective of the study and the degree of accuracy required. The fact that the continuum hypothesis ignores the fine structure of water, studied by the physicist and the physical chemist, does not prevent continuum mechanics (which includes hydraulics) from being a respectable scientific discipline or from achieving useful results, provided that the method is applied to problems appropriate to this particular approach. In a similar fashion the use of conceptual models or of black-box analysis in hydrology is a respectable way of approaching certain problems in hydrology and will, for a particular range of problem, provide useful results efficiently and economically.

1.2 The nature of conceptual models

The conceptual model approach to the rainfall—runoff problem is intermediate between the hydraulic approach based on continuum mechanics and the unit hydrograph approach based on black-box analysis. The term conceptual model can be used broadly to cover both mathematical models based on continuum mechanics and black-box models based on systems analysis. In this paper, however, the term conceptual model is used only to describe models which are formulated on the basis of a simple arrangement of a relatively small number of elements each of which is itself a simple representation of a physical relationship. This restriction is made for convenience of classification and discussion. The most widely used conceptual elements in rainfall—runoff models are linear reservoirs and linear channels. These elements represent a separation and concentration of the processes of attenuation and translation which are combined together in the case of unsteady flow in an open channel (Dooge, 1959).

There is no limit to the number of conceptual models that can be devised. Indeed, a grave defect in hydrologic research in recent years has been the proliferation of conceptual models without a corresponding effort to devise methods of objectively comparing models and developing criteria for the best choice of model in a given situation. The emphasis in the present paper will be on the nature and comparison of conceptual models of direct storm response rather than on the listing or description of individual models of total catchment response. It is hoped that by focusing on a restricted area that some general principles may become clear.

Some conceptual models can be regarded as highly simplified versions of the St Venant equations, while others can be regarded as representing mathematical approximations of the system response obtained by black-box analysis. Thus the diffusion analogy which is one of the two-parameter models used in the Workshop on Conceptual Models corresponds to a linearized version of the St Venant equations for the case of a vanishingly small Froude number and is included as such in the FRUSA program (Mugnai and Panattoni, herein). This particular model may thus be said to represent a transition between a mathematical model based on continuum mechanics and a conceptual model of the catchment as a lumped system. Similarly the conceptual model of a cascade of equal linear reservoirs each with a lateral inflow corresponds to the assumption that the system function found in black-box analysis may be approximated by the ratio of two polynomials (i.e. by a rational function). These relationships might be expected from the account given above of the position of conceptual models between hydraulic mathematical models and black-box models.

Nothing has yet been specified as to whether the rainfall input (and the corresponding runoff output) is to be considered as a deterministic or a stochastic time series. Though the nomenclature and methods of parameter estimation are different in the two cases, the conceptual models used are frequently the same (Dooge, 1972b). Thus the ARMA models used to represent stochastic time series (Box and Jenkins, 1970) correspond exactly to the model of the cascade of uniform linear reservoirs with lateral inflow widely used as a deterministic conceptual model in rainfall—runoff studies. In the present paper attention is confined to the operation of conceptual models on deterministic inputs.

1.3 Linearity and time-invariance

No matter which of the three approaches is used for the analysis of the rainfall—runoff relationship, the theory and the computations are greatly simplified if one can assume the relationship to be linear and time-invariant. The approach based on hydraulics leads to a set of partial differential equations. Linear equations are far easier to solve than non-linear equations and equations with constant coefficients are easier to solve than equations with variable coefficients. A linear equation with constant coefficients corresponds to a linear time-invariant system and such equations have been used to describe hydrologic processes both in the case of surface flow and subsurface flow. In the use of conceptual models, the assumption of time-invariance reduces the specification of a parameter from a time series to a single value and the assumption of linearity makes the determination of the optimum value of the parameter much easier than for the non-linear case. In the case of black-box analysis, the assumption of linearity and time-invariance reduces the unspecified operation of the system on the input to a convolution of the impulse response and the input. The identification of this impulse response (or kernel) is an easy matter compared with the identification of a series of kernels which would be required in a non-linear analysis. It is important therefore to be clear in regard to the nature of linearity and time-invariance in hydrologic systems.

A system is said to be linear if, and only if, the response of the system to an input x which is a linear combination of a number of elementary inputs x_i:

$$\mathbf{x} = \Sigma_i c_i x_i \tag{1}$$

is given by the output y which is the same linear combination

$$\mathbf{y} = \Sigma_i c_i y_i \tag{2}$$

of the elementary outputs y_i corresponding to the respective elementary inputs x_i.

The linearity in the systems sense, as defined above, must be clearly distinguished from a relationship between x and y which is linear in the sense of the algebraic equation:

$$y = a + bx \qquad (3)$$

It should be noted that, if an input—output pair (x, y) obeys the relationship given by equation 3, the pair (2x, 2y) which would hold for a linear system in accordance with equations 1 and 2 does not satisfy the relationship given by equation 3. Similarly it is necessary to distinguish between the superposition property of a linear system and the linearity of the regression equation:

$$Y = a_0 + a_1 X + a_2 X^2 \qquad (4)$$

in which the linearity is a linearity in the coefficients rather than the variables (Clarke, 1973).

A system is said to be time-invariant if the response of the system to any element of the input depends only on the time elapsed since that element of input and not on the point in time at which it occurs. Thus, if an element $x_i(t)$ gives rise to an element $y_i(t)$, then the displacement of that element in time in either direction results only in the displacement of the corresponding element of output by the same time, i.e. $x_i(t \pm t_0)$ gives rise to an output $y_i(t \pm t_0)$. Time-invariance in deterministic processes corresponds to strict stationarity in stochastic processes.

The importance of the distinction between linearity and non-linearity and between time-invariance and time-variance is fundamental and we can use it as the basis of the classification of mathematical models of hydrological processes. If we combine this basis with a classification based on the approaches to modelling discussed in Section 1.1 above we obtain the two-dimensional classification of mathematical models in hydrology shown in Figure 1. In all approaches to mathematical modelling of hydrologic processes, the first attempts have been on the basis of linear time-invariant systems and only in the case when such models are

	CONTINUUM MECHANICS	CONCEPTUAL MODELS	BLACK— BOX
LINEAR TIME-INVARIANT			
NON-LINEAR TIME-INVARIANT			
LINEAR TIME-VARIANT			
NON-LINEAR TIME-VARIANT			

Figure 1. Models of hydrologic processes

deficient are more complex models used. The same approach will be followed in regard to conceptual models of the rainfall—runoff process in the present paper.

1.4 Total response and component response

The hydrologic processes that comprise the hydrological cycle may be represented in a block diagram such as Figure 2. In this figure the boxes represent forms of water storage and the lines connecting the boxes indicate the individual hydrologic processes which transform the water from one form of storage to another. In applied hydrology, we are only interested in the operation of the catchment as a hydrological system. The sub-system of the hydrological cycle that represents the operation of the catchment is outlined by the dotted line in Figure 2.

This picture of the catchment operation is highly simplified insofar as all storage of one particular form is lumped together and all elements of given hydrologic processes are similarly lumped. Nevertheless it still remains too complex for the practical modelling of the rainfall—runoff process. For example, while we speak of the differing concepts of overland flow (Q_o), interflow (Q_i) and groundwater outflow (Q_g), it is not possible to distinguish between these components of outflow except on a research scale. Indeed, the separation of outflow into direct response and baseflow is frequently difficult to make in practice.

In the modelling of catchment response a simplified model of the type shown in

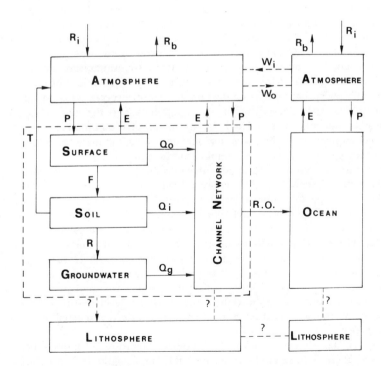

Figure 2. Block diagram of hydrologic cycle

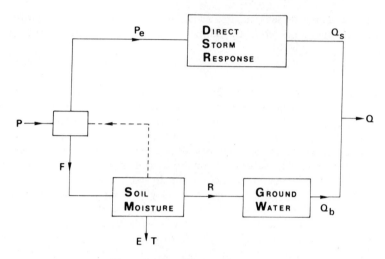

Figure 3. Simplified catchment model

Figure 3 is used. This distinguishes between direct storm response and baseflow and distinguishes between the operation of the soil moisture in the unsaturated zone and the groundwater in the saturated zone. The simplified catchment model can thus be divided into three components; (1) the component of direct storm response (i.e. conversion of P_e to Q_s); (2) the component of groundwater response (i.e. conversion of R to Q_b); (3) the component involving the unsaturated zone which must account for the depletion of soil moisture by evaporation and transpiration (E, T) and the effect of the state of soil moisture on the amount of infiltration (F). Nearly all conceptual models of the rainfall–runoff process are of the general form shown in Figure 3. They differ in the complexity and the manner in which the various components are simulated. In any model of the rainfall–runoff process all three components must be taken into account, though in many cases the manner in which they are dealt with is only implicit in the model.

It would be desirable to model the overall rainfall–runoff relationship by a linear model. However, it is generally considered that there is a threshold effect whereby recharge to groundwater only takes place to an appreciable extent when there is no soil moisture deficiency. Since a threshold effect is essentially non-linear, a linear model for the total catchment response cannot include such a feature. Accordingly, it is not surprising that the first attempts at rainfall–runoff modelling concentrated on the direct storm response where there was no such initial hindrance to the use of a linear model. In the present paper, attention will be concentrated on the use of linear conceptual models for the component of direct storm response but the application of the approach developed to the groundwater response and the soil moisture component will be briefly discussed towards the end of the paper.

There is no shortage in the hydrological literature of models of all types. However, there is little guidance on how the practising hydrologist should choose between these models when faced with a practical problem. As mentioned earlier, the best model in any particular case depends largely on the objective of the study. A rational methodology for the selection, calibration and use of a mathematical model of the rainfall—runoff process might follow a procedure such as shown in Figure 4. This involves both the choice between competing models and the determination of optimum values of the parameters of the model chosen. The remainder of the paper will be largely concerned with a first approach to the development of a rational methodology for the use of linear conceptual models with particular reference to the modelling of the direct storm component of the total rainfall—runoff relationship.

It is to be noted that the final step on Figure 4 is to embed the model in a more general model. This could represent the embedment of a validated component model into a model of the total catchment response. At a higher level of

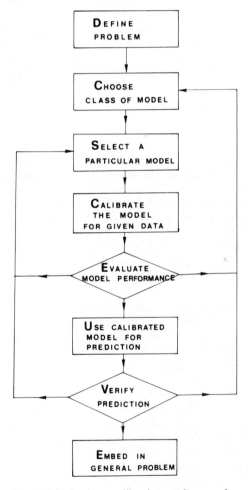

Figure 4. Selection, calibration and use of a mathematical model

78

organization it could represent the embedment of the validated model of a total catchment response into a decision-making model intended for the design or operation of a complex water resource system. In either case it is necessary to keep the objective clearly in mind. It is a misuse of human resources to develop a highly complex model in order to produce precise predictions if the precision is not warranted by the type of general model in which the the results are embedded.

2. Effective rainfall and direct runoff

2.1 The rational method

The first attempt at the modelling of the rainfall–runoff process was developed over 120 years ago in the form of the rational method for the prediction of flood peaks (Mulvany, 1850). For certain simple problems this method is probably still an appropriate and convenient method to use. The method is based on the assumption 'that the discharge will be the greatest possible under the circumstance of a fall of rain occurring at the maximum uniform rate of fall for . . . the time necessary for the rain which falls on the most remote portion of the catchment to travel to the outlet'. This description by Mulvany introduced for the first time the concept of *time of concentration*. The original rational method may be represented by the formula:

$$Q_{max} = C \cdot i_{max}(t_c) \cdot A \tag{5}$$

where Q_{max} is the peak rate of storm runoff, C is a coefficient of runoff, i_{max} is the maximum rate of rainfall for a duration equal to the time of concentration t_c, and A is the catchment area.

As originally proposed, the rational method was used to predict the maximum runoff due to a uniform intensity of rainfall throughout the storm. During the 1920s the method was modified to allow for non-uniform intensities of rainfall during the storm and also to allow for highly irregular shapes of catchment. In both of these lines of development, use was made of a time–area diagram which indicates the distribution of the time of travel from different parts of the catchment.

Figure 5(a) shows a catchment map on which have been drawn isochrones, i.e. lines passing through all points with an equal travel time from the point to the outlet. The production of an isochrone map of the catchment is quite a complicated process since it involves a knowledge of the topography of the catchment and a series of calculations of the time of travel of overland flow and channel flow. A time–area curve can be drawn by plotting against each value of the travel time the area of the catchment whose travel time is less than or equal to the specified amount (Figure 5(b)). According to the rational method, this diagram shows for any value of travel time, the area which will contribute to the flow at the outlet at a time from the start of rainfall equal to this value. In practical calculations it is often more convenient to use the time–area–concentration curve shown in Figure 5(c). The latter is the derivative of the time–area curve and its baselength is equal to the time of concentration.

Even though the rational method has for most purposes been superseded by more sophisticated methods, it nevertheless holds an important place in the

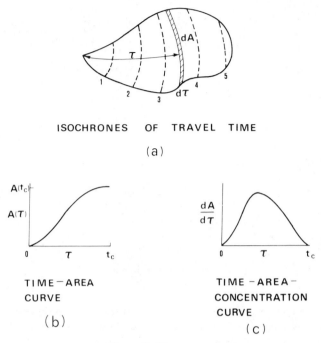

ISOCHRONES OF TRAVEL TIME

(a)

TIME—AREA
CURVE

(b)

TIME—AREA—
CONCENTRATION
CURVE

(c)

Figure 5. Time—area curves

development of systems hydrology and can be reinterpreted in the light of later concepts. Thus the prediction of the time—area—concentration curve on the basis of isochrones corresponds to the replacement of the St Venant equations by simplified wave equations such as kinematic wave theory dealt with in this Workshop by Woolhiser (herein). Similarly the time—area—concentration curve, used in the modified rational method, corresponds to the instantaneous unit hydrograph used in the black-box approach. Thus the rational method has links with both the continuum mechanics approach and the black-box approach to the analysis of the rainfall—runoff process.

2.2 The unit hydrograph approach

The unit hydrograph concept and its development was one of the highlights of the classical period of scientific hydrology. Figure 6 reproduces the first figure of the basic paper by Sherman which introduced the concept of the unit hydrograph (Sherman,1932). In this figure a triangular form of hydrograph is assumed to represent the runoff due to rain falling continuously and uniformly for the unit interval. The figure shows how superposition may be used to build up the runoff for periods of uniform rainfall longer than the unit period. It will be noted that, if the duration of this continuous effective precipitation is greater than the base of the unit hydrograph, the runoff becomes constant. For about 25 years, unit hydrograph methods were widely used in applied hydrology without a recognition

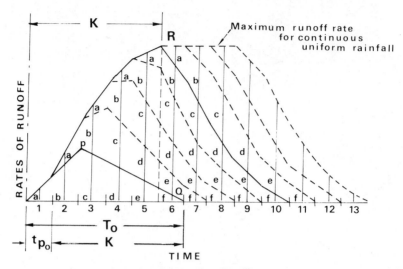

Figure 6. Superposition of unit hydrographs

of the essential assumption involved, namely that the relationship between effective precipitation and direct storm runoff was that of a linear time-invariant system.

The classical unit hydrograph approach is described in a number of textbooks published at the end of the 1940s. The book by Johnstone and Cross contains a particularly good discussion of the classical theory (Johnstone and Cross, 1949). In it they state the basic propositions of the unit hydrograph as follows:

We are now in a position to state the three basic propositions of unit graph theory all of which refer solely to the surface-runoff hydrograph:

(i) For a given drainage basin, the duration of surface runoff is essentially constant for all uniform-intensity storms of the same length, regardless of differences in the total volume of the surface runoff.

(ii) For a given drainage basin two uniform-intensity storms of the same length produce different total volumes of surface runoff, then the rate of surface runoff at corresponding times t, after the beginning of the two storms, are in the same proportion to each other as the total volumes of the surface runoff.

(iii) The time distribution of surface runoff from a given period is independent of concurrent runoff from antecedent storm periods.

Johnston and Cross make the following comment:

All these propositions are empirical. It is not possible to prove them mathematically. In fact it is a rather simple matter to demonstrate by rational hydraulic analysis that not a single one of them is mathematically accurate. Fortunately, nature is not aware of this.

In the twenty years after Sherman's basic paper the unit hydrograph approach developed into a flexible and useful tool in applied hydrology and only later was a full theory of the unit hydrograph developed.

The original unit hydrograph developed by Sherman was a continuous hydrograph of runoff due to uniform rainfall in a unit period. Later the S-hydrograph or S-curve was defined as the hydrograph of surface runoff produced by a continuous effective rainfall at a constant rate. One of the big advances in classical unit hydrograph theory was the discovery that the S-hydrograph could be used to convert a unit hydrograph from one duration to another. Before this, it was necessary to find a storm of the appropriate duration to derive the required unit hydrograph from the data. Figure 6 (taken for Sherman's original paper) shows the manner in which the S-hydrograph is derived from the unit hydrograph for the particular case of a triangular shape for the unit hydrograph. Once the S-hydrograph has been obtained from a unit hydrograph of any unit period, a unit hydrograph of a new unit period (D) can be derived from it by displacing the S-hydrograph by the required amount, subtracting the ordinates of the two S-hydrographs and then normalizing the volume. This process can be represented by the equation

$$h_D(t) = \frac{S(t) - S(t - D)}{D} \tag{6}$$

As D becomes smaller and smaller, the process represented by equation 6 comes closer and closer to the definition of differentiation and in the limit we have

$$h_0(t) = \frac{d}{dt} [S(t)] \tag{7}$$

The hydrograph defined by equation 7 is known as the instantaneous unit hydrograph (IUH).

It was soon found necessary to devise methods for the derivation of the unit hydrograph by the analysis of complex storms in which the rate of effective precipitation was not uniform throughout the storm. In the early studies, the procedure used was essentially one of trial and error. At the end of the 1930s some less subjective methods based on iteration were derived. In the early 1950s the least squares method was applied to the solution of the set of linear equations for the ordinates of the finite period unit hydrograph. At the end of the 1950s further objective methods of deriving a unit hydrograph from the rainfall—runoff data for a complex storm were derived and applied. These methods constitute techniques for the identification of black-box systems dealt with in this Workshop by Natale and Todini (herein).

2.3 Synthetic unit hydrographs

It is a commonplace of applied hydrology that such data as are available frequently do not relate to the catchment area for which information is required. Accordingly, it is not sufficient to be able to derive a unit hydrograph for a catchment area in which there are records of rainfall and runoff. It is desirable also to develop a procedure for the derivation of synthetic unit hydrographs (and hence the prediction of storm runoff) for ungauged catchments. The basic approach used is (1) to derive the unit hydrographs for the catchments in a region for which records are available and (2) to find a correlation between some parameters of these unit hydrographs and the catchment characteristics. If a satisfactory correlation can be derived, then this correlation can be used to predict the parameters of the unit hydrograph for catchments which have no records of streamflow but for which the catchment characteristics can be derived from topographical maps.

The problem of synthetic unit hydrographs has in the past been approached from a number of directions (Dooge, 1973). It is interesting to note that in the same year in which he published his basic paper on the unit hydrograph concept, Sherman published a second paper which was concerned with the relation between the parameters of the unit hydrograph and the important catchment characteristics of area and slope. However, it may be said that the first synthetic unit hydrographs were in fact derived more than ten years before the concept of the unit hydrograph itself appeared in print. In 1921, the rational method was modified to include the effect of non-uniform rainfall distribution by the use of time—area—concentration curves (see Figure 5). This modification was, in effect, an attempt to synthesize the response of the watershed on the basis of characteristics which could be read from a map. Since, in each case, the time—area—concentration curve was built up by means of hydraulic equations from the information available for the particular catchment, each unit hydrograph was unique to the catchment concerned.

A further development was the assumption by Clark and others that the unit hydrograph could be obtained by routing the time—area—concentration curve through an element of linear storage. In this case also, each unit hydrograph would be unique but the variation between them would be reduced and the differences in catchment characteristics smoothed out to a greater or lesser extent depending on the degree of damping introduced by the storage routing. O'Kelly, Nash and Farrell, working in the Irish Office of Public Works found that there was no essential loss in accuracy if the routed time—area—concentration curve was replaced by a routed isosceles triangle. The methods of Clark and O'Kelly only became synthetic unit hydrograph methods in the real sense of the word when empirical relationships between some of the parameters of their models and the catchment characteristics were derived. In the case of the routed triangle only two parameters are required; the base of the triangle (T) and the storage delay time (K) of the linear storage element. Thus the line of development which started out by treating each unit hydrograph as unique had in time developed into an empirical procedure in which there were only two unknown parameters.

In contrast to the time—area methods which treated each catchment and each unit hydrograph as unique, a number of hydrologist suggested that there was a single unique shape for the dimensionless unit hydrograph. Such a number of universal shapes for the unit hydrograph were proposed in the literature. In order to use them it was only necessary to determine a single parameter in order to fix the scale of the unit hydrograph. Since the volume under the unit hydrograph was normalized to unity, a change in the time scale was automatically compensated for by a corresponding change in the discharge scale. As further studies were made of synthetic unit hydrographs, it was realized that a one-parameter method was not sufficiently flexible and that at least two parameters were required for adequate representation. Such methods would require the use of a family of curves from which the unit hydrograph shape might be chosen. Since it is easier to represent a two-parameter model by an equation rather than a family of curves, the natural development of this approach was towards the suggestion of empirical equations which would represent all unit hydrographs. An important example of this type of development was the attempt of Japanese hydrologists to simulate the response of rivers to models consisting of either a single linear storage element or two equal linear storage elements in series.

It is remarkable that people working in a number of different countries turned to the same empirical equation for the representation of the unit hydrograph. The equation in question was the two-parameter gamma distribution or Pearson type III empirical distribution. Nash suggested the two-parameter gamma distribution as having the general shape required for the instantaneous unit hydrograph and pointed out that the gamma distribution could be considered as the impulse response for a cascade of equal linear reservoirs. He suggested that the number of reservoirs could be taken as non-integral if required. This also is a conceptual model with two parameters.

The two lines of development in regard to synthetic unit hydrographs are shown in Figure 7. It can be seen that the approach which started with the

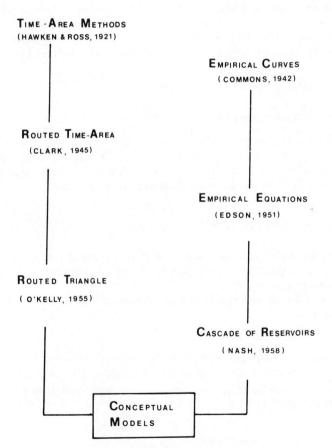

Figure 7. Synthetic unit hydrographs

84

time—area assumption that every unit hydrograph was unique had ended with the routing of a fixed shape through a linear reservoir. Similarly the line of development which had started with the assumption that there was a single universal shape for the unit hydrograph had led to the representation of the unit hydrograph by a cascade of equal linear reservoirs. Both of these were conceptual models and, from this time on, the way was open for attempts to represent the unit hydrograph by a wide variety of conceptual models.

2.4 Systems formulation

From the systems viewpoint, the basic assumptions of unit hydrograph theory, given in the quotation from Johnstone and Cross above may be restated by saying that it is assumed that the operation of the catchment on the effective precipitation is linear and time-invariant. Once the assumption has been made that effective precipitation is converted to direct storm runoff in a linear time-invariant fashion, then all the problems of unit hydrograph derivation and synthesis can be formulated in terms of black-box analysis and synthesis (Dooge, 1959, 1973; Tonini 1969).

If the record of effective precipitation is represented by a histogram, then each element of the input is represented by a pulse function P_D defined by

$$P_D(t - sD) = \frac{1}{D} \text{ for } sD < t < (s + 1)D \tag{8a}$$

$$P_D(t - sD) = 0 \quad \text{elsewhere} \tag{8b}$$

where D is the standard interval and s is the number of intervals elapsed before the beginning of the interval in question. If the area of effective precipitation in each interval is given by $X(sD)$ then the histogram of input can be expressed in terms of the volumes of input in successive standard periods as follows:

$$x(t) = \sum_{s=0}^{\infty} X(sD) \cdot P_D(t - sD) \tag{9}$$

The unit hydrograph $h_D(t)$ has been defined as the response to a unit volume of rain falling uniformly in a unit period D and hence must be the output corresponding to the input $P_D(t)$.

If we now make the assumption of time-invariance, then we can write the output corresponding to

$$P_D(t - sD) \text{ as } h_D(t - sD)$$

We now make the further assumption that the operation is linear and can write the output due to $X(sD) \cdot P_D(t - sD)$ as $X(sD) \cdot h_D(t - sD)$. Since summation is a linear process we can write the relation between input and output for the input defined by equation 9 as:

$$y(t) = \sum_{s=0}^{\infty} X(sD) \cdot h_D(t - sD) \tag{10}$$

In the above development both the output $y(t)$ and the pulse response $h_D(t)$ are taken as continuous functions. If the output is only available at discrete moments of time then the output and pulse response will become sampled functions. In the case where the sampling interval D is the same for the input and the output, the equation takes the form

$$y(rD) = \sum_{s=0}^{\infty} X(sD)h_D(rD - sD) \tag{11a}$$

which can be written without ambiguity as

$$y(r) = \sum_{s=0}^{\infty} X(s)h_D(r - s) \tag{11b}$$

In mathematical terms equation 11 states that the output at any sampling point is found by the discrete convolution of the input and the pulse response corresponding to the particular sampling interval.

The above equation of discrete convolution can also be written in the alternative notation

$$y_i = \sum_{j=0}^{\infty} x_j h_{i-j} \tag{12}$$

where x is being used to represent the volume of inputs which appear as X in equation 11. This is done in the interest of differentiating equation 12 from the matrix form of the relationship which can be written as

$$y = Xh \tag{13}$$

where y is the vector of outputs, h is the vector of unknown unit hydrograph ordinates and X is a matrix consisting of columns corresponding to the vector of inputs offset by varying amounts.

The above development has been made in terms of a finite period unit hydrograph. For the case of the instantaneous unit hydrograph a similar development results in the corresponding equation

$$y(t) = \int_0^{\infty} x(\tau)h(t - \tau)d\tau \tag{14}$$

in which the output is given as the continuous convolution of the input and the impulse response or instantaneous unit hydrograph.

In systems terms the problem of deriving the unit hydrograph is seen to correspond to that of solving a set of linear algebraic equations for the discrete case and solving an integral equation for the continuous case. Equation 12 would appear to indicate that the set of algebraic equations is infinite. However, if the assumption is made that the system is causal, i.e. that no output can occur before the coresponding input, and it is further assumed that the input is isolated, then equation 12 can be written as

$$y_i = \sum_{j=0}^{j=i} x_j h_{i-j} \tag{15}$$

in which the number of algebraic equations to be solved is finite.

If the input and output were known with absolute precision then the determination of the ordinates of the unit hydrograph would be an almost trivial problem. In practice, however, errors in the data can give rise to serious errors in the derived unit hydrograph. Even if the unit hydrograph appears to be of reasonable shape (and this is not always the case) the correlation of its parameters with catchment characteristics may become quite unreliable and physically meaningless.

The advantages of using conceptual models to represent the unit hydrograph are twofold. Firstly the conceptual model provides automatically a number of constraints on the form of the derived unit hydrograph which have the effect of filtering out some of the worst effects of the magnification of the data errors brought about by the inversion process of unit hydrograph derivation. Secondly, by using a conceptual model with a small enough number of parameters, it is possible to concentrate the information content of the data into this small number of parameters and thus increase the chances of a reliable correlation with catchment characteristics.

3. Fitting a linear conceptual model

3.1 Moments and cumulants

If a conceptual model is to be used to represent the action of a catchment area on effective rainfall, then it is necessary both to choose a conceptual model and to choose values of parameters for the model. If the model is chosen at random and the parameters are chosen by trial and error on the basis of fitting the runoff, then the approach may be even more subjective than the classical unit hydrograph method. As will be seen in Part 3 of this volume the matching of the output by a model is no guarantee that the unit hydrograph resembles closely the actual unit hydrograph. If reliable methodologies are to be developed, then every step of the process should be made as objective as possible.

The first question to be considered is the manner in which a unit hydrograph may be described. It may, of course, always be described in terms of the derived ordinates at some specified interval. In this case the number of parameters to be determined are the interval used and the values of a sufficient number of ordinates to describe the shape adequately. In order to develop synthetic unit hydrographs it would be necessary to correlate all these ordinates with catchment characteristics.

If one borrows from statistics the use of moments or cumulants as descriptive parameters (Kendall and Stuart, 1958), then the number of parameters used can be considerably reduced. Nash showed that the statistical moments of the instantaneous unit hydrograph can be determined from the corresponding moments of the effective rainfall and direct storm runoff without deriving the full unit hydrograph (Nash, 1960). The moments have the advantage that they can be used both for determining suitable values for the parameters of conceptual models and as the basis for a comparison of models. The moments used in systems hydrology are the moments of the various functions with respect to time. The moments about the time origin are defined as:

$$U'_R(f) = \int_0^\infty f(t) \cdot t^R \cdot \mathrm{d}t \qquad (16)$$

and the moments about the centre of the area are defined as:

$$U_R(f) = \int_0^\infty f(t) \cdot (t - U_1')^R \, dt \tag{17}$$

The relationship between the moment about the origin and about the centre can be found by expanding the term $(t - U_1')^R$ in equation 17.

For a linear time-invariant system there is a special relationship between the moments of the input, the impulse response and the output (Nash, 1960). For such a system we have

$$U_R'(y) = \sum_{k=0}^R \binom{R}{k} U_k'(x) U_{R-k}'(h) \tag{18}$$

which enables us to calculate the moments of the unit hydrograph $h(t)$ when the input $x(t)$ and the output $y(t)$ are known. The special case of equation 18 for $R = 1$ is:

$$U_1'(y) = U_1'(x) + U_1'(h) \tag{19}$$

which expresses the fact that the first moment of the instantaneous unit hydrograph is equal to the distance between the centre of the input and the centre of the output, i.e. equal to the lag of the catchment. The relationship between the second moments about the origin is given by

$$U_2'(y) = U_2'(x) + 2U_1'(x)U_1'(h) + U_2'(h) \tag{20}$$

which converted to moments about the centre gives

$$U_2(y) = U_2(x) + U_2(h) \tag{21}$$

and so on. For the third moment we get an equation with the simple additive form of equations 19 and 21, but for higher moments the relationship is more complex.

Moments are not the only set of parameters which may be used to describe a function and from some viewpoints they are not the most convenient set. Another set of parameters used in statistics are the cumulants or semi-invariants (Kendall and Stuart, 1958). These may be defined as a set of parameters for which the logarithm of the Fourier transform is the generating function. All cumulants except the first are unaffected by a change of origin. It can be shown that for a linear time-invariant system:

$$k_R(y) = k_R(x) + k_R(h) \tag{22}$$

which indicates that in the case of cumulants we get the simple additive relationship of equation 19 and equation 21 for all orders of the cumulants.

It can be shown that the first cumulant is equal to the first moment about the origin, the second cumulant to the second about the centre, the third cumulant to the third moment about the centre, thus verifying equations 19 and 21. The fourth cumulant is equal to the fourth moment about the centre minus three times the square of the second moment about the centre (i.e. the quantity known in statistics as excess kurtosis). It is interesting to note in passing that the Gaussian distribution is the distribution in which all cumulants above the second are zero.

There are corresponding definitions and relationships for the case of discrete data. Thus the Rth moment of a discrete distribution about the origin is defined as

$$U_R'(f) = \sum_{s=0}^{\infty} f(s)s^R \tag{23}$$

which corresponds to equation 16 for the continuous case from which we can derive the additive theorem for cumulants in the discrete case. It can be shown that for a linear time-invariant system the simple additive relationship holds for the first moment above the origin and the second and third moments about the centre as in the continuous case.

3.2 Optimization of model parameters

The parameters of the conceptual model must be optimized in some sense. In the present paper and in the Workshop session, this is done by equating the moments of the conceptual model to the estimated moments of the unit hydrograph as derived from the rainfall and runoff data. Though the use of moment matching may be criticized, it is extremely convenient in the case of most linear conceptual models. As mentioned previously, estimates of the moments of the unit hydrograph can be obtained from the records of rainfall and runoff data. Secondly, the moment relationship described in Section 3.1 can also be used to simplify the derivation of the expressions for the cumulants of some of the common conceptual models. Thirdly, the moments may be used as the basis of an objective method for the choice of model.

The derivation of the moments of a conceptual model will be illustrated for the case of a cascade of equal linear reservoirs. For a single linear reservoir with a storage delay time K the impulse response is given by

$$h(t) = \frac{1}{K} \exp\left(-\frac{t}{K}\right) \tag{24a}$$

This can also be written conveniently as

$$h(t) = a \exp(-at) \tag{24b}$$

where a is the reciprocal of K. It can be shown that the Rth moment of $h(t)$ about the origin is given by

$$U_R' = R!K^R \tag{25}$$

and the Rth cumulant by

$$k_R = (R-1)!K^R \tag{26}$$

where K is the storage delay time.

The above equations refer only to a single reservoir. For the case of a cascade of n reservoirs the derivation of the moments and cumulants is greatly simplified by the use of equations 18 and 22. Thus for the case of the cascade of n linear reservoirs, the output from one is the input to the next and so the use of equation 22 allows us to write the Rth cumulant of the cascade of n equal linear reservoirs as

$$k_R = n(R - 1)!K^R \tag{27}$$

In particular we can write

$$k_1 = U_1' = nK \tag{28a}$$

$$k_2 = U_2 = nK^2 \tag{28b}$$

$$k_3 = U_3 = 2nK^3 \tag{28c}$$

$$k_4 = U_4 = 3(U_2)^2 = 6nK^3 \tag{28d}$$

In order to determine the parameters n and K of the conceptual model, it is only necessary to use equations 28a and 28b above. Equations 28c and 28d could be used as a check on the extent to which the conceptual model matched the higher moments not used in the derivation of the parameters. A serious discrepancy in this regard would be an indication that the actual conceptual model chosen was not suitable.

Where a time—area—concentration curve is represented by a geometrical figure and routed through a linear reservoir, then the cumulants of the resulting conceptual model are obtained by adding the cumulants of the geometrical figure representing the time-area-concentration curve and the cumulants of the linear reservoir. Thus, for the case of the routed isosceles triangle, if the base of the triangle is given by T and the storage delay time of the linear reservoir by K, the cumulants of the resulting model are as follows:

$$k_1 = U_1' = \frac{T}{2} + K \tag{29a}$$

$$k_2 = U_2 = \frac{T^2}{24} + K^2 \tag{29b}$$

$$k_3 = U_3 = 2K^3 \tag{29c}$$

$$k_4 = U_4 - 3(U_2)^2 = 6K^4 - \frac{T^4}{960} \tag{29d}$$

If the respective moments (or cumulants) of the conceptual model are equated to the derived moments (or cumulants) of an empirical hydrograph, then the values of the parameters that are optimal in the sense of moment matching can be evaluated.

In optimizing the parameters of the conceptual model by moment matching, it is necessary to have as many moments for the unit hydrograph as there are parameters to be optimized. The usual practice is to use the lower order moments for this purpose. This can be justified (1) by the fact that the estimates of the lower-order moments are more accurate than higher-order moments and (2) from the consideration that the order of a moment is equal to the power of the corresponding term in a polynomial expansion of the Fourier or Laplace transform.

3.3 Effects of errors in data

Since the derivation of the unit hydrograph is essentially an inversion process, the effect of errors in the data may appear in a magnified form in the derived unit hydrograph. This error must be filtered in some way by the imposition of constraints on the solution. Constrained black-box analysis is dealt with by Natale and Todini (herein) and in the present paper the subject will only be discussed in relation to the use of conceptual models.

The effect of data error on unit hydrograph derivation can be studied systematically by combining a synthetic input and a synthetic unit hydrograph to produce a synthetic output and then adding error of a known amount (either systematic or random) to the input and output before trying to recover the known unit hydrograph from the contaminated input and output data. When this is done it is found that the direct solution of the set of linear equations given by equation 15 in Section 2.4 is highly sensitive to error. The results are shown in Table 1 for the effect of 10% error in the data on the types of input and output used in a systematic study of this problem (Laurenson and O'Donnell, 1969).

Case A in Table 1 shows that, if the only constraint on the unit hydrograph is that its length is taken as the difference between the length of rainfall and the length of runoff, then for the case of 10% error in data the error in the derived unit hydrograph becomes astronomical. In the case B the area of the unit hydrograph found by the direct solution is normalized to unity and the error is reduced but is still enormous. When the further constraint of setting all negative ordinates equal to zero is introduced, the error is still further reduced but not to a level which would be acceptable in practice.

As shown in Table 1 the introduction of a least squares solution gives a further reduction in error but is still quite sensitive to random error. The method of regularization which is a method of constrained optimization gives some further

Table 1. Effect on unit hydrograph of 10% error in data

Method of identification	Mean absolute error as % of peak		
	Error free data	Systematic error	Random error
Direct solution (case A)	0.87×10^{-3}	1×10^{9}	2×10^{9}
Direct solution (case B)	0.85×10^{-3}	251	964
Direct solution (case C)	0.85×10^{-3}	27.0	45.5
Least squares	0.29×10^{-3}	6.6	21.15
Regularization	3.1×10^{-3}	4.3	11.5
Linear programming	0.48	11.6	23.1
Harmonic analysis ($n = 9$)	3.4	5.3	7.8
Meixner analysis ($n = 5$)	1.2	4.8	6.3
Routed triangle	6.8	8.1	7.7
Cascade of reservoirs	2.8	6.0	5.2
Diffusion analogy	7.0	8.0	7.4

improvement at the cost of a big increase in computer time. Methods such as harmonic analysis and Meixner analysis which are based on expansion of the input, impulse reponse and output in truncated series of orthogonal polynomials give the best results of all the algebraic methods.

Our present interest, however, is in the fact that a number of conceptual models are more effective in filtering out the error than all the algebraic methods except those based on orthogonal series. The three conceptual models used were (a) a routed isosceles triangle, (b) a cascade of equal linear reservoirs and (c) the diffusion analogy. The success of these conceptual models in filtering out error effects is due to the constraints automatically introduced by the use of such models. Thus all of the conceptual models are normalized automatically to unit area; all of them produce only non-negative ordinates; all of them produce unimodal shapes which are appropriate in the particular case under examination. It is important to remark in connection with the latter point that if the actual unit hydrograph had a bimodal shape, these particular conceptual models would not be able to compete with harmonic analysis or Meixner analysis.

It will be noted from Table 1 that the methods successful in filtering out the errors in the data also produce an error in the derived unit hydrograph for the case of error-free data. This is because the filtering mechanisms have the effect of filtering out part of the signal as well as the error. This is unimportant in practice because the applied hydrologist is interested in maintaining the error of the unit hydrograph below a certain acceptable figure and is not concerned with very high degrees of precision obtainable only for data with an accuracy which cannot be attained in the field.

3.4 Use of shape factor diagram

The discussion in the previous section was concerned with the question of optimizing the parameters of the conceptual model once the model to be used had been chosen. The results shown in Table 1 indicated that, from the point of view of stability against data error, all three conceptual models chosen performed reasonably well. It remains to discuss whether there are any rules to be followed in choosing what particular conceptual model to use.

The first rule to be followed is to use as few parameters as possible. This may be taken as a modern interpretation of Occam's razor which warned: 'Entia non sint multiplicanda praeter necessitatem'. Keeping the numbers of parameters as low as possible increases the information content per parameter and therefore allows both a more accurate determination of the parameter and a more reliable correlation of the values obtained with catchment characteristics. In the present discussion, as in part 3 of this volume, the procedure followed is attempting at first to simulate the action of the catchment by a one-parameter model and then proceeding to increase the number of parameters until a satisfactory conceptual model has been tested and accepted.

Conceptual models with one, two or three parameters can be conveniently represented on a shape factor diagram which is obtained by plotting the dimensionless third moment S_3 against the dimensionless second moment S_2.

Dimensionless moments or shape factors may in this context be defined by

$$S_R = \frac{U_R}{(U_1')^R} \tag{30}$$

where U_R is the Rth moment about the centre and U_1' is the first moment about the origin. A one-parameter model would be represented on such a diagram by a single point. A two-parameter conceptual model would be represented by a line and a three-parameter conceptual model would be represented by a region or by a family of lines.

Once the moments are known for the unit hydrograph of a particular storm on a catchment area, this unit hydrograph can also be plotted as a point on a shape factor diagram. If data are available from a number of catchments they can be plotted on a shape factor diagram and the results used to judge the efficacy of various conceptual models. If all the plotted points for derived unit hydrographs clustered around a single point in the diagram, then a one-parameter model which plotted at the same point would be sufficient to represent all the unit hydrographs. If the points plotted along a line, then a conceptual model whose characteristic line on a shape factor diagram passed close to all the points would be a satisfactory conceptual model. If the plotted points fill a region on the shape factor diagram, then only a three-parameter conceptual model capable of spanning that region would be adequate to model all these hydrographs.

Though unit hydrographs cannot in practice be satisfactorily represented by one-parameter conceptual models, it is remarkable the degree to which runoff can be reproduced by a one-parameter model. Even in the case of one-parameter conceptual models there is a wide choice available. In the present paper, as in part 3 of this volume, we will consider conceptual models based on pure translation (i.e. linear channels), on pure storage action (i.e. linear reservoirs) and on the diffusion analogy.

Conceptual models of the relationship between effective rainfall and storm runoff involving two or three parameters are of necessity more flexible in their ability to match measured data. However, in many cases the improvement obtained by using an additional parameter is much less than might be expected. This will be illustrated for Sherman's data (Sherman, 1932) and for Nash's data (Nash, 1960) in Part 3 of this volume (Dooge and O'Kane, herein).

4. Examples of conceptual models

4.1. One-parameter models

The simplest model based on a pure translation is that of a linear channel which displaces the inflow at its upstream end by a constant amount thus shifting the inflow in time without any change of shape. The impulse response corresponds to travel time of the linear channel. Such a delta function has a first moment equal to the travel time but all its higher moments are zero. Thus the model based on a linear channel with upstream inflow (model 1 in Table 2) will have a value of $S_2 = 0$ and a value of $S_3 = 0$. It would, however, seem more appropriate in the case of catchment runoff (as opposed to a flood-routing problem) to consider a linear

Table 2. One-parameter conceptual models

Model	Elements	Type of inflow	Shape factors	
			S_2	S_3
1	Linear channel	Upstream	0	0
2	Linear channel	Lateral, uniform	1/3	0
3	Linear channel	Lateral, triangular (1:2)	1/6	0
4	Linear channel	Lateral, triangular (1:3)	7/32	1/32
5	Linear reservoir	Upstream/lateral	1	2
6	2 reservoirs	Upstream	1/2	1/2
7	2 reservoirs	Lateral, uniform	7/9	10/9
8	3 reservoirs	Upstream	1/3	2/9
9	Diffusion reach	Upstream	∞	∞
10	Diffusion reach	Lateral, uniform	7/5	124/35

channel with lateral inflow. If the inflow is taken as uniform along the length of the channel then the instantaneous unit hydrograph would have the shape of a rectangle. In this case (model 2 on Table 2), the first moment would be given by $T/2$ and the second moment by $T^2/12$ thus giving a shape factor S_2 of 1/3.

Since the instantaneous unit hydrograph is symmetrical the third moment and third shape factor would be zero. Recognizing that most catchment areas are ovoid rather than rectangular in shape, we might replace this rectangular inflow by an inflow in the shape of an isosceles triangle. In this case the first moment would again be given by $T/2$ and the second moment would be given by $T^2/24$ thus giving a value of S_2 of $1/6$. The third moment and third shape factor would again be zero. None of the three models given above would be capable of reproducing the skewness which appears in most derived unit hydrographs. This could be overcome by using a scalene triangle rather than an isosceles triangle and if the shape is kept fixed then only one parameter is involved. In fact a triangle in which the length of the recession is twice the length of the rise (model 4) was used by Sherman in his basic paper and is shown in Figure 6.

If the one parameter model is to be based on storage then the simplest model is that of the single linear reservoir. For this case (model 5) the value of S_2 and S_3 can be shown by means of equation 26 above, to be 1 and 2 respectively. In the early studies of conceptual models carried out in Japan, the single linear reservoir was replaced by two equal reservoirs in series with the inflow into the upstream reservoir. If the number of reservoirs is kept constant in this fashion, it can be considered as a one-parameter model and for the case of two reservoirs both the shape factors S_2 and S_3 will have a value of 1/2 (model 6). If on the other hand we take two equal linear reservoirs with lateral inflow divided equally between them (model 7) then the shape factors are markedly different having the values of 7/9 and 10/9. If a cascade of three equal reservoirs is taken (model 8) then the values for the shape factors are 1/3 and 2/9. Unless the number of reservoirs is predetermined, these models cannot be considered as one-parameter models.

The diffusion analogy has been used as a conceptual model for surface flow, flow in the unsaturated zone and for groundwater flow (Kraijenhoff van de Leur *et al.*, 1966). If the model is one of pure diffusion without any advective term then it can be classed as a one-parameter model. Where the inflow is taken at the upstream end of a diffusion element (model 9) the first moment is infinite, the higher moments are all infinite, and the shape factors S_2 and S_3 are also infinite. This means that the model cannot be fitted by equating the first moment of the model to the first moment of the data. However, the impulse response is given by

$$b(t) = \frac{A}{\sqrt{(\pi t^3)}} \exp\left(-\frac{A}{t}\right) \tag{31a}$$

and the single parameter A can be determined from the estimates of the unit hydrograph moments by

$$A^2 = \frac{(U_1')^3}{U_2} \tag{31b}$$

Another one-parameter model can be postulated on the basis of a diffusion reach with a uniform lateral inflow. In this case, which had been used in groundwater analysis, the moments are finite and the shape factors are given by 7/5 and 124/35.

It can thus be seen from the models described above and listed in Table 2 that the models based on translation give low values of the shape factors, those based on storage give intermediate values and those based on diffusion give high values of the shape factors. The models 1 to 10 are plotted on a shape factor diagram in Figure 8. Since they are all one-parameter models, they plot as single points.

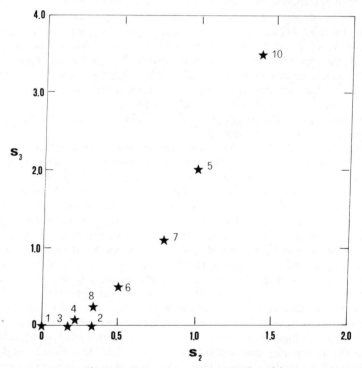

Figure 8. One-parameter conceptual models

4.2 Two-parameter models

In the case of two-parameter models there is a wide choice available. A number of them are listed in Table 3. Any shape of lateral inflow to a linear channel that involves two parameters will provide a two-parameter conceptual model of direct storm runoff. Model 11 in Table 3 involves a triangular inflow of length T with the peak at the point aT. Models 3 and 4 in Table 2 are obviously special cases of model 11.

Table 3. Two-parameter conceptual models

Model no.	Elements	Type of inflow
11	Channel	Lateral, triangular $(a:1)$
12	Channel plus reservoir	Upstream
13	Channel plus reservoir	Lateral, uniform
14	Channel plus reservoir	Lateral, triangular $(1:2)$
15	Channel plus reservoir	Lateral, triangular $(1:3)$
16	n equal reservoirs	Upstream
17	2 unequal reservoirs	Upstream
18	n equal reservoirs	Lateral, uniform
19	2 equal reservoirs	Lateral, non-uniform
20	Convective diffusive	Upstream

A two-parameter model can always be obtained by combining any of the one-parameter models based on translation with a single linear reservoir. Models 12 to 15 inclusive in Table 3 correspond to models 1 to 4 in Table 2. The moments (or cumulants) of the resulting models are obtained by adding the moments (or cumulants) of model 5 to the moments (or cumulants) of the appropriate translation model. It is also easy to construct two-parameter models based solely on storage. Models 5, 6 and 8 in Table 2 represent the cases of a cascade of one, two and three equal reservoirs respectively each with upstream inflow. These are all special cases of the Nash cascade which consists of a series of n equal linear reservoirs (model 16 in Table 3). Alternatively, model 6, which is a one-parameter model based on two equal reservoirs each with a delay time K, can be modified to give a two-parameter model based on two reservoirs with unequal delay times (K_1 and K_2) placed in series (model 17 on Table 3).

Model 7, i.e. two equal reservoirs with uniform lateral inflow, can be modified in a number of ways. The uniformity of the lateral inflow can be retained and the length of the cascade used as a second parameter (model 18) or the length of the cascade could be retained at two and the lateral inflow into each reservoir varied (model 19 in Table 3).

Finally the models based on diffusion can be modified by the introduction of a convective term (model 20). This corresponds to replacing the St Venant equations by the convective diffusion equation

$$D\frac{\mathrm{d}^2 y}{\mathrm{d}x^2} = a\frac{\mathrm{d}y}{\mathrm{d}x} + \frac{\mathrm{d}y}{\mathrm{d}t} \qquad (32a)$$

For the case of upstream inflow, this equation has the impulse response:

$$b(x, t) = \frac{x}{\sqrt{(4\pi Dt^3)}} \exp\left[-\frac{(x - at)^2}{4Dt} \right]$$ (32b)

which is a distributed model. It can, however, be considered as a lumped conceptual model with the impulse response

$$b(t) = \frac{A}{\sqrt{(\pi t^3)}} \exp\left[-\frac{(A - Bt)^2}{t} \right]$$ (32c)

where the two parameters A and B can be determined from the estimates of the moments by

$$A^2 = \frac{(U'_1)^3}{U_2}$$ (32d)

and

$$B^2 = \frac{U'_1}{U_2}$$ (32e)

and used to generate the impulse response defined by equation 32c.

It is interesting to compare the three examples of two-parameter models included in Table 1 on the basis of their position on a shape factor diagram. This is done in Figure 9 which shows the following models: a routed isosceles triangle

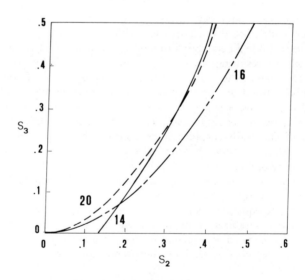

14   Routed isosceles triangle   ——————

16   Cascade with upstream inflow   —— · ——

20   Convective diffusion analogy   — — — — —

Figure 9. Comparison of conceptual models

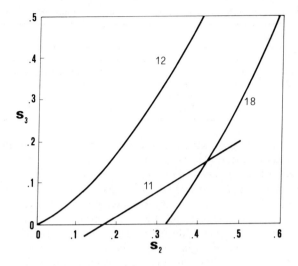

11 CHANNEL WITH TRIANGULAR INFLOW

12 CHANNEL AND RESERVOIR

18 CASCADE WITH LATERAL INFLOW

Figure 10. Comparison of conceptual models

(model 14), a cascade of equal linear reservoirs (model 16) and a model based on the convective diffusion equation (model 20). It will be noted that all three models, which are based on differing physical concepts plot close together on the shape factor diagram.

A further comparison of two-parameter conceptual models is shown in Figure 10. The conceptual models shown in Figure 10 are a linear channel with lateral inflow in the shape of a scalene triangle (model 11), a linear channel with upstream inflow followed by a linear reservoir (model 12) and a cascade of equal linear reservoirs with equal lateral inflow (model 18). It can be seen that in this case the curves plot well apart.

4.3 Three-parameter models

A very large number of three-parameter models can be synthesized in an attempt to simulate the operation of any of the components of catchment response. Thus the two-parameter model of a channel with lateral inflow in the shape of a scalene triangle (model 11 on Table 3) can be combined with a single linear reservoir to give a model based on a routed scalene triangle (model 21 in Table 4). Similarly the two-parameter models 12 and 16 in Table 3 can be combined to give a conceptual model based on upstream inflow to a channel and a cascade of equal linear reservoirs in series, i.e. a lagged Nash cascade (model 22 on Table 4). Similarly model 17 on Table 3 (two unequal reservoirs with upstream inflow) can be given an additional parameter either by modifying the cascade to three unequal reservoirs

98

Table 4. Three-parameter conceptual models

Model no.	Elements	Type of inflow
21	Channel, reservoir	Lateral, triangular (a:1)
22	Channel, n equal reservoirs	Upstream
23	3 unequal reservoirs	Upstream
24	2 unequal reservoirs	Lateral, non-uniform

(model 23 in Table 4) or by changing the inflow from inflow into the upstream reservoir only to non-uniform lateral inflow (model 24 in Table 4).

For the sake of convenience and ease of comparison with the one-parameter and two-parameter models already listed, the three-parameter models mentioned above are tabulated in Table 4. These four three-parameter models have been included in the computer program (see Dooge and O'Kane, herein).

Since they define a region in the S_3 S_2 shape factor diagram, three-parameter models cannot be compared conveniently in graphical form with derived unit hydrographs, except that they can only represent a unit hydrograph that plots within this space. They can, however, be characterized by their ability to predict the value of S_4 on the basis of fitting the three lower moments. The question of fitting a conceptual model to an individual hydrograph will be dealt with further in Part 3 of the volume (Dooge and O'Kane, herein) and the question of finding the best conceptual model for a regional study will be discussed in Section 5.3.

5. Scope of conceptual models

5.1 Non-linear conceptual models

The whole of the foregoing discussion is concerned with linear conceptual models of the rainfall-runoff relationship. Such models are far easier to handle than non-linear models and accordingly are to be preferred if they can serve the purpose of the study with sufficient accuracy. However, particularly in the case of small catchment areas, the non-linear nature of the catchment response will be too marked for linear theory to be adequate. Accordingly, this section of the paper discusses very briefly the use of non-linear conceptual models.

One approach to the problem of non-linear behaviour is to analyse the catchment for each individual event as if the operation were linear and then to study the relationship between the variations of the parameters of the linearized model and the variations of the intensity and other characteristics of the rainstorm. In this approach, the analysis of the individual event is exactly the same as in the linear approach and involves for each storm the derivation of the apparent unit hydrograph for the catchment and its representation by a conceptual model. The correlation of the parameters with storm characteristics may be carried out in the standard manner. The complete non-linear model consists of the specification of the conceptual model and of the relationship between the model parameters and storm characteristics.

A second approach is to simulate a non-linear hydrologic system by a relatively simple non-linear model built up from simple non-linear conceptual elements. An obvious element of this type is a non-linear reservoir in which we have a relationship between outflow and storage given by

$$S = K \cdot Q^n \tag{33a}$$

where S is the storage in the element, Q is the outflow from the element, K and n are parameters characterizing the element. For the case of $n = 1$ we have the familiar case of a linear reservoir with a storage delay time K. This relationship can be written in the alternative form

$$Q = aS^c \tag{33b}$$

where a and c are again parameters characterizing non-linear storage element. Similarly, we can replace the linear channel by a conceptual element giving a non-linear translation for which we would have

$$Q(t + t_0) = I(t) \tag{34}$$

where the translation time (t_0) is a function of flow. The kinematic wave solution for open channel flow is normally used in a non-linear form. For the two-dimensional case this can be considered as a distributed conceptual element in which we have at any point:

$$q = by^c \tag{35}$$

where q is the discharge per unit width, y is the depth of flow, and b and c are parameters characterizing the element. For the linear case we take $c = 1$, for turbulent flow $c = 5/3$ and for laminar flow $c = 3$.

These simple conceptual elements could be combined in the same way as linear conceptual elements to produce conceptual models and then used to simulate the non-linear catchment operation. When we do so, however, we miss the great power of linear mathematics which enables us to predict the effect of a cascade of elements by convoluting the impulse responses of the separate elements. A further disadvantage is that the relationship connecting the moments of the rainfall, the unit hydrograph and the runoff discussed in Section 3.1 no longer holds. However, many of the simplified methods used in the hydrologic analysis of surface runoff can be viewed as simple non-linear conceptual models (Dooge, 1972a).

The problem of overland flow is one in which non-linear effects are quite marked. Since the solution of the equations of unsteady flow for this case is quite difficult, applied hydrologists have used simplified approaches to the study of overland flow. One such approach is based on the replacement of the momentum equation by the assumption of a power relationship between the outflow at the downstream end and the total storage on the surface. This method was proposed by Horton (1938) for overland flow and natural catchments and later used by Izzard (1946) for paved surfaces. The basic assumption of this method is that the surface of overland flow behaves as a single non-linear reservoir.

A second widely used approach to the problem of overland flow is that based on the kinematic wave solution. This method also assumes a power relationship between discharge and depth but in this case the assumption is that of a relationship between the discharge and the depth at every point as in equation 34 and thus constitutes a distributed relationship. The results obtained from the kinematic wave approach are quite different to that obtained by the Horton–Izzard approach. It can be shown that, whereas the Horton–Izzard method uses a single non-linear reservoir, the kinematic wave approach is equivalent to the use of a cascade of a large number of very small equal non-linear reservoirs.

The author has studied the properties of the model based on a cascade of equal non-linear storage elements with lateral inflow and concluded that for such a system a dimensionless response curve can be derived which will be invariant for any set of similar inflows. Inflows of different intensities are said to be similar in this sense if the shapes are similar and if the time scales of the two inflows are related to the respective intensities by

$$\frac{t_2}{t_1} = \left(\frac{r_1}{r_2}\right)^{(c-1)/c} \tag{36}$$

where c is the degree of non-linearity as in equation 33b. For this conceptual model, which is referred to as the case of uniform non-linearity, the outflow hydrograph for uniform inflow can be represented in dimensionless form by

$$\frac{q}{q_e} = \phi\left[\frac{t}{t_0}, \frac{D}{t_0}\right] \tag{37}$$

where q is the outflow, q_e is the equilibrium outflow (equal to the rate of uniform inflow), t is the time elapsed since the start of inflow, D is the duration of uniform inflow and t_0 a characteristic time which depends on the intensity of inflow in accordance with equation 36.

It can be shown that both laboratory and field data of non-linear hydrologic systems can be plotted in such a way as to indicate the validity of equation 37 (Dooge, 1972a). A single example will be given here. Figure 11 shows a series of unit hydrographs derived by Minshall (1960) for a catchment of 27 acres (10.9 ha)

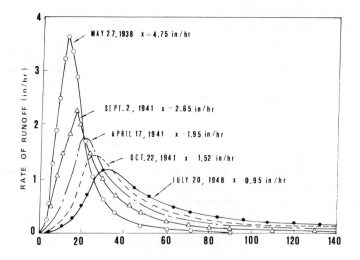

TIME FROM BEGINNING OF EXCESS RAINFALL (min)

Figure 11. Unit hydrographs derived by Minshall

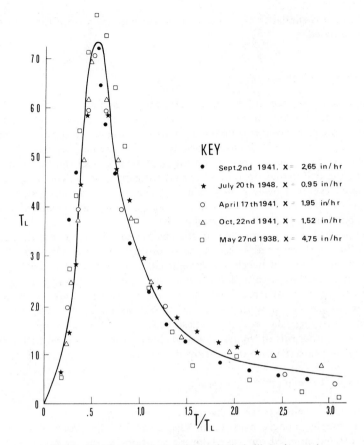

Figure 12. Dimensionless plotting of Minshall's hydrograph

and indicates that, for the range of intensity shown, there is a threefold variation in the value of the peak of the unit hydrograph. This is clear evidence of non-linearity in the behaviour of the catchment. If the unit hydrographs were plotted in accordance with equation 37 by taking the lag as the characteristic time, we get the result shown in Figure 12. Here we see that, though there is some scatter, a single curve could be used for prediction purposes. According to the hypothesis of uniform non-linearity, a single uniform hydrograph would be obtained if the ratio of duration to lag was the same in the case of each storm. In fact no knowledge of the duration is available from the published paper so the data in Figure 12 may include quite a variation in the ratio of duration to lag.

A curve such as that shown in Figure 12 together with a correlation of the lag with the intensity of storm would enable reasonable predictions to be made even in the presence of such a high degree of non-linearity. The dimensionless response function of Figure 12 can be simulated by a conceptual model in the same way as a unit hydrograph can be simulated by a linear conceptual model. However, it must be remembered that the response function is only valid for a pattern of effective rainfall which is similar in the sense of uniform non-linearity to that on which the response is based.

5.2 Models of subsurface flow

The approach described in Sections 2 and 3 above for the simulation of the direct response component of the catchment operation by conceptual models can also be applied to the groundwater component and to the soil moisture component. These further applications are discussed briefly in the present section. If all three components are modelled then a general catchment model can be constructed to represent the continuous operation of the catchment under all conditions as well as for isolated events. However, in dealing with any particular event, such a general model will of necessity be less efficient than a model of equal complexity designed for that particular type of hydrological event.

Many hydrologists assume that, in the absence of inflow, the baseflow recession curve follows an exponential decline and accordingly use a semi-log plot to identify the baseflow. It should be clearly recognized that the use of a semi-log plot to separate the baseflow is equivalent to assuming that the groundwater response can be represented by a particular linear model, i.e. by a single linear reservoir. If this is so, it would be appropriate to use the same model for the groundwater component during the recharge phase instead of an arbitrary straight-line separation or other rule of thumb. If a single linear reservoir is subjected to recharge at the uniform rate (R) then the outflow during recharge will be given by

$$Q = R \left[1 - \exp\left(-\frac{t}{K}\right) \right] + Q_0 \exp\left(-\frac{t}{K}\right) \tag{38}$$

where the time origin is taken at the start of recharge.

Other simple models have been suggested for the groundwater response. Kraijenhoff has pointed out that Glover's solution for the recession of the water table after the cessation of recharge is equivalent to taking the impulse response of the groundwater reservoir as:

$$h(t) = \frac{8}{\pi^2} \frac{1}{j} \sum_{n=1,3\ldots} \exp\left(-n^2 \frac{t}{j}\right) \tag{39a}$$

where the reservoir coefficient (j) given by

$$j = \frac{1}{\pi^2} \cdot \frac{fS^2}{Kh} \tag{39b}$$

groups into a single coefficient the values of the drainable pore space (f), the spacing of the trenches or drains (S), the saturated permeability of the soil (K), and the average value of the depth of groundwater ($\bar{h}$) (Kraijenhoff van de Leur, 1966).

The soil moisture component remains the most difficult component to model. In the conceptual models for the total catchment response that have been proposed in the literature it is frequently the weakest part of the formulation of the model. In unit hydrograph procedures, the replacement of a declining rate of infiltration by an equivalent uniform rate distorts the pattern of effective rainfall and overestimates the amount of effective rain at the beginning of the storm. This, combined with initial detention, may be reflected in the inclusion of an initial lag (or linear channel) in many conceptual models of direct storm runoff.

The infiltration equations commonly used in hydrology can be derived by postulating a relationship between the rate of infiltration capacity (f) and either the volume of actual infiltration (F) or the volume of potential infiltration (F_p). These can in turn be interpreted as special types of conceptual models. These relationships can also be postulated in terms of the rate of excess infiltration (f_e) which is defined as $f - f_c$ where f_c is the ultimate constant rate of infiltration. These relationships can also be formulated in terms of negative feedback.

Thus if we assume that the rate of infiltration is inversely proportional to the amount already infiltrated, i.e.

$$f = \frac{a}{F} \qquad (40a)$$

it is easy to show that the variation of infiltration with time is given by

$$f = \sqrt{\left(\frac{a}{2t}\right)} \qquad (40b)$$

which is the Kostiakov formula for the special value of ½ and also the dominant term of the Philip equation for initial high rate infiltration. When f_e and F_e are used in equation 40a then a constant term f_e appears on the r.h.s. of equation 40b.

Equation (40a) assumes a relationship between the rate of inflow into the soil and the amount of moisture which has already infiltrated. This is comparable to a linear reservoir in which the amount of outflow is directly proportional to the amount of water contained in the reservoir. Thus we could consider the relationship given by the equation 40 as being a conceptual element which we might refer to as a linear absorber of the inverse type.

If, alternatively, we relate the rate of infiltration (f) directly to the potential infiltration (R_p), i.e. the ultimate volume of infiltration at saturation minus the actual volume value of infiltration to date, then we have:

$$f = aF_p \qquad (41a)$$

which could be described as a linear absorber of the potential type. It can be readily shown that the assumption in equation 41a gives as the formula for the rate of infiltration excess:

$$f = f_0 \exp(-at) \qquad (41b)$$

which shows the exponential decrease found in the well-known Horton equation for infiltration. When equation 41a is posutulated in terms of infiltration excess the resulting form of equation 41b is the full Horton formula.

Thus we can identify two different types of conceptual element which correspond to the two most commonly used equations for infiltration, i.e. those of Philip and Horton. Apart from this harmonization of viewpoint in regard to the unsaturated phase, actual calculations in terms of equations 40a and 41a are more easily programmed and controlled than the direct relationships given by equations 40b and 41b.

5.3 Regional analysis

It will be recalled from Section 2.3 that conceptual models first arose in the context of synthetic unit hydrographs. Unit hydrographs can be derived for the gauged catchments within a region and made the basis of a method of synthetic unit hydrographs for the ungauged catchments in the same region. For a general synthetic scheme, it is necessary to determine (a) the degree of complexity (i.e. the number of parameters) required in the conceptual model; (b) the particular model of this degree of complexity which best represents the gauged catchments; (c) the correlation between the parameters of the chosen model and the catchment parameters. The moments of the individual unit hydrographs for each catchment area can be determined from the records of effective rainfall and storm runoff. These moments can be used systematically as the basis for a general synthetic scheme outlined in Figure 13.

The moments of the unit hydrographs of the gauged catchments can be used to estimate the number of parameters required in the conceptual model needed as the basis for the scheme of synthetic unit hydrographs. For a two-parameter conceptual model the two degrees of freedom in the model are completely absorbed by the fixing of the first and second moments and hence for this particular model the dimensionless third moment is uniquely determined by the value of the dimensionless second moment. For this reason the model will plot as a line on a shape factor diagram. Similarly for a three-parameter model the fourth dimensionless moment would be completely determined by the second and third dimensionless moments.

An estimate of the extent to which a model of given complexity will represent the unit hydrographs from a number of gauged catchments is given by the coefficients of multiple correlation of the appropriate dimensionless moment with

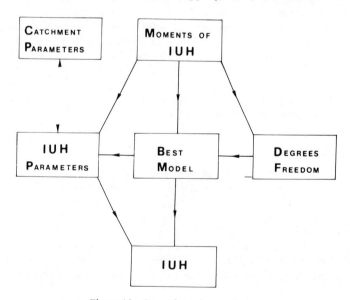

Figure 13. General synthetic scheme

the dimensionless moments of lower order. This may be exemplified for Nash's data on British catchments (Nash, 1960). The coefficient of multiple correlation of m_3 with m_2 for Nash's data is 0.717. This indicates that the variation in the third dimensionless moment (m_3) was only accounted for to the extent of about 50% by variations in the dimensionless second moment (m_2). This figure of 50% may be taken as an estimate of a lower bound of the efficiency of a two-parameter model in representing this particular data. For the same data the coefficient of multiple correlation between the dimensionless fourth moment (m_4) and the two lower dimensionless moments (m_3 and m_2) was found to be 0.93, indicating that the variance of m_4 was accounted for by the variance in the lower moments to the extent of almost 90%. Considering the basic nature of Nash's data (which were normal river observations rather than research data), this was a very high correlation and indicated that a three-parameter model would probably give as satisfactory a simulation as the data warranted.

Having determined the degree of complexity of the conceptual model to be used, it is necessary to choose the best model with the given number of parameters. This could also be done on the basis of the derived moments for the gauged catchments by determining the model which gave the best fit in the $(n-1)$-dimensional shape factor space. Once the best model has been determined, the parameters of that model could be optimized by moment matching and a check for gross error made by reproducing the flood runoff for the individual gauged catchments.

Figures 14 and 15 show Nash's data plotted for British catchment on a shape

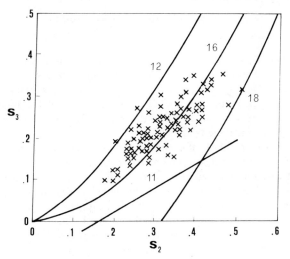

11 CHANNEL WITH TRIANGULAR INFLOW
12 CHANNEL AND RESERVOIR
16 CASCADE WITH UPSTREAM INFLOW
18 CASCADE WITH LATERAL INFLOW

Figure 14. Nash's data for British catchments

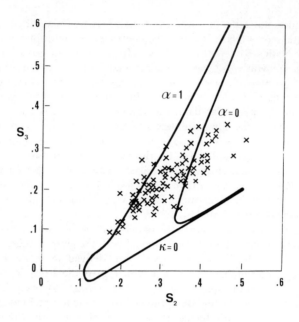

SCALENE TRIANGLE OF BASE T

WITH VERTEX AT TIME αT

ROUTED THROUGH RESERVOIR OF SIZE κ

Figure 15. Nash's data and model 21

factor diagram. The lines characterizing four different two-parameter models are also shown on Figure 14. While models 12 and 18 give a closer fit to some individual unit hydrographs it is clear that model 16 (a cascade of equal linear reservoirs with upstream inflow) gives the best overall fit. Figure 15 shows the comparison of the same data with the region covered by the three-parameter model 21 (a routed scalene triangle).

It remains to correlate the unit hydrograph parameters (or the individual moments themselves) with catchment parameters. To determine the three independent unit hydrograph parameters that would be required for a three-parameter model it is necessary to have three independent catchment parameters which between them would account for a certain proportion (e.g. 90% or more) of the variation in the shape of the unit hydrograph. It must be stressed that what is required in unit hydrograph synthesis is not necessarily a correlation with individual catchment characteristics. Each of the catchment parameters used for correlation might be made up from a number of individual catchment characteristics (such as area, slope, drainage, density, shape etc.) in the same way as the Froude and the Reynolds number are made up from a number of individual hydraulic characteristics. The determination of the significant grouping of catchment characteristics into catchment parameters remains one of the great unsolved problems of surface water hydrology. Factor analysis may help in the preliminary trial grouping of catchment characteristics but it is likely that the final significant forms of the grouping will only emerge through a better understanding of geomorphological processes.

5.4 Effects of human activity

In cases where catchment behaviour is affected by human activity, it is necessary to modify the unit hydrograph derivation and the regional analysis. For the case of a single catchment it is necessary to determine parameter values at different levels of a given factor of human influence and to attempt to find a correlation between the values of the parameters and the level of influence. In some cases, it may not be possible to obtain data on a single catchment at different stages of development and accordingly we must once again resort to a regional analysis in which the catchments have different characteristics and also different levels of development. Much less work is being done in this area than in the general field of synthetic unit hydrographs. Two examples illustrating how the problem may be approached are described below.

The first example is concerned with an attempt to simulate the effect of drainage on the runoff from peatland. The study relates to small plots of drained and undrained peatland at Glenamoy in north-west Ireland. The study was a preliminary one and is referred to as an illustration of the approach to be followed rather than a prediction of the actual effect of drainage. The plots studied were 0.5 hectares in extent.

A computer program was written to find the first three moments of the unit hydrograph for the input and output data. The necessary data for the program were the daily values of rainfall, evaporation and runoff during the period. The moments (with days as the time unit) which were obtained from the data for the 10th to the 26th January, 1968, are given in Table 5.

A conceptual model of a cascade of equal linear reservoirs was fitted to the data by moment matching and the parameter values found as indicated in Table 6. As can be seen from Table 6 the fourfold increase in lag time is simulated largely by the increase in the value of the storage constant K and only to a slight extent by the increase in the value n. This indicates that the unit hydrograph derived in this way

Table 5. Moments from Glenamoy data

Moments about the origin	Undrained plot	Drained plot
First	1.43	5.69
Second	7.55	97.85
Third	76.01	2565.06

Table 6. Parameters for conceptual model

Parameter	Undrained plot	Drained plot
n (dimensionless)	0.25	0.33
K (days)	5.81	17.02

for the undrained and drained plots would be fairly similar in shape though different in scale. This suggests that the model might be useful for predicting the effect of drainage on small areas of peat, since the greater part of the variation could be accounted for by the adjustment of a single parameter.

The second example relates to the effects of urbanization on runoff studied by Rao, Delleur and Sarma. The study reviews previous work on the subject and uses a number of approaches. Discussion here, however, will be confined to the use of the cascade of equal linear reservoirs to the problem. Data from eight urbanized and four rural watersheds in Indiana and Texas were used in the study. These varied in area from 13 hectares to 4900 hectares, in mean basin slope from 1 in 1300 to 1 in 47 and in impervious area from 0 to 35%. The number of storms used in the analysis varied from catchment to catchment but the average number of storms per catchment was ten.

It was found that the values of the parameters varied for different storms on the same catchment area, indicating that the catchment was behaving in a non-linear fashion. It was decided to attempt to correlate these variations with storm characteristics. Thus the conceptual model used was a linearized model rather than a linear one. The parameters n and K were obtained by (a) equating the product nK to the lag and (b) by optimizing the value of the parameter K so the correlation coefficient between the observed and computed runoff would be a maximum.

Regression equations were developed to estimate the lag of the catchment and the parameter K in terms of the physiographic and storm characteristics. The following regression relationships were obtained

$$nK = 0.831 \frac{A^{0.453} T_R^{0.371}}{(1 + U)^{1.662} P_E^{0.267}} \tag{42a}$$

$$K = 0.575 \frac{A^{0.389} T_R^{0.222}}{(1 + U)^{0.622} P_E^{1.06}} \tag{42b}$$

where A is the catchment area, T_R the duration of rainfall, $(1 + U)$ an urbanization factor and P_E the volume of rainfall excess.

If we take an 80% impervious area as representing complete development, the urbanization factor will have a value of 1.8 and it can be deduced from equation (42a) that the lag for a fully developed catchment will be less than 40% of the lag for the same catchment in an undeveloped condition. In this case, more of the change will be accounted for by a change in the value of n (which is 55% of its former value) than in the value of K (which is 70% of its former value).

It must be emphasized that the outline description of these two studies is not given as a basis for predicting actual values but as an illustration of the approach to modelling of particular effects of human activity. This approach could be followed in other cases with due regard to local circumstances and local data. The value of such an approach is that, once the model has been validated in respect of its ability to reproduce the effects of human activity for certain catchments in a region, it may be used with reasonable confidence to predict the continued effect of human activity in other catchments in the area.

A Constrained Parameter Estimation Technique for Linear Models in Hydrology

LUIGI NATALE
Hydraulics Institute, University of Pavia, Italy

EZIO TODINI
IBM Scientific Center, Pisa, Italy

1. Introduction

Many hydrological systems do not at present have valid 'physics based' mathematical models owing to the limited knowledge of their dynamics and to the inevitable lumping of the system parameters when real world data must be treated.

Because of the impossibility of developing a complete accurate 'physics based' model, hydrologists have introduced a plethora of empirical conceptual models each of which reflects a small portion of hydrologic reality together with gross empirical simplifying assumptions based on the personal judgements of the individual modeller.

Given that all models must resort to the approximations and simplifying assumptions it is our contention that the chosen approximations should lead to a lessening of the computational load and allow for objective parameter estimation techniques.

The introduction of linear behaviour assumptions fits both the above-mentioned criteria. In addition, many hydrological phenomena, such as flood routing (Hayami, 1951), can be regarded as being linear or at least can be successfully simulated, as in the case of rainfall—runoff, by sets of linear elements connected by extremely simple non-linear linkages.

In the following pages, a linear black-box parameter estimation technique is advocated that is extremely flexible and stable and can allow for multiple inputs.

2. A linear model of a drainage network

Following others (Linsley *et al.*, 1949; Hayami, 1951; Henderson, 1969; Price, 1973a) the St Venant set of equations can be reduced to one equation in one

The research was done with the partial contribution of the Italian National Research Council (CNR) under contract no. 72.00966.28, 'Ricostruzione dell'onda di piena di alcuni corsi d'acqua italiani'.

unknown which can be written for a natural channel without lateral inflow as

$$\frac{\partial Q}{\partial t} = D_1 \frac{\partial^2 Q}{\partial x^2} - D_2 \frac{\partial Q}{\partial x} \tag{1}$$

where D_1 and D_2 are two coefficients that take into account the characteristics of the reach.

Equation 1 can be solved in the form of a convolution integral:

$$Q_d(t) = \int_0^t u_d(\tau) Q_u(t - \tau) \, d\tau \tag{2}$$

where Q_d is the outflow of the reach, Q_u the inflow and u_d the impulse response of the reach. (In Appendix A the expressions of equations 1 and 2 have been deduced for the special case of a rectangular channel reach.)

Equation 2 can be generalized to allow for the N inputs of a natural drainage network:

$$Q_d(t) = \int_0^t u_1(\tau) \, Q_{u_1}(t - \tau) \, d\tau + \int_0^t u_2(\tau) \, Q_{u_2}(t - \tau) \, d\tau + \ldots$$

$$+ \int_0^t u_N(\tau) \, Q_{u_N}(t - \tau) \, d\tau \tag{3}$$

The different impulse responses u_i of each channel can be treated in parallel for a linear system and can be determined from the measured data by one of the several methods of parameter estimation that will be compared in the next chapter.

We can sample the individual terms of equation 3 in discrete time intervals Δt as follows:

$$\mathbf{q} = \begin{bmatrix} Q_d(1\Delta t) \\ Q_d(2\Delta t) \\ \vdots \\ Q_d(m\Delta t) \end{bmatrix} \tag{4}$$

$$\mathbf{u_i} = \begin{bmatrix} u_i(1\Delta t) \\ u_i(2\Delta t) \\ \vdots \\ u_i(k\Delta t) \end{bmatrix} \quad i = 1, \ldots, N \tag{5}$$

and omitting to write the Δt from now on (i.e. $(j \cdot \Delta t) = (j)$),

$$\mathbf{H_i} = \begin{bmatrix} Q_{u_i}(1) & & \\ Q_{u_i}(2) & Q_{u_i}(1) & \\ \vdots & \vdots & \\ Q_{u_i}(m-1) & Q_{u_i}(m-2) \ldots Q_{u_i}(m-k+2) \\ Q_{u_i}(m) & Q_{u_i}(m-1) \ldots Q_{u_i}(m-k+1) \end{bmatrix} \quad i = 1, \ldots, N \tag{6}$$

so that equation 3 can be written

$$q = (H_1 \, u_1 + H_2 \, u_2 + \ldots + H_N \, u_N) \, \Delta t \tag{7}$$

If we denote by H the (m, Nk) partitioning matrix

$$H = [H_1 \quad H_2 \quad \ldots \quad H_N] \tag{8}$$

and by u the (Nk) vector

$$u = \begin{bmatrix} u_1 \\ \cdots \\ u_2 \\ \cdots \\ \vdots \\ u_N \end{bmatrix} \tag{9}$$

and we consider $\Delta t = 1$. We can write equation 7 as follows:

$$q = H \, u \tag{10}$$

which is the discrete form of the linear model of a drainage network with N inputs.

The mathematical description equation 10 of the 'drainage network' as a linear system is, as previously stated, an approximate one; moreover the discharge measurements at the gauging stations are affected by errors that must be considered. Therefore it is more realistic to consider, instead of equation 10 the following expression of our model:

$$q = H \, u + \epsilon \tag{11}$$

where

$$\epsilon = \begin{bmatrix} \epsilon(1) \\ \epsilon(2) \\ \vdots \\ \epsilon(m) \end{bmatrix} \tag{12}$$

is an m length vector which will be called 'error' or 'noise' from now on.

The vector u of the ordinates of the impulse responses, which will be called 'parameters' from now, is to be estimated.

A discussion of the more common methods of parameter estimation follows. For a deeper discussion on parameter estimation see Sage and Melsa (1971b), whilst for the basic matricial calculus required see Ayres (1962) and Lipschutz (1968).

3. Parameter estimation of the synthetic linear model — comparison of estimators

In the following paragraph a comparison of 'efficiency' or 'goodness' of the most common estimators will be considered.

We may define

$$\tilde{u}_A = u - \hat{u}_A \tag{13}$$

as the error of estimate of the parameter u due to the estimator A.

We shall regard the estimator A more efficient than the estimator B if

$$E\{\tilde{u}_A \, \tilde{u}_A^T\} < E\{\tilde{u}_B \, \tilde{u}_B^T\} \tag{14}$$

where $E\{\,.\,\}$ is the expected value.

3.1 Maximum likelihood estimation

By definition the ML estimate is the estimate that maximizes the probability density function $p(q \mid u)$ of the observed output conditioned upon the parameter. The ML estimator gives the value of the parameter that maximizes the probability of measuring at the downstream section the actually measured output discharges, given the input discharges. The ML estimate $\hat{u}_{ML}$ is then given by

$$\frac{\partial p(q \mid u)}{\partial u}\bigg|_{u = \hat{u}_{ML}} = 0 \tag{15}$$

or by

$$\frac{\partial \ln p(q \mid u)}{\partial u}\bigg|_{u = \hat{u}_{ML}} = 0 \tag{16}$$

The use of equation 15 or of equation 16 requires the conditioned probability density function $p(q \mid u)$ that can be expressed in terms of ϵ if the distribution function of the error ϵ is known. In our case a large number of different elements concur in generating the errors, so that a Gaussian distribution of ϵ seems to be an acceptable assumption.

If the error has a Gaussian distribution with

$$E\{\epsilon\} = \mu_\epsilon \tag{17}$$

and

$$E\{(\epsilon - \mu_\epsilon)(\epsilon - \mu_\epsilon)^T\} = V_\epsilon \tag{18}$$

the conditioned probability distribution function of the observed output is still Gaussian (multinormal) with

$$E\{q \mid u\} = Hu + \mu_\epsilon \tag{19}$$

and

$$\mathrm{Var}\{q \mid u\} = V_\epsilon \tag{20}$$

The conditioned probability density function is then

$$p(q \mid u) = \frac{1}{(2\pi)^{m/2}(\det V_\epsilon)^{\frac{1}{2}}} \exp\left[-\frac{1}{2}(q - Hu - \mu_\epsilon)^T V_\epsilon^{-1}(q - Hu - \mu_\epsilon)\right] \tag{21}$$

Imposing (16) we obtain

$$H^T V_\epsilon^{-1}(q - H\hat{u}_{ML} - \mu_\epsilon) = 0 \tag{22}$$

from which we derive the expression of the ML estimate:

$$\hat{u}_{ML} = (H^T V_\epsilon^{-1} H)^{-1} H^T V_\epsilon^{-1}(q - \mu_\epsilon) \tag{23}$$

We can derive the efficiency of the estimator from the statistical characteristics of the error of estimate:

$$\tilde{u}_{ML} = u + \hat{u}_{ML} = u - (H^T V_\epsilon^{-1} H)^{-1} H^T V_\epsilon^{-1} (q - \mu_\epsilon) \tag{24}$$

Substituting (11) into (24) we obtain

$$\tilde{u}_{ML} = - (H^T V_\epsilon^{-1} H)^{-1} H^T V_\epsilon^{-1} (\epsilon - \mu_\epsilon) \tag{25}$$

Bearing in mind the characteristics of the noise (17) and (18), we obtain

$$\mu_{\tilde{u}_{ML}} = E\{\tilde{u}_{ML}\} = - (H^T V_\epsilon^{-1} H)^{-1} H^T V_\epsilon^{-1} E\{\epsilon - \mu_\epsilon\} = 0 \tag{26}$$

$$\mathrm{Var}\{\hat{u}_{ML}\} = E\{\tilde{u}_{ML} \tilde{u}_{ML}^T\} = (H^T V_\epsilon^{-1} H)^{-1} H^T V_\epsilon^{-1} E\{(\epsilon - \mu_\epsilon)(\epsilon - \mu_\epsilon)^T\}$$

$$V_\epsilon^{-1} H (H^T V_\epsilon^{-1} H)^{-1} = (H^T V_\epsilon^{-1} H)^{-1} \tag{27}$$

Concluding we can say that the ML estimator is unbiased and that the error of estimate $\tilde{u}_{ML}$ has a variance:

$$\mathrm{Var}\{\tilde{u}_{ML}\} = (H^T V_\epsilon^{-1} H)^{-1}$$

3.2 Least squares estimation

The LS estimator can be used even if the statistical characteristics of the error ϵ are not known. In fact by definition the LS estimator is the estimator that minimizes the quadratic form

$$J(\epsilon) = \frac{1}{2} \epsilon^T R^{-1} \epsilon \tag{28}$$

where R^{-1} must be a symmetrical positive definite matrix to ensure the existance of a minimum.

Equation 28 can be written in terms of u:

$$J(u) = \frac{1}{2} (q - Hu)^T R^{-1} (q - Hu) \tag{29}$$

The necessary condition for the existance of an extremum is then

$$\frac{\partial J(u)}{\partial u} \bigg|_{u=\hat{u}_{LS}} = (H^T R^{-1} H)\hat{u}_{LS} - H^T R^{-1} q = 0 \tag{30}$$

and the sufficient condition for a minimum is then satisfied by

$$\frac{\partial^2 J(u)}{\partial u^2} \bigg|_{u=\hat{u}_{LS}} = H^T R^{-1} H \tag{31}$$

being positive definite.

The LS estimate $\hat{u}_{LS}$ is

$$\hat{u}_{LS} = (H^T R^{-1} H)^{-1} H^T R^{-1} q \tag{32}$$

and the error of estimate, bearing in mind (11), is

$$\tilde{u}_{LS} = u - \hat{u}_{LS} = u - (H^T R^{-1} H)^{-1} H^T R^{-1} q = - (H^T R^{-1} H)^{-1} H^T R^{-1} \epsilon \tag{33}$$

It can be seen that if the expected value of the noise is

$$\mu_\epsilon = E\{\epsilon\} = 0 \tag{34}$$

the LS estimator is unbiased:

$$\mu_{\tilde{u}_{LS}} = E\{\tilde{u}_{LS}\} = -(H^T R^{-1} H)^{-1} H^T R^{-1} E\{\epsilon\} = 0 \tag{35}$$

And if

$$Var\{\epsilon\} = E\{\epsilon\epsilon^T\} = V_\epsilon \tag{36}$$

and we use the variance of the error as the weighting matrix of the quadratic form, i.e. $R = V_\epsilon$, the variance of the error of estimate is

$$Var\{\tilde{u}_{LS}\} \bigg|_{R = V_\epsilon} = E\{\tilde{u}_{LS}\} = (H^T V_\epsilon^{-1} H)^{-1} H^T V_\epsilon^{-1} E\{\epsilon\epsilon^T\} V_\epsilon^{-1} H (H^T V_\epsilon^{-1} H)^{-1}$$
$$= (H^T V_\epsilon^{-1} H)^{-1} \tag{37}$$

However, it should be pointed out that the generalized least squares estimator

$$\hat{u}_{GLS} = \hat{u}_{LS} \bigg|_{R = V_\epsilon} = (H^T V_\epsilon^{-1} H)^{-1} H^T V_\epsilon^{-1} q \tag{38}$$

does not require the knowledge of the probability distribution function of the error ϵ; it only requires that the first two moments of the error be known.

3.3 Bayesian estimation

We can show that the ML estimator and the GLS estimator in the case of zero mean noise are the most efficient estimators. It is useful at this point to recall the generalities of Bayesian estimators and of the minimum variance estimator.

We shall refer to the most general case of the estimate of a stochastic parameter u, first, and subsequently drive the estimate of a deterministic parameter.

The Bayes estimate problem is solved when the value of the parameter which minimizes the risk of Bayes:

$$\mathscr{B} = \int_{-\infty}^{+\infty} \int_{-\infty}^{+\infty} C(\tilde{u}) p(q,u) dq du = E\{C(\tilde{u})\} \tag{39}$$

is found.

In 39 $C(\tilde{u})$ is a cost function of the error of estimate, and $p(q, u)$ is the joint probability density function of observing q when the stochastic parameter assumes the value of u. By definition, the Bayes risk is then the expected value of the cost function of the error of estimate.

Different cost functions, such as the squared error, the absolute-value-of-error and the uniform error and the uniform error cost functions, lead to different Bayes estimators; but it can be shown that under certain assumptions (Sage and Melsa, 1971b) the estimate is independent of the choice of the cost function and it is always a minimum variance estimate.

We saw that the ML and GLS estimators are linear functions in q. Therefore we now wish to obtain expression of the linear unbiased estimator of minimum variance.

Without specifying the probability distributions of the parameters and of the error we can assume that their first two moments are known.

$$E\{u\} = \mu_u \tag{40}$$

$$Var\{u\} = E\{(u - \mu_u)(u - \mu_u)^T\} = V_u \tag{41}$$

$$E\{\epsilon\} = 0 \tag{42}$$

$$Var\{\epsilon\} = E\{\epsilon\epsilon^T\} = V_\epsilon \tag{43}$$

Further, without loss of generality we suppose that

$$E\{\epsilon u^T\} = E\{u\epsilon^T\} = 0 \tag{44}$$

The generic linear estimate:

$$\hat{u}_L = \xi + \Phi q = \xi + \Phi(Hu + \epsilon) \tag{45}$$

is unbiased if

$$E\{\tilde{u}_L\} = E\{u - \hat{u}_L\} = E\{u - \xi - \Phi(Hu + \epsilon)\} = \mu_u - \xi - \Phi H\mu_u = 0 \tag{46}$$

If we substitute in (45) the value of ξ derived from (46) we obtain the expression of the generic unbiased linear estimate:

$$\hat{u}_{UL} = \mu_u + \Phi(q - H\mu_u) \tag{47}$$

It can be shown that this estimator will minimize equation 39 with a quadratic cost function if it minimizes:

$$Var\{\tilde{u}_{UL}\} = E\{\tilde{u}_{UL}\tilde{u}_{UL}^T\} \tag{48}$$

where

$$\tilde{u}_{UL} = u - \hat{u}_{UL} = u - \mu_u - \Phi(q - H\mu_u) \tag{49}$$

Thus the minimum variance estimator will be found.

Bearing equation 11 in mind, and the first two moments of the parameter and of the noise, it is useful to derive the expressions of the following expectations:

$$
\begin{aligned}
&E\{u - \mu_u\} = 0 \\
&E\{q - H\mu_u\} = 0 \\
&E\{(u - \mu_u)(u - \mu_u)^T\} = V_u \\
&E\{(q - H\mu_u)(q - H\mu_u)^T\} = HV_uH^T + V_\epsilon \\
&E\{(q - H\mu_u)(u - \mu_u)^T\} = HV_u \\
&E\{(u - \mu_u)(q - H\mu_u)^T\} = V_uH^T
\end{aligned}
\tag{50}
$$

Expanding (48) we obtain

$$E\{\tilde{u}_{UL}\tilde{u}_{UL}^T\} = E\{[u - \mu_u - \Phi(q - H\mu_u)][u - \mu_u - \Phi(q - H\mu_u)]^T\} \tag{51}$$

To obtain the expression of the unbiased linear estimator of minimum variance we must find the value of Φ which minimizes (51), bearing in mind equation (50):

$$\frac{\partial E\{\tilde{u}_{UL}\tilde{u}_{UL}^T\}}{\partial \Phi}\bigg|_{\Phi=\hat{\Phi}} = -2E\{[q - H\mu_u][u - \mu_u - \hat{\Phi}(q - H\mu_u)]^T\} =$$

$$-2[HV_u - (HV_uH^T + V_\epsilon)\hat{\Phi}^T] = 0 \qquad (52)$$

from which we obtain

$$\hat{\Phi} = V_uH^T(HV_uH^T + V_\epsilon)^{-1} \qquad (53)$$

and from the matrix inversion lemma (Sage and Melsa, 1971b) we may have an alternative expression of $\hat{\Phi}$:

$$\hat{\Phi} = V_uH^T[V_\epsilon^{-1} - V_\epsilon^{-1}H(H^TV_\epsilon^{-1}H + V_u^{-1})^{-1}H^TV_\epsilon^{-1}] = \qquad (54)$$

$$= V_u[I - H^TV_\epsilon^{-1}H(H^TV_\epsilon^{-1}H + V_u^{-1})^{-1}]H^TV_\epsilon^{-1} =$$

$$= V_u[H^TV_\epsilon^{-1}H + V_u^{-1} - H^TV_\epsilon^{-1}H](H^TV_\epsilon^{-1}H + V_u^{-1})^{-1}H^TV_\epsilon^{-1} =$$

$$= (H^TV_\epsilon^{-1}H + V_u^{-1})^{-1}H^TV_\epsilon^{-1}$$

Substituting (54) into (47) we obtain the expression of the unbiased linear estimate of minimum variance:

$$\hat{u}_{ULMV} = \hat{u}_{UL}\bigg|_{\Phi=\hat{\Phi}} = \mu_u + (H^TV_\epsilon^{-1}H + V_u^{-1})^{-1}H^TV_\epsilon^{-1}(q - H\mu_u) =$$

$$= (H^TV_\epsilon^{-1}H + V_u^{-1})^{-1}H^TV_\epsilon^{-1}q$$

$$+ [I - (H^TV_\epsilon^{-1}H + V_u^{-1})^{-1}H^TV_\epsilon^{-1}H]\mu_u =$$

$$= (H^TV_\epsilon^{-1}H + V_u^{-1})^{-1}H^TV_\epsilon^{-1}q \qquad (55)$$

$$+ (H^TV_\epsilon^{-1}H + V_u^{-1})^{-1}(H^TV_\epsilon^{-1}H + V_u^{-1} - H^TV_\epsilon^{-1}H)\mu_u =$$

$$= (H^TV_\epsilon^{-1}H + V_u^{-1})^{-1}(H^TV_\epsilon^{-1}q + V_u^{-1}\mu_u)$$

Finally substituting (53) into (51) we obtain the expression of the variance of the estimate due to the ULMV estimator:

$$E\{\tilde{u}_{ULMV}\tilde{u}^T_{ULMV}\} = V_u - \hat{\Phi}HV_u - V_uH^T\hat{\Phi}^T + \hat{\Phi}(HV_uH^T + V_\epsilon)\hat{\Phi}^T =$$

$$= V_u - V_uH^T(HV_uH^T + V_\epsilon)^{-1}HV_u - V_uH^T$$

$$(HV_uH^T + V_\epsilon)^{-1}HV_u + V_uH^T(HV_uH^T + V_\epsilon)^{-1} \qquad (56)$$

$$(HV_uH^T + V_\epsilon)(HV_uH^T + V_\epsilon)^{-1}HV_u =$$

$$= V_u - V_uH^T(HV_uH^T + V_\epsilon)^{-1}HV_u$$

and from the matrix inversion lemma:

$$E\{\tilde{u}_{ULMV}\tilde{u}^T_{ULMV}\} = (V_u^{-1} + H^TV_\epsilon^{-1}H)^{-1} \qquad (57)$$

If we compare equation 57 with equation 27 and equation 37 it is easy to see that the variance of the error of estimate of a stochastic parameter obtained by the ULMV estimator is smaller than the corresponding variance obtained by the ML or by GLS estimators. This can be explained by the fact that the Bayesian estimator uses the *a priori* knowledge of the first two moments of the stochastic parameter u, which means that it utilizes more information than the two estimators described before. However, when the parameters to be estimated are constant (deterministic case), the estimation cannot be helped by a non-existing probability density function of the parameter. We must admit in this case that the estimate of u may assume any value in the real field which means that $V_u^{-1} = 0$ in (55) and (57) so that the expression of the ULMV estimator becomes equal to the expressions of the ML and of the GLS estimators and all the three estimators show the same variance of the error of estimate, that is with the same level of information all the three estimators have the same efficiency.

It is concluded that the Bayes estimator is superior only if we are able to enter additional *a priori* information, as for instance the first two moments of the stochastic parameter.

In the next section we will show how to introduce some physical information in the estimate of a deterministic parameter and hence augment the efficiency of the estimator.

4. Constrained estimation

In Section 3 it has been shown how we can use the available statistical information on a stochastic parameter u to improve the estimate. In the same way we will produce an improvement in the goodness of the estimate of a deterministic parameter if we introduce in the estimator some information which can reduce the field of the choice of û.

A natural way of obtaining this reduction is to impose a set of constraints that are satisfied by the true value of the parameters and hence should be satisfied by the estimate

$$Gu = i \Rightarrow G\hat{u} = i \tag{58}$$

where G is an (r, Nk) matrix and i is the unitary vector of length r

$$i = \begin{bmatrix} 1 \\ 1 \\ \vdots \\ 1 \end{bmatrix} \tag{59}$$

where r is the number of linear constraints.

Using the ML criterion the equality constrained estimate $\hat{u}_{EC}$ is the solution of the following problem:

$$\begin{cases} \min F(u) = \tfrac{1}{2}(q - Hu - \mu_\epsilon)^T V_\epsilon^{-1}(q - Hu - \mu_\epsilon) \\ \text{s.t. } Gu = i \end{cases} \tag{60}$$

which is equivalent to

$$\min L(u, \lambda) = \tfrac{1}{2}(q - Hu - \mu_\epsilon)^T V_\epsilon^{-1}(q - Hu - \mu_\epsilon) + \lambda^T(Gu - i) \tag{61}$$

having introduced the equality constraints into the functional by the classic Lagrange method (Dorn, 1963) where λ are the Lagrange multipliers.

By setting the derivative of $L(u, \lambda)$ with respect to u^T and λ^T equal to zero, we obtain in the following system of linear equations:

$$\begin{cases} H^T V_\epsilon^{-1} H \hat{u}_{EC} + G^T \lambda = H^T V_\epsilon^{-1}(q - \mu_\epsilon) \\ G \hat{u}_{EC} = i \end{cases} \tag{62}$$

which can be solved by inversion of the partitioning matrix of the system to give the expression of the equality constrained estimate

$$\hat{u}_{EC} = K^{-1} H^T V_\epsilon^{-1}(q - \mu_\epsilon) - K^{-1} G^T (GK^{-1} G^T)^{-1} GK^{-1} H^T V_\epsilon^{-1}(q - \mu_\epsilon)$$
$$+ K^{-1} G^T (GK^{-1} G^T)^{-1} i \tag{63}$$

where

$$K = (H^T V_\epsilon^{-1} H) \tag{64}$$

If we suppose, without loss of generality, that $\mu_\epsilon = 0$, and remembering $q = Hu + \epsilon$, we find after expansion,

$$\hat{u}_{EC} = K^{-1} H^T V_\epsilon^{-1} Hu + K^{-1} H^T V_\epsilon^{-1} \epsilon - K^{-1} G^T (GK^{-1} G^T)^{-1}$$
$$GK^{-1} H^T V_\epsilon^{-1} Hu - K^{-1} G^T (GK^{-1} G^T)^{-1} GK^{-1} H^T V_\epsilon^{-1} \epsilon$$
$$+ K^{-1} G^T (GK^{-1} G^T)^{-1} i = \tag{65}$$
$$= u + [I - K^{-1} G^T (GK^{-1} G^T)^{-1} G] K^{-1} H^T V_\epsilon^{-1} \epsilon$$
$$- K^{-1} G^T (GK^{-1} G^T)^{-1} (Gu - i)$$

To simplify notation we introduce the symbol D as

$$D = I - K^{-1} G^T (GK^{-1} G^T)^{-1} G \tag{66}$$

remembering that $Gu = i$ we obtain the expression of the error of estimate of the equality constrained estimator

$$\tilde{u}_{EC} = u - \hat{u}_{EC} = u - u - DK^{-1} H^T V_\epsilon^{-1} \epsilon = -DK^{-1} H^T V_\epsilon^{-1} \epsilon \tag{67}$$

with its first two moments as

$$E\{\tilde{u}_{EC}\} = -DK^{-1} H^T V_\epsilon^{-1} E\{\epsilon\} = 0 \tag{68}$$

$$E\{\tilde{u}_{EC} \tilde{u}_{EC}^T\} = DK^{-1} H^T V_\epsilon^{-1} E\{\epsilon \epsilon^T\} V_\epsilon^{-1} HK^{-1} D^T = \tag{69}$$
$$= DK^{-1} H^T V_\epsilon^{-1} V_\epsilon V_\epsilon^{-1} HK^{-1} D^T = DK^{-1} D^T$$

If we substitute the expression for D from (66) into equation 69, bearing in mind that the equality constrained estimator is unbiased, we obtain

$$\mathrm{Var}\{\tilde{u}_{EC}\} = E\{\tilde{u}_{EC} \tilde{u}_{EC}^T\} = [I - K^{-1} G^T (GK^{-1} G^T)^{-1} G] K^{-1}$$
$$[I - K^{-1} G^T (GK^{-1} G^T) G]^T = K^{-1} - K^{-1} G^T (GK^{-1} G^T)^{-1}$$
$$GK^{-1} - K^{-1} G^T (GK^{-1} G^T)^{-1} GK^{-1} + K^{-1} G^T (GK^{-1} G^T)^{-1}$$
$$GK^{-1} G^T (GK^{-1} G^T)^{-1} GK^{-1} = K^{-1} - K^{-1} G^T (GK^{-1} G^T)^{-1}$$
$$GK^{-1} \tag{70}$$

from which it can be proved that

$$\mathrm{Var}\{\tilde{u}_{EC}\} = \mathrm{Var}\{\tilde{u}_{ML}\} - K^{-1} G^T (GK^{-1} G^T)^{-1} GK^{-1} < \mathrm{Var}\{\tilde{u}_{ML}\} \tag{71}$$

because

$$K^{-1}G^T(GK^{-1}G^T)^{-1}GK^{-1}$$

is a symmetric positive definite matrix.

In the trivial case in which we have as many independent equality constraints as unknown parameters, i.e. $r = Nk$, G becomes a square matrix and from (58) we obtain

$$\hat{u}_{EC} = u = G^{-1}i \tag{72}$$

Moreover, from (70), G being a square matrix

$$\text{Var}\{\tilde{u}_{EC}\} = K^{-1} - K^{-1}G^T(G^T)^{-1}KG^{-1}GK^{-1} = 0 \tag{73}$$

In the preceding discussion we have shown analytically that introducing equality constraints (satisfied by the true parameter value) reduces the variance of the estimate and in the limit can reduce the variance to zero. However, our knowledge of the physical system is often inadequate for specifying enough equality constraints to markedly reduce the variance of the estimate.

Inequality constraints may be easier to specify and their inclusion can lead to a reduction in the variance of the parameter estimate, but unfortunately the statistical characteristics of such estimates are at present analytically intractable (Judge and Yancey, 1969) and we must resort to Monte Carlo methods.

5. Numerical solution of the parameter estimation

5.1 The unconstrained and the constrained algorithms

The unconstrained estimate of the parameter u is usually obtained from equation 23 via inversion of the matrix $(H^T V_\epsilon^{-1} H)$. This matrix appears to be ill-conditioned in most of the usual (Abadie, 1970). Moreover, when the number of inputs used in the model is greater than one, the level of the errors due to inversion becomes comparable to the values of the parameter that are to be estimated.

Many iterative methods have been proposed to avoid this inconvenience (Sage and Melsa, 1971a; Taha, 1971), for instance the solution of the estimate problem can be found searching for the minimum of the quadratic form

$$J(u) = \tfrac{1}{2}(q - Hu - \mu_\epsilon)^T V_\epsilon^{-1}(q - Hu - \mu_\epsilon) \tag{74}$$

where V_ϵ^{-1} is a symmetrical positive definite matrix.

Eliminating the constant terms after expansion of equation 74 we obtain the estimate $\hat{u}$ as the solution of the unconstrained problem:

$$\min \Theta(u) = \tfrac{1}{2}u^T H^T V_\epsilon^{-1} Hu - u^T H^T V_\epsilon^{-1}(q - \mu_\epsilon) \tag{75}$$

which is solved using a gradient technique, $\Theta(u)$ being a convex form which ensures the existence and the uniqueness of the solution.

The constrained estimator in our case, as it will be shown, is defined as the solution of the following problem:

$$\begin{cases} \min \Theta(u) = \tfrac{1}{2}\, u^T H^T V_\epsilon^{-1} Hu - u^T H^T V_\epsilon^{-1}(q - \mu_\epsilon) \\ \text{s.t.} \qquad u \geqslant 0 \\ \qquad Gu = i \end{cases} \qquad (76)$$

which can be solved by quadratic programming, $\Theta(u)$ being convex.

5.2 The linear constrained model of a drainage network

To solve (76) as a drainage network problem it is necessary to specify the necessary equality and inequality constraints for the network. For each channel of the drainage network u is the response to a unitary impulse and represents the percentage of the impulse measured at subsequent time lags at the outlet. We therefore have that each percentage must be greater than or equal to zero and for each impulse response the sum of the percentages should equal unity — a deeper discussion of this problem can be found in Appendix A — so that the constrained estimation problem for a drainage network with N inputs is to find the solution of (76) where G is an (N, Nk) matrix:

$$G = \begin{bmatrix} 11 \ldots 1 & & & & & 0 \\ & 11 \ldots 1 & & & & \\ & & \cdots \cdots & & & \\ & & & 11 \ldots 1 & & \\ 0 & & & & 11 \ldots 1 \end{bmatrix} \qquad (77)$$

and i is a unity vector of length N:

$$i = \begin{bmatrix} 1 \\ 1 \\ \vdots \\ 1 \end{bmatrix} \qquad (78)$$

6. Simulation

To evaluate the improvement of the estimate due to the introduction of the inequality constraints Monte Carlo experiments are needed.

6.1 Description of the synthetic linear drainage network

The linear system used in the simulation represents the confluence of two linear channels where a given hypothetical flood was routed (in Figure 1 the upstream hydrographs are shown).

The downstream hydrograph was numerically obtained by convoluting the upstream hydrographs with two given unit hydrographs so as to represent the linear routing process (in Figure 2 the two unit hydrographs u_A and u_B are shown). u_A represents a pure delay relevant to a pure cinematic routing process while u_B

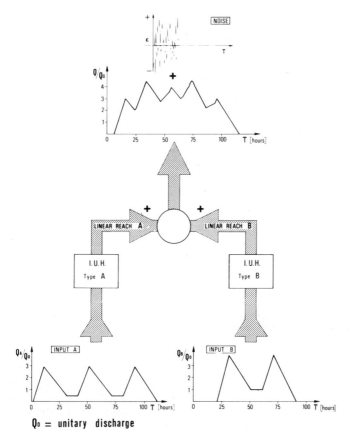

Q₀ = unitary discharge

Figure 1. Scheme of a linear system confluence set up for the Monte Carlo experiments with synthetic data

represents a unit hydrograph relevant to a typical dynamic routing process, which can be described for instance by equation 1.

The values of q of equation $q = Hu + \epsilon$ were obtained by adding to the downstream hydrograph a zero mean randomly generated noise ϵ (see Figure 1).

We produced in this manner one thousand q strings and for each we estimated $\hat{u}_A$ and $\hat{u}_B$ which were then compared to the true values of u_A and u_B known *a priori*. It should be stressed that even with this simple linear model the individual parameter estimates were very different from each other, and those who regard such a phenomenon as an indication of system non-linearity should be cautioned.

6.2 Assumptions about the variance matrix of errors used in the estimates

As stated previously, all the estimates need an *a priori* evaluation of the variance matrix of the errors. In real world problems the covariance elements are usually unknown and difficult to estimate.

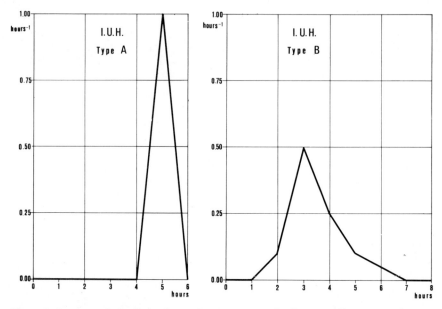

Figure 2. Instant unit hydrographs used to represent the linear routing process for the Monte Carlo experiments with synthetic data

Unfortunately it is not possible to resolve the nature of ϵ by looking at the fitting errors $\hat{\epsilon}$. In fact, the fitting error and the noise have different statistical characteristics.

If $q = Hu + \epsilon$ is the measured output of the system and $\hat{q} = H\hat{u}$ is the computed output, the fitting error will be

$$\hat{\epsilon} = q - \hat{q} = Hu + \epsilon - H\hat{u} = H(u - \hat{u}) + \epsilon = H\tilde{u} + \epsilon \qquad (79)$$

If we set, as usual,

$$\mu_\epsilon = E\{\epsilon\} = 0; \quad \text{Var}\{\epsilon\} = E\{\epsilon\,\epsilon^T\} = V_\epsilon$$

and we use for instance the GLS estimator, we obtain

$$\tilde{u} = -(H^T\,V_\epsilon^{-1}\,H)^{-1}\,H^T V_\epsilon^{-1}\epsilon; \quad \mu_{\tilde{u}} = E\{\tilde{u}\} = 0;$$

$$\text{Var}\{\tilde{u}\} = E\{\tilde{u}\,\tilde{u}^T\} = (H^T\,V_\epsilon^{-1}\,H)^{-1}; \quad E\{\epsilon\,\tilde{u}^T\} = -H(H^T\,V_\epsilon^{-1}\,H)^{-1};$$

$$E\{\tilde{u}\,\epsilon^T\} = -(H^T\,V_\epsilon^{-1}\,H)^{-1}\,H^T$$

and hence

$$\mu_{\hat{\epsilon}} = E\{\hat{\epsilon}\} = E\{H\tilde{u} + \epsilon\} = 0$$

$$\text{Var}\{\hat{\epsilon}\} = E\{\hat{\epsilon}\,\hat{\epsilon}^T\} = E\{(H\tilde{u} + \epsilon)(H\tilde{u} + \epsilon)^T\} = HE\{\tilde{u}\,\tilde{u}^T\}\,H^T + HE\{\tilde{u}\epsilon^T\} + \{\epsilon\tilde{u}^T\}H^T$$

$$+ E\{\epsilon\,\epsilon^T\} = H(H^T\,V_\epsilon^{-1}\,H)^{-1}\,H^T - 2H(H^T\,V_\epsilon^{-1}\,H)^{-1}\,H^T + V_\epsilon$$

$$= V_\epsilon - H(H^T\,V_\epsilon^{-1}\,H)^{-1}\,H^T \qquad (80)$$

which shows that, even if the embedded noise in the system is white, the errors which are estimated *a posteriori* as fitting errors have a full variance matrix unless for an impulsive input function. That is we always see correlated fitting errors except for the trivial case of impulsive inputs, and care should be taken not to confuse ϵ with its *a posteriori* estimate $\hat{\epsilon}$.

Lacking information about the true nature of $\epsilon(t)$ it is assumed to be white noise so that the error variance matrix becomes:

$$V_\epsilon = \begin{bmatrix} \sigma_{11}^2 & & & 0 \\ & \sigma_{22}^2 & & \\ & & \ddots & \\ 0 & & & \sigma_{mm}^2 \end{bmatrix} \tag{81}$$

To set up the (81) matrix we may choose different criteria:

(1) The error $\epsilon(t)$ is stationary in the mean and the variance (wide sense stationarity) so that

$$V_\epsilon = \sigma^2\, I \tag{82}$$

and if we substitute this into (38) we obtain the expression which is used to produce the ordinary least squares estimate

$$\hat{u}_{OLS} = (H^T\,H)^{-1}\,H^T\,q \tag{83}$$

where $H^T H$ is the autocorrelation matrix of the input and $H^T q$ is the cross-correlation vector of the input and the output (Eagleson *et al.*, 1965).

(2) An alternative assumption that was also used in our study was that the standard deviation of $\epsilon(t)$ varied proportionally to the discharges $q(t)$ while the noise was still stationary in the mean:

$$\sigma_{ii} = \sigma q(i)$$

from which

$$V_\epsilon = \sigma^2 \begin{bmatrix} q(1)^2 & & & 0 \\ & q(2)^2 & & \\ & & \ddots & \\ 0 & & & q(m)^2 \end{bmatrix} \tag{84}$$

6.3 Types of errors used in Monte Carlo simulation

Three different types of errors were superimposed upon the outflow discharges of the synthetic linear model previously described in Section 6.1. They are briefly described below and further details can be found in Appendix B.

The first type of error was a Gaussian white noise with zero mean and standard deviation equal to 20% of a standardized outflow (unitary discharge): $\sigma_{\epsilon(i)} = 0.2$.

The second type of error was also Gaussian independent with zero mean, but with standard deviation proportional to the actual outflow discharge $\sigma_{\epsilon(i)} = 0.04\, q(i)$.

The third type of error was a persistent zero mean Gaussian noise, so that the variance matrix had the covariance terms different from zero, with the standard deviation proportional to discharge $\sigma_{\epsilon(i)} = 0.04q(i)$. This coloured noise was generated by an Autoregressive-Integrated-Moving Average, ARIMA (p, d, q) process. The ARIMA domain of stochastic processes have been fully documented elsewhere (O'Connell, 1974) but for those who have not yet been introduced to its terminology we include a brief explanation.

The p term of our ARIMA process represents the number of autoregressive terms; in our example, $p = 1$ with value of $\varphi = 0.95$. The q term represents the number of moving average terms that are included in the process; in our case $q = 1$, with value of $\theta = 0.70$. The d parameter of the ARIMA (p, d, q) process represents the number of integrations performed to generate the process. We used $d = 0$ because $d > 0$ makes the ARIMA process non-stationary.

The values of φ and θ that we used were picked from examples of sample functions that can be found in O'Connell's work. The kernel from our ARIMA had

$$\rho_1 = \frac{(1 - \varphi\theta)(\varphi - \theta)}{1 + \theta^2 - 2\varphi\theta} = 0.5234375 \quad \text{with} \quad \rho_k = \varphi\rho_{k-1} \quad \forall k \geq 2$$

6.4 Experiments and results

6.4.1 Experiment 1 — Stationary and non-stationary Gaussian noise with correct assumptions about the nature of errors, constrained versus unconstrained estimations. None of the results for the stationary noise will be presented being so similar to those obtained for the non-stationary Gaussian noise wich is a more general case.

For the error proportional to discharges the probability density functions of the errors of estimate for the 1000 repetitions are shown as histograms in Figures 3, 4, 5 and 6.

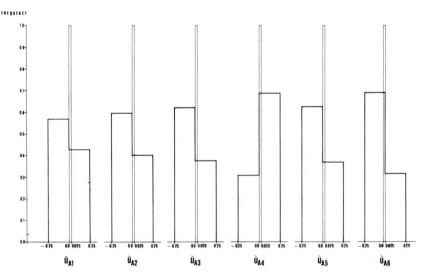

Figure 3. Frequency histograms for unconstrained and constrained estimators (sample size 1000)

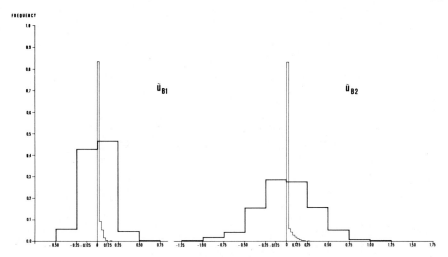

Figure 4. Frequency histograms for unconstrained and constrained estimators (sample size 1000)

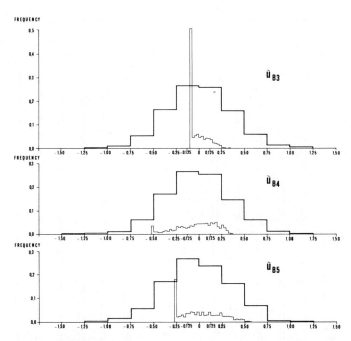

Figure 5. Frequency histograms for unconstrained and constrained estimators (sample size 1000)

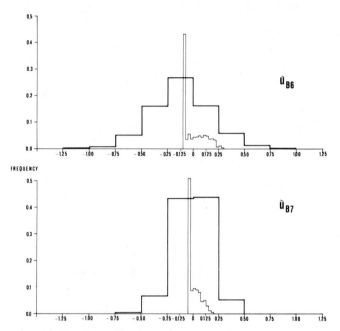

Figure 6. Frequency histograms for unconstrained and constrained estimators (sample size 1000)

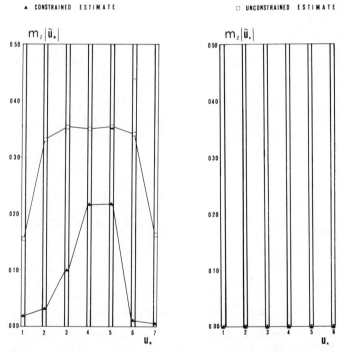

Figure 7. Second moments of the error of estimate. Unconstrained versus constrained estimator (sample size 1000)

It can be seen that the constrained estimator histograms are asymmetric with non-zero mean, a consequence of the inequality constraints, while the unconstrained are Gaussian with zero mean. However, the disperson of $\tilde{u}$ about zero for the constrained estimator is noticeably reduced compared to the dispersion of the error of estimate of the constrained parameter. This reduction in variance is also very apparent in Figure 7 where the second moments about zero of each individual parameter error of estimate are plotted.

It can be seen from Figure 8 where the square root of the sum of the square means of the error of estimate of the parameter are plotted versus sample size, that, in the field of 'small samples' (<100 rainfall—runoff records) usual hydrological range, the constrained estimator is much better than the unconstrained estimator; that is to say, the mean value of the parameter, estimated on a 'small' sample using the constrained estimator, is closer to the true value.

6.4.2 Experiment 2 — Errors proportional to discharges, constrained versus unconstrained estimator and correct and incorrect assumptions about the nature of errors.
In this experiment we have used a correct matrix $\mathbf{V}_\epsilon$ and an incorrect variance

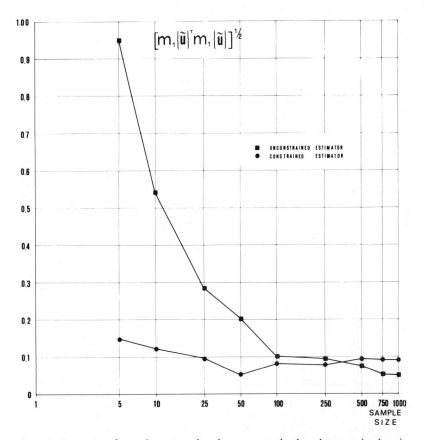

Figure 8. Departure from the true value for unconstrained and constrained estimators versus sample size

matrix $\bar{V}_\epsilon = \sigma^2 I$. Using the incorrect variance matrix $\bar{V}_\epsilon$ our estimate will be from (38).

$$\hat{u}_I = (H^T \ \bar{V}_\epsilon^{-1} \ H)^{-1} \ H^T \bar{V}_\epsilon^{-1} \ q \tag{85}$$

which is unbiased if $\mu_\epsilon = 0$.

But it can be shown (Sage and Melsa, 1971b) that

$$\mathrm{Var}\{\tilde{u}_I\} \geqslant \mathrm{Var}\{\tilde{u}_{ML}\} \tag{86}$$

where the equality sign holds only for $\bar{V}_\epsilon = \alpha \ V_\epsilon$ with α a constant. In fact from (85)

$$\mathrm{Var}\{\tilde{u}_I\} = (H^T \ V_\epsilon^{-1} \ H)^{-1} \ H^T \ \bar{V}_\epsilon^{-1} \ V_\epsilon \ \bar{V}_\epsilon^{-1} \ H(H^T \ V_\epsilon^{-1} \ H)^{-1} =$$
$$= (H^T \ V_\epsilon^{-1} \ H)^{-1} = \mathrm{Var}\{\tilde{u}_{ML}\} \tag{87}$$

Figure 9 gives the second moments of the error of estimate for each individual parameter for correct and incorrect assumptions for both the constrained and unconstrained estimators. From equation 27 we can also evaluate the expected value of the second moments of the error of estimate for the unconstrained case which has also been marked upon the figure. It is evident that the nature of the assumptions concerning the variance matrix of the errors is much more critical in

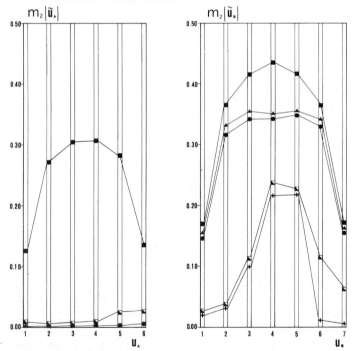

Figure 9. Second moments of the error of estimate for correct and incorrect assumptions both for unconstrained and constrained estimators (sample size 1000)

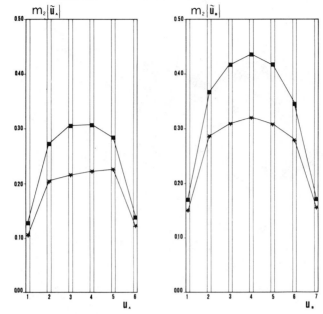

■ W H I T E   NOISE UNCONSTRAINED INCORRECT ESTIMATE
✳ COLOURED NOISE UNCONSTRAINED INCORRECT ESTIMATE

Figure 10. Second moments of the error of estimate for white noise and coloured noise (sample size 1000)

the unconstrained case than it is in the constrained one: the difference between the constrained incorrect and correct estimates is slight, while it is really noticeable between the unconstrained ones. Moreover, the second moments of the errors of estimate of the parameter are far lower when the constrained estimator is used.

6.4.3 Experiment 3 — Comparison between incorrect estimates for Gaussian white and ARIMA noises proportional to discharge. It can be seen in Figure 10 that when an incorrect evaluation $\bar{V}_\epsilon = \sigma^2 I$ of the variance matrix of the noise is provided to the estimator, the coloured noise is less of a nuisance to the estimate than the white noise. Reiterating this means that our preceding tests were conducted under the damaging error type (white noise) and yet the model still gave very good results.

7. An application to a real world junction problem

As previously stated a certain amount of information obtained by a physical–mathematical analysis of the phenomenon under study can be introduced into the estimating procedure by imposing a set of constraints: the constrained estimator is then more 'efficient' than the ordinary maximum likelihood or least squares estimators. Moreover when the estimate is 'incorrect' i.e. the estimator has been provided by an incorrect variance matrix of the noise, the introduction of the constraints reduces dramatically the variance of the estimate.

In Figure 7 it can be seen how the second moment about the origin of the error

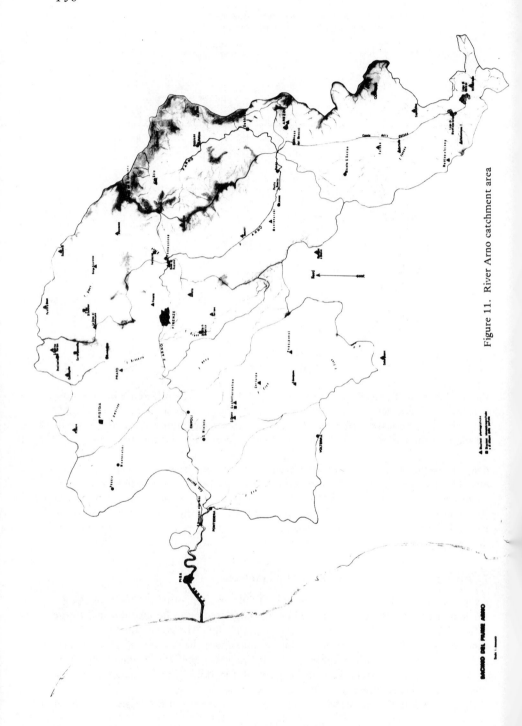

Figure 11. River Arno catchment area

of estimate of each individual parameter is reduced to less than half of its value when the constraints are introduced into the 'incorrect' estimator. This reduction is particularly noticeable for a pure delay IUH, previously introduced as the A type IUH.

On the base of the results obtained by the simulation on the synthetic linear model, it can be stated that the constraints can also give an improvement in a real world hydrologic application. In this case the noise $e(t)$ is so high that it will affect in a non-negligible way the estimates, especially when an unconstrained estimator is used.

For our real world example we studied the flood routing through a confluence of two water courses of the Arno basin.

7.1 Description of the junction

The Arno river and the Chiana main channel flow towards the confluence from opposite directions (Figure 11). The Arno flows through the valley of Casentino in north–south direction and the Chiana main channel through the Chiana valley in south–north direction. Close to the confluence, two hydrometrographic stations measure the levels of the two incoming streams: at Subbiano for the Arno (13.50 km from the confluence) and at the Rome–Florence railway bridge for the Chiana (5.75 km from the confluence). At Ponte Romito, 12.00 km after the confluence a third hydrometrographic station operated till 1955.

The Arno river in Subbiano has 738 km^2 of catchment area with a mean altitude of 720 m above mean sea level and the Chiana at the Rome–Florence railway has a bigger catchment area, 1272 km^2, flatter than the Arno catchment, with a mean altitude of 409 m.

The Arno catchment area contributes twice as much as the Chiana catchment area to the outflow below the confluence. Their runoff per unit area is 25.0 l/s km^2 for the Arno basin and 6.8 l/s km^2 for the Chiana basin (mean values computed on a 30-year period).

The catchment area which lies between the two hydrometrographic stations before the confluence and the Ponte Romito station is 326 km^2 so that the total basin with outlet at Ponte Romito has an area of 1.16 times the total catchment area of the two tributaries. For this reason the flood waves from the upstream station to the downstream one are amplified (Figure 12).

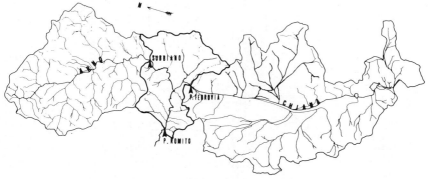

Figure 12 Arno–Chiana junction catchment areas

7.2 Experiments and results

The two IUH of the water courses were identified on the hypothesis that the phenomenon of wave propagation in the network could be considered as linear. To estimate the parameters we used the hourly recordings of six flood waves of the period 1934—1951. The hydrographs of the flood waves recorded in the three stations are shown in Figures 13—18 together with the mean daily discharge due to the direct rainfall (daily values) on the catchment area which lies between the three stations.

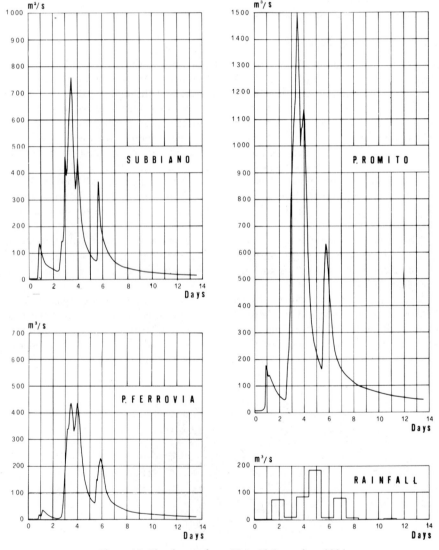

Figure 13 Flood wave from 10 to 23 December, 1934

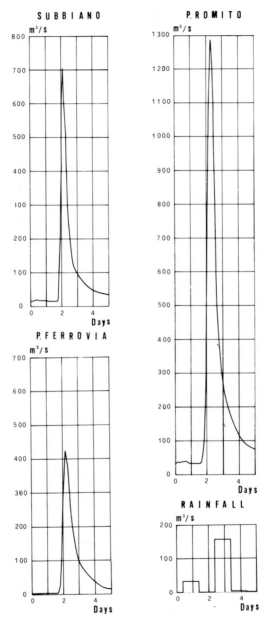

Figure 14. Flood wave from 16 to 20 November, 1935

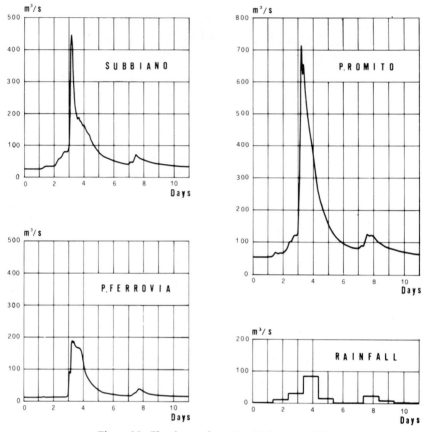

Figure 15. Flood wave from 1 to 11 January, 1936

In Table 1 some characteristics of the flood events are shown.

7.2.1 Assumptions about the noise. An *a priori* evaluation of the statistical distribution of the noise ϵ is clearly impossible. We empirically provided to the estimator the values of μ_ϵ and V_ϵ which gave the best estimates in the sense of the

Table 1.

Date	Volumes (m³ × 10⁶)			Duration (hours)	Volume increment	Outflow mean discharge (m³/s)
	Chiana	Arno	Outflow			
10.12.34	85	115	263	317	1.31	230.5
16.11.35	31	34	83	120	1.27	192.0
1.1.36	22	41	78	264	1.24	82.0
2.12.37	131	193	391	708	1.21	153.5
12.2.41	81	110	229	436	1.20	146.0
4.2.51	16	94	129	344	1.17	104.0

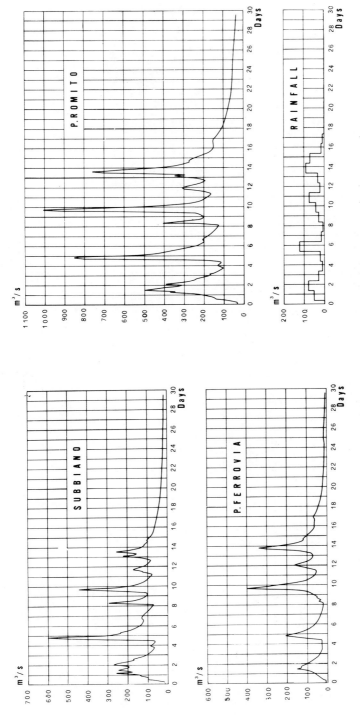

Figure 16. Flood wave from 2 to 31 December, 1937

136

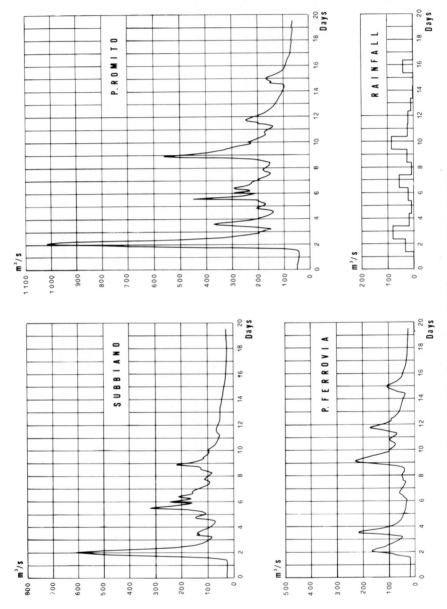

Figure 17. Flood wave from 12 February to 3 March 1941

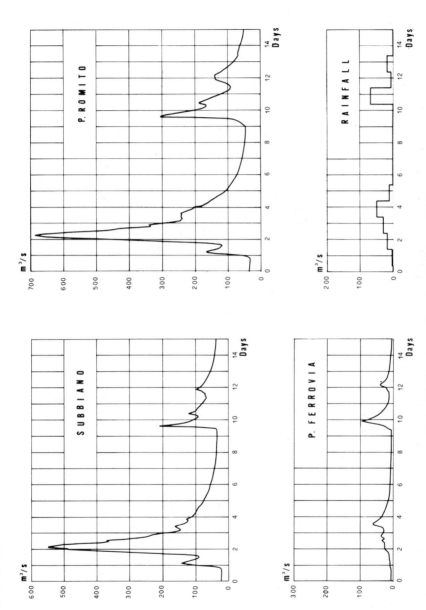

Figure 18. Flood wave from 4 to 18 February 1951

least dispersion of the estimates. It was found that

$$\mathbf{V}_\epsilon = \sigma^2\,\mathbf{I} \tag{88}$$

was the most satisfactory hypothesis.

The mean value of the error $\boldsymbol{\mu}_\epsilon$ takes into account the difference between the inflow volumes v_i and the outflow volumes v_0:

$$\sum_{i=1}^{m} \mu_\epsilon(i) \cong v_0 - v_i \tag{89}$$

Therefore we supposed that the value of the discharge which enters as direct rainfall into the confluence catchment area, and which is responsible for the amplification of the flood waves could be taken as an estimate of the mean value of the error $\epsilon(t)$.

If $p(t)$ is the direct rainfall which enters into the basin and

$$\mathbf{p} = \begin{bmatrix} p(\Delta t) \\ p(2\,\Delta t) \\ \vdots \\ p(m\Delta t) \end{bmatrix} \tag{90}$$

is the vector which is obtained after discretization, we set:

$$\boldsymbol{\mu}_\epsilon = \mathbf{p} \tag{91}$$

This assumption implies the hypothesis, not strictly true, that the measurement errors and the mathematical modelling errors are zero mean random errors.

Preliminary tests with the unconstrained model showed that using $\boldsymbol{\mu}_\epsilon = \mathbf{p}$ gave a smaller dispersion than $\boldsymbol{\mu}_\epsilon = \mathbf{0}$ even if the rainfall data were not of the same order of precision as the streamflows. Moreover, we have found, using the synthetic model described in Section 6.1, that if the direct inflow $\mathbf{p}$ is not taken into account it affects in a sensible way the estimate which will vary with the different shapes of $\mathbf{p}$.

For the Arno the direct inflow might be better considered as a third input of the linear system together with the two upstream inflows. We did not use this approach to evaluate the effectiveness of the equality constraints (77).

7.2.2 Description of estimators and results. For each of the six events of Table 1 the IUH of the two inputs model confluence were determined using the different estimators.

Estimator I: Unconstrained maximum likelihood, $\boldsymbol{\mu}_\epsilon = \mathbf{p}$
Estimator II: Positivity constrained maximum likelihood, $\boldsymbol{\mu}_\epsilon = \mathbf{p}$
Estimator III: Positivity and equality constrained maximum likelihood, $\boldsymbol{\mu}_\epsilon = \mathbf{p}$
Estimator IV: Positivity and equality constrained maximum likelihood, $\boldsymbol{\mu}_\epsilon = \mathbf{0}$

For each estimator and flood wave in IUH was determined and the mean value for each estimator is shown in Figure 19.

With the ordinary unconstrained estimator (estimator I) oscillating IUH were obtained, with positive and negative ordinates as also happened in the synthetic model when its mean values were computed on a small sample (Figure 20).

If the analogy between synthetic and the real case holds, this inaccuracy depends

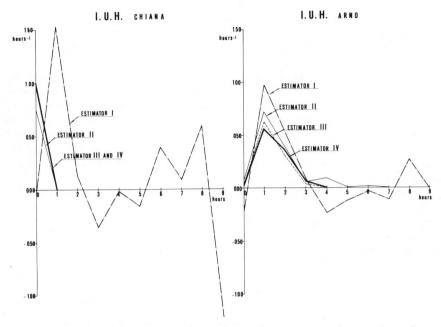

Figure 19. Mean instant unit hydrographs computed on a small sample (sample size 6) from real world data

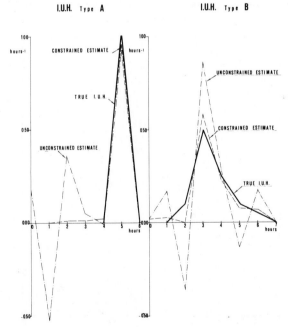

Figure 20. Mean instant unit hydrographs computed on a small sample (sample size 5) from synthetic data

only on the noise which is superimposed upon the data, and in fact the introduction of the positivity contraints reduces the inaccuracy.

The areas under the mean IUH (estimator II) are still non-unitary as the continuity equation requires, when the outflow volumes are equal to the inflow volumes. This error has been completely eliminated by estimator III where the equality constraints were introduced. Moreover the imposition of both the types of constraints gives a stable estimate quite independent from the value assumed by μ_ϵ as it is shown by the comparison of the mean IUH obtained by estimators III and IV. It can be seen that the IUH for the Chiana are identical both for $\mu_\epsilon = \mathbf{p}$ and $\mu_\epsilon = 0$ while the IUHs for the Arno are very close to each other. The tail of the Arno IUH, owing to pure numerical errors is greatly reduced by the introduction of the equality constraints.

Following the criteria exposed in the preceding sections we compared the dispersion of the results. However, in a real world system analysis we cannot properly speak of errors of estimate as we do not know the values of the true IUH.

The measure of the dispersion and of the 'goodness' of the estimate will be provided by the standard deviation of each individual parameter estimate:

$$\sigma_{\hat{u}_j} = \sqrt{\left(\frac{1}{n-1} \sum_{j=1}^{n} \left[\hat{u}_{ij} - \frac{1}{n} \sum_{j=1}^{n} \hat{u}_{ij} \right]^2 \right)} \tag{92}$$

where $n = 6$ is our sample size.

When the constraints are imposed the dispersion is reduced (see Figure 21).

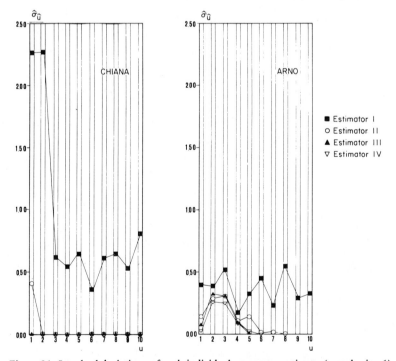

Figure 21. Standard deviations of each individual parameter estimate (sample size 6)

Further, we can say that the mean IUH of the Chiana obtained by the classic method is completely unacceptable as the dispersion is greater than the individual parameter values, while it can be seen that the dispersion goes to zero when we introduce the constraints. The dispersion of the estimates of the IUH of the Arno is also reduced significantly when the constraints are introduced. It can be seen that, in this case, estimator IV is more precise than estimator III: it seems that with the hypothesis $\mu_\epsilon = p$ the data used are so modified because of the poor definition of p that an estimator as accurate as the constrained estimator has been negatively influenced.

We may conclude at this point that the constraints *a priori* imposed upon the parameters contain by themselves as much information as is needed to produce a sufficiently accurate estimation and that the introduction of $\mu_\epsilon = p$ will only be helpful if p is defined as accurately as the other inputs to the system.

7.2.3 'Serial' or 'parallel' estimation. A 'parallel' estimate is done if the individual values of the parameters are determined from each single flood event and then the mean value of those estimates is taken as to represent the mean IUH (as the ones in Figure 19).

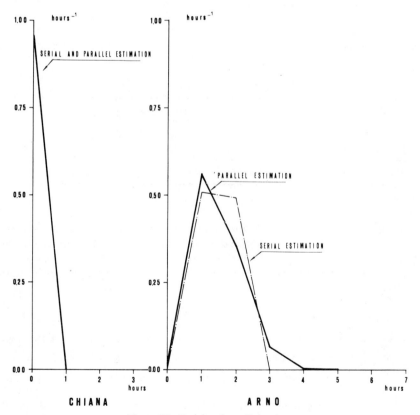

Figure 22. Serial and parallel estimates

In an alternative approach, which we shall call a 'serial' estimate, the estimate is produced as a single calculation from a multiple flood wave series that has been set up putting in succession individual events that are not necessarily in historic order (Natale and Todini, 1972, 1973). If the estimator is unbiased and mean-square-consistent, the results should be asymptotically the same for a parallel estimate on an infinite number of samples and for a serial estimate on an infinite length sample.

Actually we generally have only a small number of sample events to produce the parallel or the serial estimates. We may expect in that case different results for the parallel and for the serial estimates: in Figure 22 the parallel and serial hydrographs estimates that were obtained by estimator IV are shown.

Even if they have different shapes, the IUHs so determined do not present significant practical differences; in fact both with the parallel and the serial estimated IUH the predictions of the flood waves are the same.

The different error indexes that measure the residual between predicted and measured waves coincide in the examined cases to the third significant digit.

7.2.4 Prediction of a flood wave: a split sample test. Among the other flood waves measured at the Arno—Chiana confluence, the flood event which began on 21 February, 1942, was peculiar in that no direct precipitation was measured in the confluence catchment area, so that the total amount of water entering the system through the two inflow stations was found unchanged at the outflow station (see Table 2). It was decided to use this event as the basis of a split sample test.

Table 2

Date	Volumes ($m^3 \times 10^6$)			Duration (hours)	Volume increment	Outflow mean discharge (m^3/s)
	Chiana	Arno	Outflow			
21.2.42	35	67	104	264	1.02	109.5

In Figure 23 the results of the prediction are plotted versus the actual measured discharges at Ponte Romito station and it can be seen that the predictions are quite accurate.

A more objective evaluation of the goodness of the prediction can be found from the following indexes:

Percentage error at the peak	=	2.8%
Standard deviation of the residuals	=	8.3 m^3/sec
Maximum deviations between predicted and measured flows	max. positive	= + 22.5 m^3/sec
	max. negative	= − 50.8 m^3/sec

The validity of the results obtained by this application is encouraging and we feel that the proposed method may be useful in other hydrologic situations.

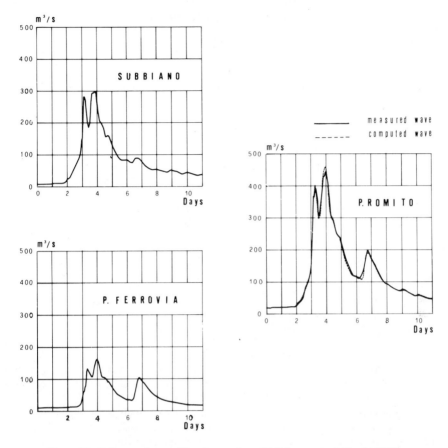

Figure 23. Split sample test. Flood wave from 21 February to 3 March, 1942

8. Conclusions

We may conclude by emphasizing that many hydrologic systems, such as the one we have examined, may be sufficiently well represented by linear models for which the proposed technique may be applied.

The enormous variability of the IUH determined with the 'classical' estimators may induce one to think that the examined system is strongly non-linear, but we think that the dispersion of the estimates may merely be a result of using the classical computational techniques, which are unable to separate the noise from the signal that bears the information.

In fact, when the number of recorded events is small, as frequently happens in hydrological practice, the classical estimators will provide estimates of the parameters which are so inaccurate that they do not deserve our confidence.

The use of a constrained estimator which uses the *a priori* physical information of the system, can significantly improve the results, providing an effective, fast and automatic means for the solution of the hydrological problems concerning the estimation of river flows.

Appendix A

The St Venant equations for a reach without lateral inflow:

$$\begin{cases} \dfrac{\partial Q}{\partial x} + \dfrac{\partial A}{\partial t} = 0 \\[2ex] \dfrac{\partial y}{\partial x} + \dfrac{1}{g}\left(\dfrac{\partial V}{\partial t} + V\dfrac{\partial V}{\partial x} \right) = S_0 - S_f \end{cases} \tag{93}$$

can be written by ignoring the inertial terms of the momentum equation (Cunge, 1969):

$$\begin{cases} \dfrac{\partial Q}{\partial x} + \dfrac{\partial A}{\partial t} = 0 \tag{94} \end{cases}$$

$$\dfrac{\partial y}{\partial x} = S_0 - S_f \tag{95}$$

where $Q(x, t)$ and $y(x, t)$ are the unknown discharges and water levels, S_0 is the bed slope, $S_f = n^2 Q^2 / A^2 R^{4/3}$ represents the friction slope and A is the wetted area while R is the hydraulic radius.

For a river of sufficiently gentle slope such as the Arno it can be shown (Henderson, 1969) that the terms that have been omitted from (93) were only small contributors to the value of the momentum equation.

The systems (94), (95) can be further reduced to a single linear equation in one unknown in such a way that we finish with a model that relates the unknown discharges at the downstream section to the discharges at the upstream section and the hydraulic characteristics of the intermediate reach.

Taking the derivative of (95) with respect to time we obtain

$$\frac{\partial}{\partial t}\left(\frac{\partial y}{\partial x} \right) = \frac{\partial S_0}{\partial t} - \left(\frac{2n^2 Q^2}{A^2 R^{4/3}}\frac{\partial Q}{\partial t} - \frac{4n^2 Q^2}{3A^2 R^{7/3}}\frac{\partial R}{\partial t} - \frac{2n^2 Q^2}{A^3 R^{4/3}}\frac{\partial A}{\partial t} \right) \tag{96}$$

Assuming an infinite rectangular channel of width B

$$A(x, t) = By(x, t) \tag{97}$$

the continuity equation (94) can be written as

$$\frac{\partial y}{\partial t} = -\frac{1}{B}\frac{\partial Q}{\partial x} \tag{98}$$

Supposing that the channel is wide $R(x, t) \cong y(x, t)$ and substituting in (96) we obtain

$$\frac{\partial}{\partial x}\left(-\frac{1}{B}\frac{\partial Q}{\partial x} \right) = \frac{2n^2 Q^2}{A^2 y^{4/3}}\frac{\partial Q}{\partial t} - \frac{4n^2 Q^2}{3A^2 By^{7/3}}\frac{\partial Q}{\partial x} - \frac{2n^2 Q^2}{A^3 y^{4/3}}\frac{\partial Q}{\partial x} \tag{99}$$

which, after simplification can be written:

$$\frac{\partial Q}{\partial t} = D_1 \frac{\partial^2 Q}{\partial x^2} - D_2 \frac{\partial Q}{\partial x}$$ (100)

where

$$D_1 = \frac{A^2 y^{4/3}}{2n^2 QB} \text{ and } D_2 = \frac{5}{3} \frac{Q}{A}$$

This non-linear equation can be solved, as proposed by Hayami (1951) with a parameter perturbations method (Nayfeh, 1973), looking for the solution of equation 100 where Q can be written as a perturbation expansion

$$Q(x, t, \epsilon) = Q_0(x, t) + \epsilon Q_1(x, t) + \epsilon^2 Q_2(x,t) + \ldots$$ (101)

The solution $Q_0(x, t)$ is obtained assuming constant the coefficient D_1 and D_2 of the derivatives in equation 100:

$$D_1* = \frac{A_*^2 y_*^{4/3}}{2n^2 Q_*B} \qquad D_2* = \frac{5}{3} \frac{Q*}{A*}$$ (102)

where the quantities with the * subscript are the mean values for the flood event, i.e. $Q*$ represents the mean flood discharge and so on.

Equation 100 becomes a linear differential equation with constant coefficients:

$$\frac{\partial Q}{\partial t} = D_1* \frac{\partial^2 Q}{\partial x^2} - D_2* \frac{\partial Q}{\partial x}$$ (103)

$Q_0(x, t)$ will be regarded, as is usual in hydrologic practice, as a close enough approximation of $Q(x, t)$ which means that all the terms which compare in equation 101 except the first are negligible, or in other words that the instantaneous values of the coefficients of the derivatives in (100) vary only a little about the mean values D_1* and D_2*.

This hypothesis is not strictly accurate, but other model errors can be expected to be larger, so that this bias can be regarded as negligible.

Equation 103 can be solved for different boundary conditions. Its solution can be obtained by fixing the downstream condition and solving it as a convolution integral

$$Q_d(L, t) = \int_0^t u(L, \tau)Q_u(t - \tau)d\tau$$ (104)

which is commonly used to describe the linear synthetic models (Bravo *et al.*, 1970), well known in hydrology as methods of the IUH.

If we suppose that in the rectangular infinite channel the flood wave will be superimposed on the preexisting steady flow conditions without interfering with it (which is congruent with the linearity of the system) we can write the following conditions:

(a) $Q(0, t) = \delta(t)$ $t \geq 0$ unitary impulse inflow

(b) $Q(x, t) \neq \infty$ $x \to \infty, t \geq 0$ infinite length reach

(c) $Q(x, 0) = 0$ $\qquad\qquad$ $x \geqslant 0$ zero initial discharge

To integrate equation 103 under the conditions (a), (b), (c) the developments can be found in many books of applied mathematics (Pipes and Harvill, 1970).

With the hypothesis of the existence of Laplace transform of $Q(x, t)$ in respect of t, we can write (Kaplan, 1962):

$$\mathcal{L}[Q(x, t)] = W(x, s) \tag{105}$$

$$\mathcal{L}\left[\frac{\partial Q(x, t)}{\partial t}\right] = sW(x, s) + Q(x, 0) \tag{106}$$

Imposing condition (c) on (106) the Laplace transform of equation (103) can be written

$$D_{1*}\frac{d^2 W}{dx^2} - {}^{l}D_{2*}\frac{dW}{dx} - sW = 0 \tag{107}$$

This is the equation of free vibrations, for which the general solution is

$$J = C_1 e^{K_1 x} + C_2 e^{K_2 x} \tag{108}$$

where K_1 and K_2 are the two real numbers:

$$K_1 = \frac{D_{2*} + \sqrt{(D_{2*}^2 + 4D_{1*}s)}}{2D_{1*}} > 0 \tag{109}$$

$$K_2 = \frac{D_{2*} + \sqrt{(D_{2*}^2 + 4D_{1*}s)}}{2D_{1*}} \tag{110}$$

Condition (b) implies $C_1 = 0$ while condition (a) implies $W(0, s) = 1$ from which $C_2 = 1$.

Equation 108 becomes

$$W(x, s) = \exp\left[\frac{D_{2*} - \sqrt{(D_{2*}^2 + 4D_{1*}s)}}{2D_{1*}} x\right] \tag{111}$$

The inverse of the Laplace transform:

$$\mathcal{L}^{-1}[W(x, s)] = Q(x, t) \tag{112}$$

gives the solution 103:

$$Q(x, t) = \frac{x}{2t\sqrt{(\pi t D_{1*})}} \exp\left[\frac{D_{2*}}{2D_{1*}} x - \frac{D_{2*}^2}{4D_{1*}} t - \frac{x^2}{4D_{1*}t}\right] \quad \forall t > 0 \tag{113}$$

From equation 113, rearranging the terms of the exponential and substituting $x = L$ where L is the length of the reach we obtain (Dooge, 1969):

$$Q(L, t) = \frac{L}{2t\sqrt{(\pi t D_{1*})}} \exp\left[-\frac{(D_{2*}t - L)^2}{4D_{1*}t}\right] = u(L, t) \quad \forall t > 0 \tag{114}$$

which is by definition the expression of the impulse response of the linear system described by equation 104 under the condition (b). And because of respect for the continuity equation the integral of $u(L, t)$ must equal unity. It should be noted in (114) that

$$u(L, t) \geqslant 0 \quad \forall t > 0 \qquad (115)$$

Appendix B

The program used to obtain the constrained and the unconstrained estimate (see Section 5) is mainly based on a concave programming routine SOLVER, due to Wilson (1963), which is used for the special case of quadratic programming.

The program reads the input and the output data and by means of the MATR2 subroutine sets up the matrix of the quadratic form and the vector of the linear form of equation 74. Then the INP subroutine provides SOLVER with the specification of the constraints in the case of the constrained problem.

The solution given by SOLVER is then convoluted with the input data and statistics on the residual of the model are given by the subroutine ERRORE.

For the simulation on the synthetic data, a group of three subroutines which generate the pseudo-random noise, described in Section 6.3, was inserted into the program. All these subroutines were based on the uniform pseudo-random number generator subroutine GGL, which can be found in the IBM System/360 and System/370, Subroutine Library—Mathematics (Program Number 5736-XM7).

The Gaussian pseudo-random number generator is based on the Box and Muller algorithm (1958), while the ARIMA (1, 0, 1) process generator, the subroutine ARIMA, is based on the Box and Jenkins (1970) algorithm.

Using CLS for Daily or Longer Period Rainfall—Runoff Modelling

Ezio Todini
IBM Scientific Center, Pisa, Italy

James R. Wallis
IBM Scientific Center, Pisa (while on leave from IBM Research Center, Yorktown Heights, New York, USA)

1. Introduction

The processes by which rainfall is converted into runoff are complex and variable both in space and in time, and the devising of algorithms for modelling the rainfall—runoff phenomenon on a continuous, as opposed to an event type, basis has been a research area of much recent interest. Note in the above context the word continuous does not mean that we are modelling with continuous functions, but rather that we are dealing with long, uninterrupted, hydrologic records sampled at Δt time intervals. Furthermore it is reasonable to expect that the increasingly widespread use of large, fast electronic computers will heighten this interest, and that bigger and ever more complex rainfall—runoff models will continue to be developed as computational constraints are removed from the developers. Some optimism about the future of continuous rainfall—runoff modelling is possible because of two recent developments. First, Freeze (1972) has presented a physics based model of the rainfall—runoff process; and, second, the World Meteorological Organization has made the first attempt at an unbiased statistical evaluation of the ability of various models to predict runoff (WMO, herein).

In this paper we intend to develop constrained linear systems, CLS, as a systems approach to continuous daily or longer period rainfall—runoff modelling, and to interpret the usefulness of this method primarily in the light of the Freeze and WMO results.

2. A physics based model

In a series of articles published in *Water Resources Research*, Freeze (1972) has documented a physics based model of the rainfall—runoff process. To quote:

> ... a deterministic mathematical model that couples three-dimensional, transient, saturated—unsaturated subsurface flow and one-dimensional, gradually varied, unsteady channel flow. The channel flow model uses the single step

Lax—Wendroff explicit technique to solve numerically the full shallow water equations. The subsurface flow model uses the line successive overrelaxation technique to solve numerically the Jacob—Richards diffusion equation. The results of the simulations on a hypothetical basin suggest a wide variability in watershed response under the influence of variations in rainfall properties, antecedent moisture conditions, and saturated and unsaturated subsurface hydrogeologic properties. This evidence for a wide range of watershed response functions leads to the development of a healthy scepticism toward ... the concept of basin linearity, and the rationality of hydrograph separation.

The Freeze model can be regarded as a very useful research tool for studying individual hydrologic events on a subwatershed scale. Unfortunately the computer implementation of the model uses programs that are large and complex with up to 30 000 nodes; in addition the physics based model uses large amounts of computer time and, to be operational, needs almost limitless data, or the introduction of other approximations that tend to pollute the elegant purity of the model. For discrete time rainfall—runoff modelling of whole watersheds over long time spans we must leave the sublime world of physics based models and enter the realities of gross empirical models that use lumped parameters and arbitrary assumptions about average watershed response and geometry.

3. ESMA models

Most discrete time rainfall—runoff models operable over long uninterrupted periods can be classified as explicit soil moisture accounting models, ESMA, and of these models probably the most famous is the Stanford Watershed Model (Crawford and Linsley, 1966). A typical flowchart for an ESMA-type model is shown in Figure 1 where one observes that soil moisture storage has been modelled as three reservoirs, upper zone, lower zone, and active or deep groundwater storage, and that overland flow occurs from impervious as well as from non-impervious areas. The channel flow routing by ESMA type models is either a Muskingum routing, a kinematic wave, or more frequently an arbitrary linear transfer function. The more complex ESMA models usually make provision for multiple subwatershed inputs within the channel routing phase. Various other mechanisms are provided by most ESMA type models that tend to make the overall model highly non-linear, and some of these mechanisms can be observed in Figure 1 where they are displayed with appropriate conceptual names.

It is obvious that ESMA models with flowcharts similar to Figure 1 are at best a poor approximation to hydrologic reality, and many of their lumped parameter concepts are at variance with the more recent hydrologic concepts embodied in the physics based model approach developed by Freeze. At this point it must be stressed that model inaccuracies are a major contributor to the phenomenon of model divergence (Sage and Melsa, 1971a) a subject that will be alluded to again in later sections.

ESMA models do not use the very large amounts of CPU time that are needed by a Freeze-type model; nor are they cheap, either in their data requirements or in terms of operator time and experience. Reliably to estimate the parameters for an ESMA-type model needs skill, as well as experience; and, in fact, it is not at all

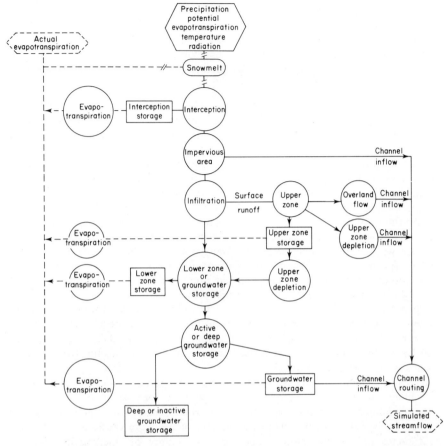

Figure 1. A typical flowchart for a rainfall—runoff model of the explicit soil moisture accounting type, ESMA, redrawn from Linsley and Crawford (1974)

unknown for would-be practitioners to require several days of carefully guided specialized training before being able to use a specified model. How much of this slow and perhaps painfully acquired experience is transferable from one ESMA model to the next is unknown and the relative merits of the current bewildering array of ESMA models are largely unknown.

4. Model divergence

Proponents and expounders of rainfall—runoff models are often guilty of intemperate justification of the product. For instance Linsley and Crawford (1974) while discussing urban hydrology stated

For most planning efforts data on probability of occurrence of events of various magnitudes is required and in most (urban) situations this can only be provided by use of a continuous simulation model.

... the urgent need in (urban) hydrology is a technique which can define the probability of peak flows, and where storage is being considered, the volume characteristics of the streamflow as well. It is precisely this kind of a service that a continuous simulation model can provide. Given a reasonable basis for calibrating the model, available long precipitation records can be transformed into flow records of equivalent length.

Unfortunately just what constitutes a reasonable basis for calibration of a rainfall—runoff model has never been documented in a statistically meaningful manner. But, even if we were to assume perfect calibration we are usually only talking about a single rainfall record of considerably less than 100 years in length — an inadequate basis for estimating either the true volume characteristics of streamflow (Wallis and O'Connell, 1973), or the probability of peak flows, given recent findings on the regionalization of the skew coefficient for hydrologic records (Wallis, Matalas and Slack, 1974b). It is clear that rainfall—runoff models are not the only way to arrive at an estimate of peak flow or volume probabilities for a stream and, in fact, they may not even be either the cheapest or the most accurate way to make such estimates. Many even more bizarre possible uses for ESMA type models have been proposed and for many, if not all, of these other fringe forecast situations the same criticism applies, namely that cheaper and more accurate forecasts can be made by other methods.

Apart from research, the probable ultimate and principal use for rainfall—runoff models will be for making deterministic runoff forecasts for specific short future or past periods, which incidentally is also the domain of statistical filtering. It is to be hoped that the future will see increased activity in the realm of objective testing of alternative forecast procedures.

It is in the realms of forecasting that the phenomenon of model divergence starts to become critical. Model divergence as paraphrased from Sage and Melsa (1971a) is the phenomenon that the error variance for the forecast flows is greatly in excess of the error variance for the fitting period. One of the major causes of divergence is inaccuracies in the modelling process due to failure of linearization, lack of complete knowledge of the physical problem, or the simplifying assumptions necessary for mathematical tractability. In hydrology we are also faced with other even more important mechanisms leading to model divergence, namely, noisy data, short unrepresentative calibration periods and possibly even non-stationarity in the data or the system being modelled.

While Freeze (1972) predicted divergence for all who attempt continuous rainfall—runoff or even event-type modelling with less detailed models than a physics based model, he did not show that his model was operationally free of the divergence phenomenon when it was applied to a real world site, nor that a simple 'black-box rainfall—runoff correlation' approach about which he expressed 'a healthy scepticism' would not yield forecasts within acceptable tolerance limits. In the next section we intend to develop such an approach, CLS, and later to show that CLS forecasts may be no more divergent than ESMA forecasts and that they are certainly a great deal easier to obtain.

5. CLS

Most linear systems are conceptually simple and always mathematically more tractable than non-linear systems. In this paper we shall restrict our search for a simple black-box correlation method to time-invariant linear systems that can be linked together in such a manner that the overall system may appear to be strongly non-linear and even time-variant (Dooge, herein). While we appreciate that the use of a systems approach to rainfall—runoff modelling will lead to model errors we feel that in many hydrologic situations the errors in the data are so large that a sophisticated least squares filtering mechanism may lead to forecasts that are as good if not better than those obtainable by more complex conceptual models.

We may define a discrete time linear system in N inputs as

$$q = H \cdot u + \epsilon \tag{1}$$

where u is an (Nk) length vector of the impulse responses, k being the length of each individual impulse response, q an (m) length vector of discrete outputs sampled with a time interval Δt, H an (m,Nk) partitioned matrix of discrete time input vectors, and ϵ an (m) length error vector.

Usually the estimate of u (namely $\hat{u}$) in the linear system represented by equation 1 is obtained via the inversion of the matrix $(H'V_\epsilon^{-1}H)$ with $V_\epsilon = I$, the variance of the errors assumed Gaussian and independently distributed. The matrix $(H'V_\epsilon^{-1}H)$ is frequently ill-conditioned (Abadie, 1970) and, in addition, we have found that when $N > 1$ the level of the errors due to the inversion becomes comparable to the values of the parameters that are to be estimated.

Natale and Todini (1973, 1974) have shown that excellent estimators of u are obtainable by the introduction of equality and inequality constraints into the least squares solution of a linear hydrologic system. For a linear rainfall—runoff model we have *a priori* information about the nature of the parameter u, and it seems reasonable that the estimating technique for u should incorporate all of the available knowledge and hence reduce the field of choice for $\hat{u}$. For instance if the process is linear we may hypothesize that $u \geqslant 0$, which is equivalent to saying that water does not flow up the stream channel.

In addition, if the rainfall—runoff process is regarded as time invariant then

$$\sum_{j=1}^{k} u_{(i-1)k+j} = \Phi_i \quad i = r + 1, \ldots, N \tag{2}$$

with Φ_i a constant runoff coefficient which takes into account the water losses between the P_i precipitation input and the output, r being the number of tributary flow inputs.

For $r > 0$, tributary flow inputs P_i $i = 1, \ldots, r$ are present, and hence by the conservation of mass

$$\sum_{j=1}^{k} u_{(i-1)k+j} = 1 \quad i = 1, \ldots, r \tag{3}$$

The CLS estimate of the parameter u is then given by the following constrained estimator

$$\min \quad J(\epsilon'\epsilon) = \frac{1}{2} \, \mathbf{u'H'Hu} - \mathbf{u'H'q}$$

s.t. $\mathbf{u} \geqslant 0$ (4)

$\mathbf{Gu} = 1$

where the $\mathbf{G}$ matrix is defined below.

If $r = 0$ $\mathbf{G}$ is a $(1, Nk)$ matrix for which the elements are:

$$g_{1, (i-1)k+j} = \frac{\displaystyle\sum_{\tau=1.}^{m-j+1} P_i(\tau)}{\displaystyle\sum_{\tau=1}^{m} Q(\tau)} \qquad \begin{array}{l} i = 1, \ldots, N \\[1em] j = 1, \ldots, k \end{array}$$ (5)

to represent the following constraint

$$\sum_{i=1}^{N} \sum_{j=1}^{k} u_{(i-1)k+j} \sum_{\tau=1}^{m-j+1} P_i(\tau) = \sum_{\tau=1}^{m} Q(\tau)$$ (6)

which takes into account the water losses between the N precipitation inputs P_i and the output Q, if $P_i(\tau) = 0$ for $1 - k \leqslant \tau \leqslant 0$.

If $r > 0$ $\mathbf{G}$ is an $(r + 1, Nk)$ matrix for which the elements are all zeros except:

$$g_{s,(s-1)k+j} = 1$$

$$g_{r+1,(i-1)k+j} = \frac{\displaystyle\sum_{\tau=1}^{m-j+1} P_i(\tau)}{\displaystyle\sum_{\tau=1}^{m}\left[Q(\tau) - \sum_{s=1}^{r} P_s(\tau) \right]} \qquad \begin{array}{l} s = 1, \ldots, r \\[0.5em] i = r + 1, \ldots, N \\[0.5em] j = 1, \ldots, k \end{array}$$ (7)

to represent equation 3 and the following water balance equation

$$\sum_{i=r+1}^{N} \sum_{j=1}^{k} u_{(i-1)k+j} \sum_{\tau=1}^{m-j+1} P_i(\tau) = \sum_{\tau=1}^{m}\left[Q(\tau) - \sum_{s=1}^{r} P_s(\tau) \right]$$ (8)

relevant to the whole system or r input tributary flows, $N - r$ precipitation discharges and one outflow discharge vector, provided $m \gg k$.

Once the parameters $\mathbf{u}$ have been estimated, CLS provides an estimate of the *a priori* unknown runoff coefficient relevant to each P_i precipitation input by means of equation 2, i.e.

$$\hat{\Phi}_i = \sum_{j=1}^{k} \hat{u}_{(i-1)k+j} \qquad i = r + 1, \ldots, N$$ (9)

All the above equations have been written for convenience with k equal for all N inputs, but the CLS program (Martelli, Todini and Wallis, herein) allows for variable k.

Using CLS with a single precipitation input we observe that the resulting û has hydrologically reasonable shape that is quite smooth unless the data has a large noise to signal ratio (Figure 2). Small bumps may occur in the tail of the impulse response function, if these irregularities occur interspersed with zeros it is an indication that the length k has been chosen longer than can be reasonably resolved with the available data.

The û obtained by CLS with a single rainfall as input may appear hydrologically desirable but the plot of the observed versus the predicted flows are rarely very good. Figure 3 shows a plot of hypothetical observed discharge q and computed q̂ for the impulse response function of Figure 2. Characteristically one finds that the peaks are underestimated and the low flow overestimated when one treats rainfall—runoff as a single linear system with parameters estimated from a long record of discrete data. To improve upon the inadequate results displayed in Figure 3 we must combine two or more linear systems with the inputs varied in either time or space.

To consider inputs that vary in space it is necessary to have multiple rainfall measurements. Consider the hypothetical watershed shown in Figure 4, which is shown with two principal tributaries, four well-distributed raingauges and one streamgauge.

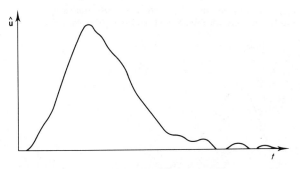

Figure 2. Hypothetical impulse response obtained by CLS from an averaged single precipitation input

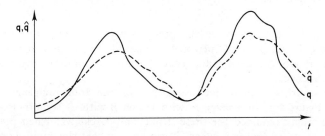

Figure 3. Portion of a plot of q versus q̂ obtained using a single input and the hypothetical kernel of Figure 2

Providing that there are no orographic or other strong reasons for weighting one raingauge more heavily than another it is customary to use these raingauges as a single lumped input, often with weights assigned by simple averaging or by means of Thiessen polygons. However, if two inputs are used, A+B and C+D, in CLS then we notice a reduction in the calibration error variance,

$$\sum_{\tau=1}^{m} (q(\tau) - \hat{q}(\tau))^2 / (m - 1)$$

that may become particularly pronounced in arid regions. In arid regions one

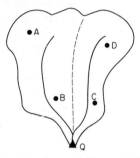

Figure 4. Map of a hypothetical watershed with four raingauges (A, B, C and D) and one streamgauge, Q, and two principal tributaries

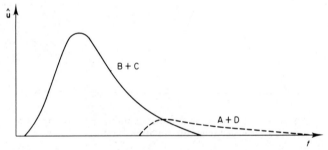

Figure 5. Typical CLS derived kernels for a watershed of the type shown in Figure 4

tributary may be in flood while the other is dry, a phenomenon observed on Wollombi brook (A. J. Hall personal communication), and having separate precipitation inputs for each tributary can reduce calibration errors as well as reducing divergence.

For humid areas a more interesting use of the four raingauge watershed pictured in Figure 4 is to average A with D and B with C. Hypothetical impulse response functions obtained for these 'front' and 'back' watershed precipitation inputs are pictured in Figure 5, where it can be seen that the impulse response for the front of the basin controls the magnitude and timing of the peaks, while the impulse response for the back is delayed, more prolonged, and of lesser quantitative importance to the analysis. For large tropical basins such as the Sanaga river (at Edea, Cameroun, 131.500 km^2) and Nam Mune river (above Ubol, Thailand, 104.000 km^2) we have found that the impulse responses from the back of the watersheds were so flat that it was hardly worth considering them as separate inputs to CLS.

Very little quantitative literature is available concerning the effect upon divergence of altering the precipitation weighting function in those fortunate situations where multiple rainfall measurements are available. One interesting published study (Sugawara et al., 1974) came to the conclusion that the only acceptable weights to apply to multiple raingauges when performing rainfall—runoff modelling were 0, 1, or 1/2. It is evident that more emphasis could be placed on this aspect of modelling, and that CLS offers a unique tool for this purpose.

So far in our discussion of CLS as a rainfall—runoff model we have followed the history so succinctly stated by Dooge (herein): 'In all approaches to mathematical modelling of hydrologic processes the first attempts have been on the basis of linear time-invariant systems and only in the case when such models are deficient are more complex models used'.

Having suggested that a simple use of CLS will rarely produce forecasts that are sufficiently accurate we shall now introduce the concept of using CLS in a more complex fashion. Following Dooge's classification scheme we shall develop a procedure for using CLS as a time-invariant non-linear system; the resulting model can be thought of as being a conceptual model or as a black-box model depending upon the whim of the classifier. The specific method advocated is not the most objective nor rigorous algorithm that can be imagined; but it is simple to use and it is yet to be shown that an alternative method would consistently result in a lessening of forecast divergence.

A simple example of a time-invariant non-linear system is shown in Figure 6. The CLS solution to non-linearity is to separate the input stream into two or more separate input vectors, as shown in the figure and to calculate separate impulse response functions for each input. The separation mechanism used by the current computer implementation of CLS (Martelli, Todini and Wallis, herein) is based upon the use of zero, one or two thresholds. For those who demand a conceptual model interpretation, the CLS thresholds can be thought of as an antecedent moisture condition, if the total precipitation in a prior counting period, L, is greater than a specified value, the threshold T, then today's precipitation plus that of M preceding days are put into a separate input vector and removed from the first vector. Expressed algebraically we can say that the thresholds operate on a precipitation input $P(\tau)$ in the following two-step manner:

(1) $\quad P'(\tau) = P(\tau) \quad \tau = 1, \ldots, M$
$\quad\quad P''(\tau) = 0$

(2) if $\quad \displaystyle\sum_{I=\mathrm{MAX}(1,\tau-L)}^{\tau-1} P(I) > T$

$\quad\quad\quad\quad\quad\quad\quad\quad J = \mathrm{MAX}(1, \tau-M), \ldots, \tau$
$\quad$ then do $\quad P'(J) = 0$
$\quad\quad\quad\quad\quad\quad P''(J) = P(J)$

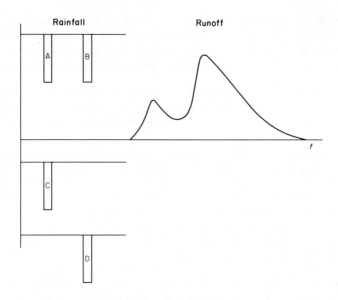

Figure 6. An illustration of a time-invariant non-linear system, two identical impulse inputs, A and B, result in output peaks of differing magnitudes. If A and B are treated with a single least squares derived impulse response function the first peak will be overestimated while the second will be underestimated. If separate input streams can be prepared, C and D, then separate impulse response functions can be generated which will allow the predicted peaks to match the observed peaks

We have found that L and M can usually be rather small integers as long as $L > M$, and that many combinations of L and M yield seemingly similar solutions. However, CLS is responsive to the threshold value and if little precipitation is moved then the extreme peaks are fitted well but average error variance does not decrease appreciably.

We have found that one threshold is usually sufficient for humid area watersheds because data errors rarely warrant additional complexity in the system. For watersheds in arid regions we have found that two thresholds are adequate for modelling the high and intermediate flows, although there is some indication that extreme drought conditions might be more accurately handled by means of additional input vectors or by the introduction of time-variance into the threshold mechanism. However, to warrant such extra effort the available data and forecast conditions would both have to be rather unusual.

In our CLS modelling to date we have not looked for an objective fitting procedure for L, M or T, especially as two or three trial-and-error guesses are usually sufficient to arrive at an acceptable CLS configuration for a rainfall–runoff problem. Our current computer program operates under a time-sharing system CP-CMS, and the operator time and CPU time are both so low that the need for further refinement has not yet become evident.

6. WMO results

The World Meterorological Organization Department of Hydrology and Water Resources conceived the idea of an objective, definitive, evaluation of rainfall—runoff models. A full report on this most interesting study has been published by WMO, and no attempt to summarize the full study findings or recommendations will be made here.

To obviate having to evaluate 75—100 models, a constraint that the models be existing and operational was imposed (Němec, personal communication). Each remaining modelling group was to choose at least one watershed and to provide the WMO with a complete set of a calibration and verification inputs and outputs. The WMO would then provide all the modellers with complete sets of input data and output data for only the calibration periods. Modellers were to send their predicted results for the calibration period and their forecast results for the verification period to WMO, who would derive the values for a prior, agreed-upon set of statistics for both the calibration and verification periods. All modellers were to model all watersheds, not just a judicious selection of watersheds. It was hoped that by making the calibration period long the problem of an unrepresentative calibration period could be eliminated and, further, that, by having a long verification period (say ten years) and a very large number of watersheds, there would be sufficient observations to attach some statistical reliability to the verification statistics. Finally, a meeting restricted to the participants was to be held to analyse the results and to see whether or not conclusions could be derived from the results. Through no fault of the WMO not all these study objectives were found feasible although the project must still be regarded as a milestone in the history of hydrology.

Ten modelling groups participated in the WMO study, of which one was CLS and at least three were of the ESMA type. The small number of participants made the logistics of the final meeting easier but it leaves many unanswered questions about the relative merits of non-competing models. A much more serious shortcoming of the study was the small number of watersheds that were represented, six (see Table 1), and the short verification periods, which prevents any truly meaningful

Table 1. The six watersheds of the WMO study

Name	Area (km²)	Length of calibration period (years)	Length of verification period (years)	Number of tributary flows provided	Number of precipitation inputs provided
Sanaga river	131 500	6	2	0	13
Nam Mune river	104 000	6	2	1	4
Kizu river	1 445	2 ½	2	0	1*
Bikin river	13 100	6 summer periods	2 summer periods	0	1†
Bird creek	2 344	6	2	0	1†
Wollombi brook	1 580	6	2	0	1†

*Based upon more than one raingauge, weighting function described in Sugawara *et al.* (1974).
†Based upon more than one raingauge, weighting function unknown to most participants.

statement being made about the reliability of the differences that were observed. To paraphrase this remark, for the verification period we cannot definitely state whether or not the average statistics represent noise, or valid quantitative differences in the ability of various models to control divergence. The graphical presentations of the verification period results in the WMO report do show some trends that allowed the participants to make some qualitative statements (value judgements) about the results.

Further, while the calibration periods are longer than the verification periods no valid statistical inferences of comparative model performance can be draw from any calibration period results. The reason for this aforementioned unfortunate property of calibration period results is apparent if we consider CLS modelling. With CLS it is mathematically possible and computationally feasible to keep on adding more and more linear systems, and ultimately reduce the calibration error variance to any desired level. The CLS modeller is deterred from such foolishness only by the knowledge that he would be surely fitting the noise as well as the signal, and that forecasts with the resulting model would be no less divergent than if he stopped his fitting procedure with a simpler model. What is not obvious to many hydrologist modellers is that the same criticism can be applied to all overly refined rainfall–runoff calibrations. In summary, a good fit to the calibration period may comfort the individual hydrologic model builder but it does not guarantee a model with minimum forecast divergence, and it imparts no substantial message to those concerned with comparative model quality unless the data used in the calibration were error-free or very nearly error-free.

In the light of the above remarks we will present only a portion of the verification period graphical results from the WMO study. We shall present the verification period double mass plots of observed versus forecast flows for CLS compared with those obtained by one of the ESMA-type models. The other graphical plot from the verification period that we shall present is the scatter diagram plot of the predicted versus observed highest daily flow values for each month of the verification period. Whenever possible we have selected the SRFC model (Burnash *et al.*, 1973) for comparison with the CSL as we have been informed by others that this is the best of the ESMA-type models; and when this comparison was not available to us we have selected the more versatile SSARR model (US Army Corp of Engineers, 1972) for comparison with the CLS.

The objective in presenting these graphs is not to single out one model as being 'better' than another as this is not possible from the limited data available to us, but to show that in many situations a simple, quick, CLS approach to rainfall–runoff modelling can yield forecasts that are not appreciably more divergent than those obtainable with more complex models. We regard this negative information as encouraging because we believe that there are many watersheds where data is too sparse to support a more detailed model, or where the benefits to accrue from the forecast may not warrant the considerable extra investment in computer time and trained personnel that are demanded by more complex models.

In Figures 7(a) and 7(b) the results for the Sanaga river are presented. The CLS modelling was by means of a single Thiessen polygon lumped input and a single threshold. The verification period contains a year with 11% more runoff that the highest year recorded in the calibration period although the precipitation recorded for this year was not particularly high by the calibration period standard. Because of the extreme length of the wet period recession, 90 days, we found it convenient to model the Sanaga river using two-day averages. A two-day averaging procedure does not influence the volume forecasts, but it does exert a downward bias on the montly highest one-day forecasts.

The Nam Mune river results are presented in Figures 8(a) and 8(b). CLS was used with the Nam Chi as a separate flow input. A single lumped precipitation input was derived between the four raingauges using weights of Korat 0.17, Khon Kaen 0.17, Surin 0.33 and Roiet 0.33. Like the Sanaga this is a large river and a two-day average time period and a single threshold was used. The verification period contains a peak monsoon flow that is some 40% greater than that observed during the calibration period. CLS maintains a permanent record of the maximum total precipitation volume in the antecedent moisture accounting period, L; with experience it is hoped that this will aid in the updating of forecasts that have to be made beyond the range of the calibration data. The solution of the Nam Mune river rainfall—runoff problem presented here was obtained by two students during the course of the two-hour training workshop session held in Pisa on 12 December, 1974. The students had had no prior experience with CSL and were not privy to the forecast period flows.

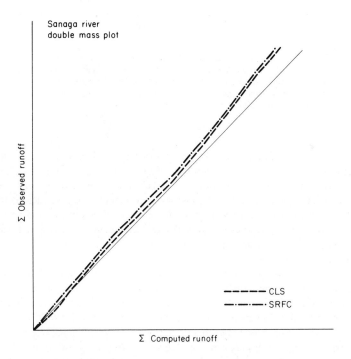

Figure 7(a). Double mass plot of forecast versus observed flows for a two-year period on the Sanaga river. Forecasts made without updating. Redrawn from WMO (1975)

162

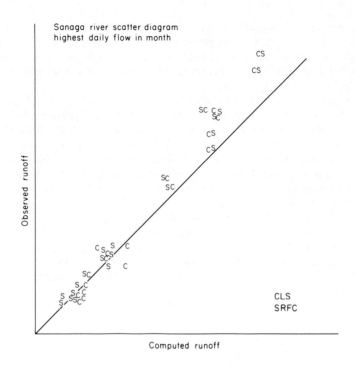

Figure 7(b). Scatter diagram of the highest daily forecast and observed flow for each month of a two-year verification period. All forecasts made without updating CLS forecasts based upon two-day averages. The two biggest values refer to a single wet season peak. Redrawn from WMO (1975)

The Kizu river (Kiuki region, Japan, 1445 km^2) Figures 9(a) and 9(b), is a particularly interesting, and important modelling problem. CLS as a modelling group entered the WMO study at a comparatively late date (end of April, 1974), by which time it had been determined (Sugawara, personal communication) that large errors existed in the early portions of the Kizu river calibration period and that the calibration should be conducted on only the last 2½ years of the original calibration period. Some of the other modelling groups recalculated with the shorter calibration period but none of their results are strictly comparable to the CLS results. The CLS results presented in the WMO report were computed with a single threshold using the calibration period September, 1962, to December, 1965, while the CLS results presented in this paper were computed after the conference with the same threshold value using the calibration period July, 1962, to December, 1965. Before the conference we observed that the runoff coefficient for 30-day periods surrounding the big storms of August, 1962, and September, 1965, were 0.4 and 0.8. By truncating the calibration period so as to start with September, 1962, we developed a prediction based upon only two large storms, which was an insufficient calibration and resulted in forecasts for the two big storms of the

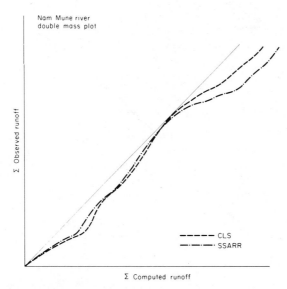

Figure 8(a). Double mass plot of forecast versus observed flows for a two-year period on the Nam Mune river. Forecasts made without updating. SSARR results redrawn from WMO (1975). CLS results obtained by students at the CLS workshop held in Pisa on 12 December, 1974

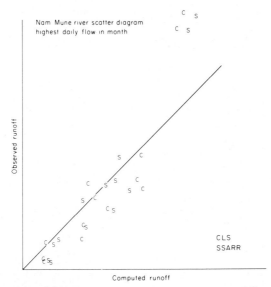

Figure 8(b). Scatter diagram of the highest daily forecast and observed flow for each month of a two-year verification period. All forecasts made without updating. CLS forecasts based upon two-day averages. The two biggest values refer to a single monsoon peak. SSARR results redrawn from WMO (1975). CLS results obtained by students at the CLS workshop held in Pisa on 12 December, 1974

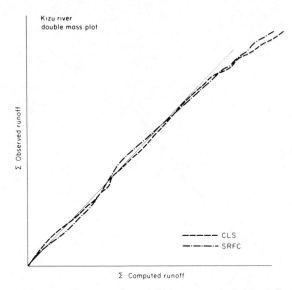

Figure 9(a). Double mass plot of forecast versus observed flows for a two-year period on the Kizu river. Forecasts made without updating. CLS forecasts based upon a 2½-year calibration, SRFC forecasts based upon a six-year calibration

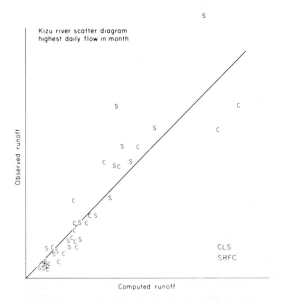

Figure 9(b). Scatter diagram of the highest daily forecast and observed flow for each month of a two-year verification period. All forecasts made without updating. CLS forecast based upon a 2½ calibration, SRFC forecasts based upon six-year calibration

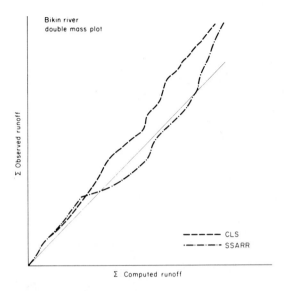

Figure 10(a). Double mass plot of forecast versus observed flows for two summer periods on the Bikin river. Forecasts made without updating. Redrawn from WMO (1975)

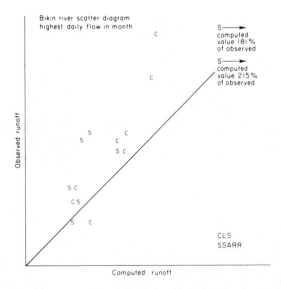

Figure 10(b). Scatter diagram of the highest daily forecast and observed flow for each month of the summer seasons. Forecasts made without updating. Redrawn from WMO (1975)

166

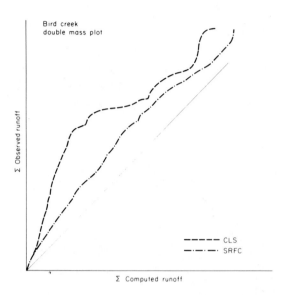

Figure 11(a). Double mass plot of forecast versus observed flows for a two-year period on Bird creek. Forecasts made without updating. Redrawn from WMO (1975)

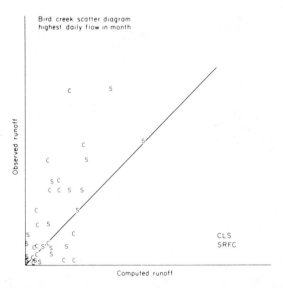

Figure 11(b). Scatter diagram of the highest daily forecast and observed flow for each month of a two-year verification period. All forecasts made without updating. Redrawn from WMO (1975)

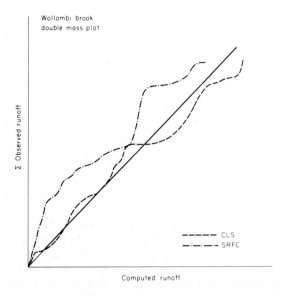

Figure 12(a). Double mass plot of forecast versus observed flows for a two-year period on Wollombi brook. Forecasts made without updating. Redrawn from WMO (1975)

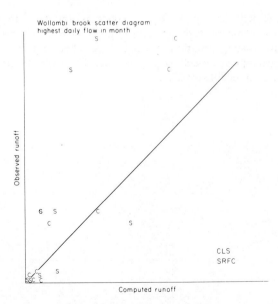

Figure 12(b). Scatter diagram of the highest daily forecast and observed flow for each month of a two-year verification period. All forecasts made without updating. Redrawn from WMO (1975)

verification period that were greatly in excess of the observed values. The wisdom of having only WMO retain knowledge of the verification period flows was illustrated by the ease with which we were able to alter our verification period results after merely a glance at the forecast period data. We are led to the unmistakable conclusion that it may be far harder than it originally appeared to design a fair test of rainfall—runoff models, and maybe even impossible until the flexibility and computer costs of other models are greatly reduced.

The Bikin river (coastal region, USSR, 13.100 km^2 results Figures 10(a) and 10(b) show that it is difficult to model continuous daily rainfall—runoff with discontinuous calibration periods. The unsatisfactory results obtained by CLS can be partially explained by the fact that the whole watershed was treated as a single linear system without the non-linearity introduced by thresholds, and without regard to the intermitted nature of the data (Table 1). The Bird creek results, Figures 11(a) and 11(b), represents one of the two arid region watersheds encompassed in the WMO study. The calibration period for this watershed was deliberately selected to include an unusually severe 18-month drought. The CSL results were obtained using thresholds and short antecedent moisture accounting periods, 7 and 15 days. It would be interesting to model this watershed with six-hourly time increments and multiple rather than lumped precipitation inputs. The other arid region watershed, Wollombi brook, Figures 12(a) and 12(b) would similarly benefit from a more detailed analysis with shorter time periods and subwatershed precipitation measurements.

7. Summary

CLS is an extremely fast, easy to use, systems approach to rainfall—runoff modelling that has comparatively low data requirements. It is suggested that there may be many forecasting situations in hydrology where data is so sparse that a more complex attempt at modelling may not provide forecasts that are any more reliable than those obtainable by CLS.

Perspective on Mathematical Models of Flood Routing

MARIO GALLATI
Hydraulics Institute, University of Pavia, Italy

UGO MAIONE
Hydraulics Institute, University of Pavia, Italy

1. Introduction

From the hydraulic point of view, the propagation of flood waves in river beds is a typical problem of gradually varied unsteady flow for which the theoretical basis was developed principally by French scientists in the last half of the nineteenth century until the formulation, in 1871, of the classic equations of St Venant.

Before the end of the century, simplified forms of these equations, that is solutions that ignore inertial terms, were already being developed. These studies led to defining the speed of propagation of the kinematic wave as the ratio of the increment of discharge to the increment of wetted area of the channel.

The result was obtained in a theoretical way by Graeff (1875) and Kleitz (1877) and by means of experimental observations of the Mississippi—Missouri Rivers by Seddon (1900).

The first method of graphic integration of the St Venant equations based on the concept of characteristic lines was principally due to Massau (1889) and was established at the end of the century.

One can say, therefore, that the theoretical bases of the problem were well known at the beginning of the twentieth century even if they received many important clarifications by mathematicians during the next twenty years. Nevertheless, while theoretical development of unsteady open channel flow was well advanced, the practitioners paid scant attention to these developments. Applications of open channel flood routing relied heavily of the equation of continuity and the development of empirical coefficients and methodologies for estimating the stored volume of water in every reach as a function of the levels or of the discharge in one or both of the extreme sections. In the text that follows such practical models will be referred to as 'hydrologic models'.

A great many processes of this type were obtained and applied in many practical cases (especially by American hydraulic engineers) beginning in the early part of this century (the study of the March, 1907, flood propagation in the Sacramento and S. Joaquin basins in California dates from 1908). It was only in the 1950s that the advent of high-speed computers permitted the reformulation and resolution of the problem according to the hydrodynamic principles with the use of numeric calculus, taking into account the irregular complex geometry of river beds.

It is necessary to note, nevertheless, that after accurate calibration the hydrologic models are usually able to supply the major part of the needed information for practical problems with sufficient reliability. This is especially true in the case of large rivers that have flood waves of long period and slow variation with time.

The most famous among these practical hydrologic models is certainly the so-called Muskingum method that will be described in detail later, together with the storage method studied and applied by Italian hydraulic engineers (the Fantoli method).

In 1951 Hayami published a study in which he examined a method of flood routing on the basis of the diffusion equation. The application of this method to the Yedo river, after calibration of the coefficients, furnished excellent results and from it a whole class of mathematical models originated, which became more and more sophisticated in the attempt to link the value of the coefficients to the geometrical characteristics of the river.

Finally, in 1953, Stoker's classic study on the numerical integration of St Venant equations applied to the Mississippi—Missouri system appeared and gave origin to a new approach to the problem which was widely followed. In fact, in the wake of this study, numerous authors produced a notable quantity of numerical integration methods for the St Venant equations, obtained using the most varied schemes of discretization of the partial derivatives. Furthermore, the characteristics of stability of such methods were investigated in relation to the space and time steps.

The principal mathematical models of flood routing are discussed, starting with the most complete one based on the St Venant equations and concluding with appropriate models. The latter, it will be shown, can be derived from the same equations making use of various simplifications.

2. Complete model based on the St Venant equations

Given that x and t are the abscissa along the river bed and the time (independent variables), that Q, A and Z are respectively discharge, water area and water level measured with respect to an arbitrary horizontal reference and that J is the energy slope due to continuous resistance, the St Venant equations in the absence of lateral inflow and outflow have the form:

$$\frac{\partial Q}{\partial x} + \frac{\partial A}{\partial t} = 0 \tag{1}$$

$$\frac{\partial Q}{\partial t} + \frac{\partial}{\partial x}\left(\frac{Q^2}{A}\right) + gA\left(\frac{\partial Z}{\partial x} + J\right) = 0$$

the first of which represents the continuity equation and the second that of motion.

It is well know that the validity of these equations is dependent on the following hypotheses, all more or less verified in reality, except in particular cases:

(a) that the current is linear, that is that the trajectories are reasonably parallel and rectilinear so that the transversal sections are plain and vertical and the pressure is distributed on them according to the hydrostatic law;

(b) that the velocity distribution coefficient can be taken as unity;

(c) that the friction resistence can be evaluated by a uniform flow formula which also takes into account the effects of eventual eddy losses;

(d) that, as already stated, there is no lateral inflow or outflow. This last limitation can obviously be eliminated by adding additional terms in the equations which, nevertheless, are not always easy to define quantitatively because of the embedded difficulties in the determination of the lateral inflow and outflow.

If berms are present additional modifications to the St Venant equations must be introduced, defining by further hypothesis the nature of motion in the over bank areas themselves.

In the literature the St Venant equations are reported in various forms depending on the unknown functions chosen for identifying the current in each section: the above form is usually applied to the problems of natural river beds while h (water level with respect to the bottom of the section) is preferred for artificial channels.

Without entering into detailed mathematical theory of partial differential equations, it is noted that the properties of the St Venant equation are essentially linked to the existence of characteristic lines which constitute a double family of curves in the (x, t) plane defined by the ordinary differential equations:

$$\frac{dx}{dt} = \frac{Q}{A} \pm \sqrt{(g\,A/B)} \tag{2a}$$

(B is the width of the river bed on the free surface) along which the dependent variables are linked among themselves and to the time by total differentials:

$$-B\left[\frac{Q}{A} \mp \sqrt{\left(g\,\frac{A}{B}\right)}\right]\frac{dZ}{dt} + \frac{dQ}{dt} + gJ = 0 \tag{2b}$$

In the case of subcritical flow, as usually happens in fluvial river beds, the two families of characteristics have contrary slopes and form a network in the (x, t) plane.

The resolution of the system can be carried out only by means of numerical computations following one of two principal methods:

(a) integration of the system of the four ordinary differential equations (2a, 2b) obtained following the method of the characteristics;

(b) direct integration of the system of partial differential equations following explicit or implicit methods.

In every case the technique of numerical solution is based on the substitution of the derivatives (continuous operators) with quotients of the differences of the estimated variables on a discrete field such as the points of an intergration network. In the first method the network is obtained from the intersection of the characteristic lines (Figure 1) and, in the second, from the intersection of a double family of straight lines parallel to the coordinate axes x and t (Figure 2).

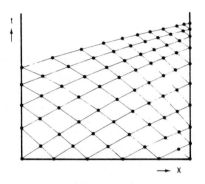

Figure 1

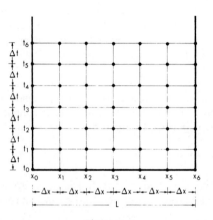

Figure 2

Since the integration field is finite, it is necessary to know the conditions of the stream at the boundary of the integration field, that is at the upper and lower end section of the considered reach. The flow being subcritical, the theory of characteristics easily shows that the numerical integration of the equations on a strip of the $(x; t)$ plane (Figure 3) is possible provided (a) the initial conditions of the dependent variables are known and (b) the boundary conditions $Q(t)$ or $Z(t)$ in both the initial and the final sections of the reach are known.

On the other hand, intuition also permits one to affirm that the hydrometric conditions of the flow in a given instant and in a certain section must depend on the conditions existing in preceding times in upstream and downstream sections, given that in subcritical flow the perturbations can influence the flow either upstream or downstream.

Moreover, experience tells us that, except in very particular cases, downstream perturbations influence the motion of the flood waves only in limited reaches next to the cause of the perturbation itself. Hence it appears that one is justified in simulating the behaviour of the river bed downstream from the extreme section by means of a rating curve estimated for the steady flow, neglecting that a one-to-one

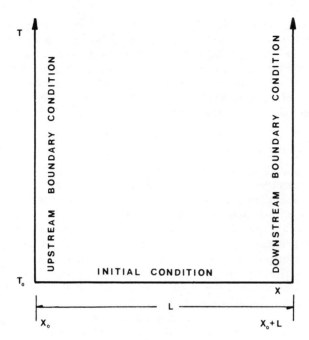

Figure 3

relationship between discharge and stage during the unsteady motion does not exist, when studying the flood propagation in a river reach far from its mouth. In this way it is possible to substitute a downstream condition of the type $Q(t)$ or $Z(t)$, with a condition of the 'impedance' type, $f(Q, Z) = 0$. Therefore, the knowledge of the flood hydrograph $Z(t)$ or $Q(t)$ in the initial section and of the rating curve (or another hydrograph) in the end section presents the possibility of numerically integrating the St Venant equations and arriving at an estimate of $Z(t)$ and $Q(t)$ in all the intermediate sections of the river reach up to the end section.

As already stated, the integration of St Venant equations requires knowledge of the geometry of the river bed, which in practice is based on a relief map of a certain number of cross-sections spaced at a distance which assures the desired precision from a hydraulic point of view. Naturally it is not possible to permanently and absolutely establish the value of this distance, which must be fixed from time to time in relation to each particular problem by means of numerical recalibration of the model.

It is worthwhile noting that one of the major burdens in the construction of such models lies in the algebraic representation of the geometry of the river bed and it is therefore convenient to simplify these models features as much as possible.

The only parameter present in the St Venant equations — the roughness coefficient — is usually fixed by calibrating the model on the bases of available experimental observations.

Some authors suggest the adoption of values of such coefficients which vary with the depth of water to get a better reproduction of the phenomenon.

Moreover, the values of the roughness coefficient must be constantly brought up to date in relation to the variations in time of the river bed. Actually, as was recognized for the Arno model, it seems possible to take into account certain modifications of the river bed by varying only the value of such a coefficient and leaving the initial geometric representation unaltered.

3. Simplified models

As already pointed out, experience shows that during the motion of flood waves the energy transformation from potential into kinetic and vice versa' are wholly insignificant: it is therefore natural to neglect the kinetic terms in the equation of motion to arrive at simpler mathematical models.

For rivers it is possible to establish that such kinetic terms are effectively negligible with respect to the others on the basis of theoretical considerations — based on a kinematic schematization of the phenomenon. These observations show that the ratio of the kinetic terms with respect to $\partial z/\partial x$ is of the order of magnitude of the square of the Froude number of the flow, which often has a value much less than unity in all natural streams.

This observation leads us to formulate a mathematical model of flood propagation — called 'parabolic' — which takes into consideration, together with the continuity equation, the simplified equation of steady flow:

$$\frac{\partial Z}{\partial x} = -J$$

The time derivative of this equation shows that during the passage of the flood the variation of the energy slope equals instant by instant the variation of the slope of the water surface. If, moreover, one can suppose that during the passage of the wave the free surface moves parallel to itself and therefore to the bottom of the river bed — as if the successive unsteady flow profiles were uniform flow profiles — the time derivative of the energy slope J is equal to zero for the whole duration of the phenomenon. The mathematical model called 'kinematic' corresponds to this schematization.

Since

$$\frac{\partial Z}{\partial x} = \frac{\partial b}{\partial x} - i$$

one can accept this hypothesis as being approximately verified when the slope i of the river bed is much greater than $\partial b/\partial x$, as usually happens in mountain watercourses. Such a term cannot be neglected for the valley reaches, usually characterized by a very small value for the slope of the river bed.

It should be emphasized, however, that holding the energy slope J invariable during the unsteady motion means that one assumes uniform flow with its one-to-one relation between the stage and discharge. This hypothesis holds good for very slow flood phenomena.

The parabolic and the kinematic models are therefore obtained by associating respectively the first and the second of the following relations to the equation of continuity:

$$\frac{\partial J}{\partial t} = -\frac{\partial}{\partial t}\left(\frac{\partial Z}{\partial x}\right)$$

$$\frac{\partial J}{\partial t} = 0$$

Since J is a function of Q and Z, and remembering the continuity equation, it can be shown that:

$$\frac{\partial J}{\partial t} = \frac{\partial J}{\partial Q}\left[\frac{\partial Q}{\partial t} - \frac{1}{B}\frac{\frac{\partial J}{\partial Z}}{\frac{\partial J}{\partial Q}}\frac{\partial Q}{\partial x}\right]$$

from which:

$$C = -\frac{1}{B}\frac{\partial J/\partial Z}{\partial J/\partial Q} = -\frac{1}{B}\frac{\partial Q}{\partial Z}$$

from which can be deduced the equation of the kinematic model:

$$C\frac{\partial Q}{\partial x} + \frac{\partial Q}{\partial t} = 0 \tag{3}$$

and, from a simple manipulation of the continuity equation, that of the parabolic model:

$$D\frac{\partial^2 Q}{\partial x^2} = C\frac{\partial Q}{\partial x} + \frac{\partial Q}{\partial t} \tag{4}$$

where

$$D = \frac{1}{B}\left(\frac{\partial J}{\partial Q}\right)^{-1}$$

With analogous considerations one can deduce similar expressions for the water levels.

The examination of (3) immediately leads to the recognition that moving along the river bed with a speed equal to C a discharge that does not vary with time is observed; and therefore it is natural to attribute to C the significance of the celerity of propagation of this same discharge. Since, on the other hand, for open sections, C is an increasing function of the water level and therefore of the discharge, one concludes that the downstream edge of waves becomes steeper and steeper during their motion due to the greater celerity of propagation of bigger discharges.

The mathematical model that is based on (3) therefore describes a propagative phenomenon characterized by a translation of the flood wave without subsidence of the peak.

On the other hand the subsidence of height that one observes moving along a river bed with speed C is reproduced by the parabolic model and is equal to:

$$D \frac{\partial^2 Q}{\partial x^2}$$

a term which, as $D > 0$, has a sign dependent on the concavity of the wave; it is negative precisely in correspondence with the maximum discharge and positive in correspondence to the minimum. As a consequence the model describes a motion in which the maximum discharge decreases during the downstream motion of the wave and because of the conservation of mass the wave extends and flattens out.

The solution of equations 3 and 4, must necessarily be obtained by means of finite difference methods as the coefficients C and D are functions of the solutions themselves. And, in addition, as for the St Venant complete model, a knowledge of the geometry of the river bed and an estimate of the roughness coefficient is required.

If, however, linearizing the problem one supposes that the coefficients are constant, it is possible to express the solution in analytical form with the expressions

$$Q(x, t) = Q\left(x_0, t - \int_0^x \frac{dx}{C} \right) \tag{3'}$$

for the kinematic linearized model and

$$Q(x, t) = \int_0^t I(x, \tau) \cdot Q(x_0, t - \tau)\, d\tau \tag{4'}$$

with

$$I(x, t) = \frac{\Delta x}{2t \sqrt{(\pi\, tD)}} \exp \frac{-(Ct - \Delta x)^2}{4Dt}$$

for the parabolic linearized model — which thus becomes a model of the 'diffusion' type.

The solutions, therefore, depend on the form of the known wave in the upstream section of the reach $Q(x_0, t)$, and on the values of the coefficients present in the models (C for the kinematic model, D and C for the parabolic model) which are fixed by calibrating the model on the basis of available experimental observations.

The values of the constant D of the parabolic model deduced for several rivers, are of the order $10^4 - 10^6$ m^2/s while the speed C is of the order $1.5 - 1.8$ V in which V m/s is the average velocity of the stream.[*]

It is worthwhile underlining that the presence of two coefficients gives the model of diffusion based on the (4') the possibility, after calibration, of reproducing with precision the two most important practical characteristics of the phenomenon: the attenuation of the peak and its time of occurrence.

In the linearized kinematic model (Cunge, 1969), which 'naturally' has only one calibration coefficient it is also possible to introduce 'artificially' a second

---

[*] It will be noted that for very wide rectangular sections the kinematic schematization of the phenomenon, using constant χ in the Chezy formula for the calculation of J, leads to the value $1.5V$ m/s for the speed of propagation.

coefficient using an opportune implicit schematization of the partial derivatives based on the following expressions:

$$\frac{\partial Q}{\partial x} = \frac{0.5 \cdot (Q_2(t + \Delta t) + Q_2(t)) - 0.5 \cdot (Q_1(t + \Delta t) + Q_1(t))}{\Delta x}$$

$$\frac{\partial Q}{\partial t} = \frac{K(Q_1(t + \Delta t) - Q_1(t)) + (1 - K) \cdot (Q_2(t + \Delta t) - Q_2(t))}{\Delta t}$$

where numbers 1 and 2 indicate the upstream and downstream sections of the Δx reach and where K is a weight coefficient.

Introducing these expressions into the linearized equation of the kinematic model one can obtain the value of the downsteam discharge at the time $t + \Delta t$ as a linear function of the known upstream discharge at the times t and $t + \Delta t$ and the downstream discharge at the time t and the two coefficients C and K:

$$Q_2(t + \Delta t) = A_1 \cdot Q_1(t) + A_2 Q_1(t + \Delta t) + A_3 Q_2(t) \tag{5}$$

$$A_1 = \frac{C^{-1} \cdot x \cdot K + 0.5 \cdot \Delta t}{C^{-1} \cdot x \cdot (1 - K) + 0.5 \cdot \Delta t}$$

$$A_2 = \frac{0.5 \cdot \Delta t - C^{-1} \cdot \Delta x \cdot K}{C^{-1} \cdot \Delta x (1 - K) + 0.5 \cdot \Delta t}$$

$$A_3 = \frac{C^{-1} \cdot \Delta x \cdot (1 - K) - 0.5 \cdot \Delta t}{C^{-1} \cdot \Delta x \cdot (1 - K) + 0.5 \cdot \Delta t}$$

An identical expression is obtained with an opportune finite difference representation of the diffusion equation after putting:

$$D = (1/2 - K) . C . \Delta x$$

and this clarifies why two calibration coefficients give the kinematic model the possibility of representing the reduction of peaks.

It is interesting to note that the preceding formula obtained by discretizing the kinematic and parabolic linearized models, was historically obtained in a completely different manner. The original solution was based on only the continuity equation* and the hypothesis that the stored volume in the reach Δx of the river bed is a linear function of the discharges in the end sections of the reach itself:

$$V = H \cdot (KQ_1 + (1 - K) \cdot Q_2) \tag{6}$$

where $H = \Delta x/C$.

Such a model, known in the technical literature as the 'Muskingum method', has had notable success and generally preferred to other hydrologic models for it seems to be more flexible in the calibration. Traditionally, its calibration was carried out with empirical graphic verification of the linearity of equation 6 using simultaneous recordings of flood discharges, in the extreme section of the reach.

Among the numerous hydrological methods of flood routing we will point out finally the storage method devised by Italian hydraulic engineers. It assumes the

*Continuity equation written as: $dW/dt = Q_2 - Q_1$.

following expression for stored volume:

$$V = K \cdot \Delta x \cdot A_2 \tag{7}$$

where A_2 represents the area of the downstream section of the reach Δx, and K is a coefficient which takes account of the major stored volume in a natural river bed with respect to that evaluated in the hypothesis of prismatic river beds for which the water profile is parallel to the bottom (Fantoli, 1925; De Marchi, 1945; Supino, 1965).

The evaluation of $Q_2(t + \Delta t)$ is obtained from the equation of continuity where Q_1 and Q_2 are expressed as means between their values at time t and $t + \Delta t$ and the stored volume is computed on the basis of equation 7. In this equation the wetted area A_2 is computed using a uniform flow rating curve* in accordance with the kinematic schematization from which the method takes its justification.

The calibration consists of the evaluation of the coefficient K on the basis of observed recordings.

4. Conclusion

In the literature there is available a wide spectrum of usable and reasonably accurate mathematical models for flood routing. This variability can be attributed to the fact that the phenomenon is very important from a physical point of view, and the rigorous mathematical schematization can be readily simplified in many different ways.

Among the models reviewed, those based upon the complete St Venant equations are undoubtedly the most descriptive. It is worthy of note that in such models the presence of only one parameter (the roughness coefficient) gives a notable simplicity in calibration. However, the use of such models can become numerically complex when the river bed has a significant length and abruptly varying section, so that sophisticated, time consuming implicit methods may be needed for the solution of the equations in some reaches.

With regard to other models, those based on only the continuity equation are certainly the oldest and even today earn wide acceptance for their intrinsic simplicity. In these simpler models the dynamic phenomena of the flood wave propagation are implicitly resolved during the calibration, and if all one requires is certain simple characteristics of the flood wave, such as the speed and flattening rate of the crest, then the results obtained are usually acceptable.

Among these models, the Muskingum method presents the notable advantage of not requiring a knowledge of the river bed geometry (required by the Fantoli method) as the phenomenon can be reproduced well enough on the basis of the calibration carried out using experimental data relative to the extreme sections of not significantly long reaches (such data therefore are the essential elements for the construction of the model).

There is perhaps another reason for the widespread use of the Muskingum method. The method has two parameters which can be closely linked to the speed and subsidence of the wave crest, and hence the method gives often good estimates of these two important propagative characteristics.

*Using Chézy formula.

Similar considerations apply to the 'diffusion' type models which can be calibrated on two parameters of the same type.

Between these two categories of models are those derived from the St Venant equations (the parabolic and kinematic models) by the elimination of the kinematic terms which, in many cases, are much smaller than the others and which may therefore be safely ignored.

It can be unequivocally stated that the parabolic model is always as precise as the one based on the complete St Venant equations since the effect of the neglected terms is not even slightly comparable with the effect caused by the imprecisions linked to the definition of geometric and hydraulic characteristics of the river bed. On the contrary, the kinematic model can be held valid only for rather steep reaches situated some distance from sections whose water levels are imposed by external phenomena (for example, invariable in time). Nevertheless, it constitutes a fundamental reference point in all the problems of flood wave propagation in river beds representing the junction among the models based on secure theoretical principles which we can define as 'rational' and the 'practical' or 'hydrologic' models, which can also be derived from a kinematic interpretation of the phenomenon. However, according to its kinematic derivation, the Muskingum method should not be able to reproduce the subsidence of the flood crest and its success in reproducing this phenomenon must be attributed solely to the numerical procedures.

With the demonstrated convergence of these different methods confronting the problem, some turned more towards theoretical investigations, and others more towards concrete applications, it can be accepted that the general principles of flood wave propagation in open channels are now well understood.

Nevertheless, very complex equations of a strictly hydrological nature, among which are those regarding the interactions between the propagative phenomenon, sediment transportation, and fluvial dynamics, still remain to be resolved.

Numerical Solution Methods of the St Venant Equations

FRANCESCO GRECO
IBM Scientific Center, Pisa, Italy

LORENZO PANATTONI
IBM Scientific Center, Pisa, Italy

1. Introduction

To study the propagation of flood waves in open channels, the one-dimensional differential equations of gradually varied unsteady flow, established by Barré de Saint Venant, have been used in the following form:

$$\frac{\partial Q}{\partial x} + B \frac{\partial z}{\partial t} = 0 \tag{1}$$

$$\frac{\partial z}{\partial x} + S_f + \frac{1}{g} \left[\frac{\partial Q/A}{\partial t} + \frac{Q}{A} \frac{\partial Q/A}{\partial x} \right] = 0 \tag{2}$$

in which x = current abscissa (positive in the direction of flow), t = time, Q = discharge, B = width of water surface, z = water level as referred to a horizontal datum, g = acceleration due to gravity, A = cross-sectional area, S_f = friction head losses.

A solution of the above equations attains when it is possible to determine the values of the unknowns z and Q in the region of the (x,t) plane, delimited by the horizontal line of the initial conditions (that is, the values of z and Q all along the considered river reach, at the time $t = t_0$) and the two vertical lines of the boundary conditions at the extreme sections (for instance, the incoming wave, $z(t)$ or $Q(t)$, at the upstream section, and the rating curve $f(z,Q) = 0$ at the downstream section).

Except for a few particular cases (Yevdjevich, 1964), remote from the real world, a general analytical solution of the St Venant equations cannot be found. The particular solutions must be considered by adopting finite differencce methods.

Essentially, two different approaches can be followed. The first, the well known method of characteristics, consists in converting the original system into an equivalent system of ordinary differential equations and then replacing the total derivatives by the corresponding incremental ratios; the second in replacing directly the partial derivatives by quotients of finite differences.

The solution of such systems consists in the computation of the quantities z and

182

Q at a given time, from the known values of the same quantities at the previous time and from the given boundary conditions.

2. The method of characteristics

The St Venant equations can be converted with some transformations, as it is well known, into the following system of four ordinary differential equations (Evangelisti, 1966; Amein, 1966):

$$\frac{dx}{dt} = \frac{Q}{A} + c \tag{3}$$

$$- B\left(\frac{Q}{A} - c\right) \frac{dz}{dt} + \frac{dQ}{dt} + g A S_f - \frac{Q^2}{A^2} \frac{\partial A}{\partial x}\bigg|_{y=\text{const}} = 0 \tag{4}$$

$$\frac{dx}{dt} = \frac{Q}{A} - c \tag{5}$$

$$- B\left(\frac{Q}{A} + c\right) \frac{dz}{dt} + \frac{dQ}{dt} + g A S_f - \frac{Q^2}{A^2} \frac{\partial A}{\partial x}\bigg|_{y=\text{const}} = 0 \tag{6}$$

where $y = A/B$ and $c(= \sqrt{(gy)})$ is the celerity of small disturbances.

Equations 3 and 5 define, for each point of the (x,t) plane, the characteristic lines passing through it and along which equations 4 and 6 are satisfied.

A solution of the above system of equations can be obtained replacing the total derivatives by the corresponding incremental ratios.

The values of the quantities z and Q at a given time T in a generic point P of the (x,t) plane can be obtained from the knowledge, at time $T - \Delta t$, of the values which the same quantities have along the characteristics lines (c_1 and c_2) passing through the considered point P (see Figure 1). It follows that the time and space intervals, which are obtained from equations 3 and 5, are functions of the unknowns z and Q. The computation grid is then not regular. This is a significant restriction, especially in the case of natural watercourses for which the geometrical description is given by means of fixed cross-sections. Furthermore, because of the short distance between two successive sections, necessary to have a sufficiently accurate geometrical description of natural watercourses, and because of the usual values of A and Q that are recorded during floods, the time interval must be very small with respect to the duration of the phenomenon.

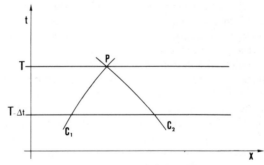

Figure 1. Characteristics grid

3. Direct difference methods

Direct difference methods are based on replacing the partial derivatives by difference quotients. In this way the original partial differential equations are transformed into an algebraic system. It is clear that, by adopting different approximations for the partial derivatives and the coefficients, different numerical systems are obtained.

The numerical grid, on the vertices of which the values of the unknowns are computed, together with the system of difference equations, form the so-called difference scheme.

Referring to the computation grid of Figure 2, the following general expression of a quantity, for instance the discharge Q, and its partial derivatives, can be written

$$Q \simeq P_s P_t Q_{i+1}^{k+1} + (1 - P_s)P_t Q_i^{k+1} + P_s(1 - P_t)Q_{i+1}^{k}$$
$$+ (1 - P_s)(1 - P_t)Q_i^{k} \tag{7}$$

$$\frac{\partial Q}{\partial x} \simeq \frac{P_t}{\Delta x}(Q_{i+1}^{k+1} - Q_i^{k+1}) + \frac{1 - P_t}{\Delta x}(Q_{i+1}^{k} - Q_i^{k}) \tag{8}$$

$$\frac{\partial Q}{\partial t} \simeq \frac{P_s}{\Delta t}(Q_{i+1}^{k+1} - Q_{i+1}^{k}) + \frac{1 - P_s}{\Delta t}(Q_i^{k+1} - Q_i^{k}) \tag{9}$$

in which the upper index (k) refers to time and the lower (i) refers to space. In these formulae P_s and P_t are suitable weighting coefficients between 0 and 1 with which the different variables and their derivatives are averaged in relation to space (P_s) and time (P_t).

The substitution of the previous expressions in the St Venant equations transforms them into an algebraic system in which, assuming that the state of the river is known at time $k\Delta t$, the unknowns are the values of z and Q at time $(k+1)\Delta t$. The solution of such a system leads to the knowledge of the unknown quantities at the same time all along the river. For the complete solution of the problem, the calculation has to be repeated for each time step into which the duration of the phenomenon has been subdivided.

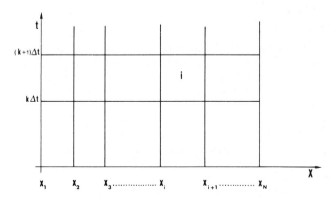

Figure 2. Numerical grid

Particularly important for the solution of the algebraic system is the value of the time averaging coefficient P_t. In fact by choosing $P_t = 0$ it is possible, for any choice of P_s, to express the unknowns at the time $(k+1)\Delta t$ in terms of the known quantities only at the time $k\Delta t$; such a scheme is called an explicit scheme. For values of P_t other than zero only implicit expressions are obtainable for the unknowns, so that the resulting schemes are called implicit schemes.

In choosing a finite difference scheme, it is necessary to take into account the most important properties of the approximations summarized under the concepts of accuracy, efficiency and stability.

The accuracy of a numerical scheme is mainly concerned with truncation error caused by the approximation in replacing the differential equations by the difference equations. The accuracy of a scheme can be improved by reducing the time and space intervals. The efficiency is related to the total number of arithmetic and logical operations necessary to obtain a solution. Contrary to accuracy, efficiency is improved by an increase of the time and step intervals. Finally the stability is related to the growth or decay of numerical errors from one time step to another. More precisely, a scheme is stable if small errors become smaller at any step.

While it is clear how the choice of time and space steps influences accuracy and efficiency, there does not exist any direct way to relate stability to the characteristics of the numerical scheme. In fact there is no general criterion to decide if a numerical scheme is stable or not (Richtmyer and Morton, 1967). For a system of hyperbolic partial differential equations, like the St Venant equations, only the original Von Neumann's method can be used (Strelkoff, 1970), and following this approach it is possible to obtain only a necessary condition for the stability of an approximate system of equations obtained by locally linearizing the original ones and assuming constant coefficients. Applying this criterion (an example is given in the Appendix) to the numerical schemes of the St Venant equations, it follows, provided $P_t \geqslant 1/2$ (Cunge and Wegner, 1964), that an implicit scheme is stable for any chosen time and space intervals, while on the other hand an explicit scheme can be unstable or only conditionally stable (Panattoni, 1974).

The necessary condition of the stability for an explicit scheme is the well known Courant condition:

$$\Delta x/\Delta t \geqslant Q/A + \sqrt{(g\,A/B)} \tag{10}$$

This relationship, with the equals sign between the time and space intervals is the same as that arising from the characteristics method and, as previously stated, this is a very restrictive condition for natural watercourses. For this reason implicit schemes are usually preferred to the explicit schemes, even though the latter lead to easily solvable algebraic systems.

4. Application to the Arno river

In order to study flood wave propagation along the Arno river, an implicit method has been adopted (Greco and Panattoni, 1975). In this way there are no restrictions for the time and space intervals and, furthermore, it is possible to adopt a computation grid perfectly fitting the experimental data.

In this computation grid the vertical lines represent the cross-sections (the distance between two successive sections is variable) and the horizontal lines refer to the time. 1 and ½ are the values adopted for the weighting coefficients P_t and P_s respectively. With these values and referring to the generic grid element i, the following system containing the four unknowns z_i^{k+1}, Q_i^{k+1}, z_{i+1}^{k+1}, Q_{i+1}^{k+1} is obtained:

$$G_i \equiv \frac{B_i^{k+1} + B_{i+1}^{k+1}}{2} \frac{\Delta x_i}{2\Delta t} (z_i^{k+1} - z_i^k + z_{i+1}^{k+1} - z_{i+1}^k) + Q_{i+1}^{k+1} - Q_i^{k+1} = 0 \quad (11)$$

$$F_i \equiv z_{i+1}^{k+1} - z_i^{k+1} + \frac{\Delta x_i}{2} (S_{f_i}^{k+1} + S_{f_{i+1}}^{k+1}) + \frac{\Delta x_i}{2g\Delta t} \left[\frac{Q_{i+1}^{k+1}}{A_{i+1}^{k+1}} - \frac{Q_{i+1}^k}{A_{i+1}^k} + \frac{Q_i^{k+1}}{A_i^{k+1}} - \frac{Q_i^k}{A_i^k} \right]$$

$$+ \frac{1}{2g} \left[\frac{Q_{i+1}^{k+1}}{A_{i+1}^{k+1}} + \frac{Q_i^{k+1}}{A_i^{k+1}} \right] \left[\frac{Q_{i+1}^{k+1}}{A_{i+1}^{k+1}} - \frac{Q_i^{k+1}}{A_i^{k+1}} \right] = 0 \quad (12)$$

in which $\Delta x_i = x_{i+1} - x_i$.

For simplicity, from this point onwards, the variables without upper indexes are referred to time $(k+1)\Delta t$. While there is a rich bibliography about implicit methods, only the original method developed as part of the Arno flood study project will be presented here. The advantages of the Arno method will be made clear in the concluding sections of this paper.

5. The Arno method

The method exploits the linearity in the discharge of the mass equation. It is possible, in fact, to rewrite the mass equation for the grid element i, as follows:

$$Q_i - Q_{i+1} = f(z_i, z_{i+1}) \quad (13)$$

Using this equation for all the grid elements, it is possible to express the discharge at a generic section as a function of the discharge Q_0 at an extreme section and of the water levels at all the sections between them (the generic section and the extreme one).

When the rating curve or the discharge at an extreme section is given as boundary condition, then the discharge Q_0 will be relevant to this section. For simplicity, Q_0 is generally supposed relevant to the section N and indicated by Q_N.

With the previous assumptions, it is possible to write

$$Q_i = Q_N + g(z_i, z_{i+1}, \ldots, z_N) = Q_i(z_i, z_{i+1}, \ldots, z_N, Q_N) \quad (13')$$

Thus, by replacing the discharge value in the equation of motion with equation $13'$, it follows that

$$f_i \equiv F_i(z_i, z_{i+1}, Q_i(z_i, z_{i+1}, \ldots, z_N, Q_N), Q_{i+1}(z_{i+1}, z_{i+2}, \ldots, z_N, Q_N)) = 0 \quad (12')$$

By applying the previous expression at all the $N - 1$ grid elements, the following system of $N - 1$ equations for the $N + 1$ unknowns $z_1, z_2, \ldots, z_N, Q_N$ is obtained:

$$f_1(z_1, z_2, \ldots, z_N, Q_N) = 0$$
$$f_1(z_2, z_3, \ldots, z_N, Q_N) = 0$$
$$\cdots\cdots\cdots\cdots\cdots\cdots$$
$$\cdots\cdots\cdots\cdots\cdots\cdots \tag{14}$$
$$f_{N-1}(z_{N-1}, z_N, Q_N) = 0$$

By adding the two boundary conditions the problem becomes feasible. The Newton method has been adopted to solve the resulting system of non-linear equations.

The method consists in assigning trial values for the unknowns and, in computing the corrections, solving the following linear system, in which the derivatives are estimated in correspondence with trial values:

$$\frac{\partial f_1}{\partial z_1}\, dz_1 + \frac{\partial f_1}{\partial z_2}\, dz_2 + \ldots + \frac{\partial f_1}{\partial z_N}\, dz_N + \frac{\partial f_1}{\partial Q_N}\, dQ_N = -f_1$$

$$\frac{\partial f_2}{\partial z_2}\, dx_2 + \ldots + \frac{\partial f_2}{\partial z_N}\, dz_N + \frac{\partial f_2}{\partial Q_N}\, dQ_N = -f_2$$

$$\cdots\cdots\cdots\cdots\cdots\cdots\cdots\cdots\cdots \tag{15}$$
$$\cdots\cdots\cdots\cdots\cdots\cdots\cdots\cdots\cdots$$

$$\frac{\partial f_{N-1}}{\partial z_{N-1}}\, dz_{N-1} + \frac{\partial f_{N-1}}{\partial z_N}\, dz_N + \frac{\partial f_{N-1}}{\partial Q_N}\, dQ_N = -f_{N-1}$$

together with the two given boundary conditions.

It can be readily shown that all the coefficients of the linear system can be grouped into just four vectors thus saving storage. In fact from equation $12'$ it follows that:

$$\frac{\partial f_i}{\partial z_i} = \frac{\partial F_i}{\partial z_i} + \frac{\partial F_i}{\partial Q_i}\frac{\partial Q_i}{\partial z_i} \equiv b_i \tag{16}$$

$$\frac{\partial f_i}{\partial z_{i+1}} = \frac{\partial F_i}{\partial z_{i+1}} + \frac{\partial F_i}{\partial Q_i}\frac{\partial Q_i}{\partial z_{i+1}} + \frac{\partial F_i}{\partial Q_{i+1}}\frac{\partial Q_{i+1}}{\partial z_{i+1}} \equiv a_i \tag{17}$$

and with $j > i + 1$

$$\frac{\partial f_i}{\partial z_j} = \frac{\partial F_i}{\partial Q_i}\frac{\partial Q_i}{\partial z_j} + \frac{\partial F_i}{\partial Q_{i+1}}\frac{\partial Q_{i+1}}{\partial z_j} \tag{18}$$

and

$$\frac{\partial f_i}{\partial Q_N} = \frac{\partial F_i}{\partial Q_i} + \frac{\partial F_i}{\partial Q_{i+1}} \equiv c_i \tag{19}$$

From equation 13 it can be deduced that

$$\frac{\partial Q_i}{\partial z_j} = \frac{\partial Q_{i+1}}{\partial z_j} = \ldots = \frac{\partial Q_{j-1}}{\partial z_j}$$

Then the relationship (18) becomes

$$\frac{\partial f_i}{\partial z_j} = \frac{\partial Q_{j-1}}{\partial z_j}\left(\frac{\partial F_i}{\partial Q_i} + \frac{\partial F_i}{\partial Q_{i+1}}\right) \equiv c_i d_j \tag{18'}$$

The coefficients $\partial f_i/\partial z_i$, $\partial f_i/\partial z_{i+1}$ and $\partial f_i/\partial Q_N$ depend on the index i in relation to the grid element in which the function F is calculated; while the coefficient $\partial f_i/\partial z_j$ depends on the same index i and on the index j in relation to the water level z on the basis of which the function F is derived.

As an example, the case in which water levels and rating curve are the boundary conditions, will now be considered.

By adding the two boundary conditions

$$z_1 = \bar{z}_{,1}(t) \tag{20}$$

$$f_N(z_N, Q_N) = 0$$

to the system (14), and the corresponding expressions

$$dz_1 = 0 \tag{21}$$

$$\frac{\partial f_N}{\partial z_N} \, dz_N + \frac{\partial f_N}{\partial Q_N} \, dQ_N = -f_N$$

to the system (15), the matrix of coefficients becomes a Hessemberg matrix:

$$
\begin{bmatrix}
a_1 & c_1 d_3 & \cdots & c_1 d_{N-1} & c_1 d_N & c_1 \\
b_2 & a_2 & \cdots & c_2 d_{N-1} & c_2 d_N & c_2 \\
 & b_3 & \cdots & c_3 d_{N-1} & c_3 d_N & c_3 \\
 & & \cdots\cdots\cdots\cdots\cdots\cdots\cdots & & & \\
 & & b_{N-1} & & a_{N-1} & c_{N-1} \\
 & & & & b_N & a_N
\end{bmatrix}
\tag{22}
$$

where $b_N = \partial f_N/\partial z_N$ and $a_N = \partial f_N/\partial Q_N$.

By adopting other boundary conditions it is easy to see that the number of rows and columns ranges from $N-1$ to $N+1$ depending on the chosen boundary conditions, but that the form of the matrix always remains a Hessemberg matrix.

The linear system of equations can then be immediately and easily solved by means of the direct factorization method and the complication that often arises in implicit methods, namely the solution of a system of non-linear equations at each time step, no longer exists.

6. Computational experience

The method described has been applied to the study of flood wave propagation in the downstream part of the Arno river from the station at Callone (54 km from the river mouth) to the sea (Figure 3). Other hydrometric stations are operated in this reach and, in particular, at S. Giovanni alla Vena (35.8 km from the river mouth) a rating curve is available.

The morphology of the river bed is well defined by a considerable number of cross-sections (150–300 m apart). The form and dimension of the cross-sections and the bottom slope vary greatly. For each section, described by points of its boundary, all the geometical characteristics have been determined as functions of depth.

Several experiments have been performed in order to determine model sensitivity to the number of cross-sections. To describe the chosen reaches, sections

188

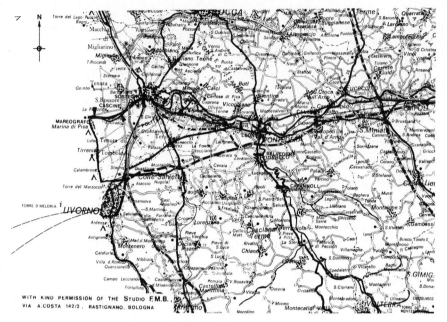

Figure 3. Downstream reach of the Arno river

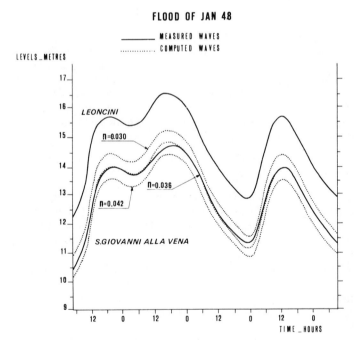

Figure 4. Measured and computed waves using different values of the roughness coefficient 'n'

on an average of 400 m apart are required. Pronounced deviations occur with a smaller number of sections, while with a greater number the results are about identical.

As in other practical cases, water levels and discharges are not recorded in all sections for this reach of the Arno river, and the initial conditions have therefore been obtained by a backwater computation, starting from the known values of water level at the downstream section and assuming the discharge at S. Giovanni alla Vena constant all along the reach.

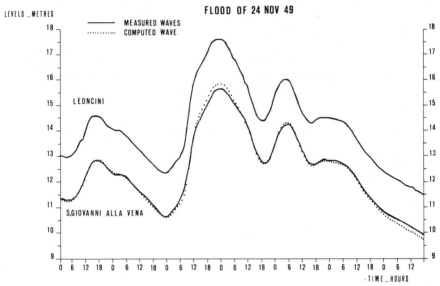

Figure 5. Measured waves at Leoncini and S. Giovanni alla Vena and the computed one at S. Giovanni alla Vena

While the initial conditions were obtained by using a rough approximation the initial conditions influence the solution for only a short time compared to the duration of the phenomenon being studied. Furthermore the importance of these initial errors can be still further reduced by choosing suitable values of the weighting coefficient P_t. As previously pointed out, the coefficient P_t must have, for stability reasons, a value between ½ and 1. Experiments have shown that, assuming $P_t = 1$, the errors introduced in the initial conditions become negligible after fewer time steps than with other values of P_t.

The model has been calibrated using several historical flood waves, on various reaches and with differing boundary conditions. In particular the results relating to two different reaches are reported here: the first from Leoncini (40.6 km from the river mouth) to S. Giovanni alla Vena, the second from Leoncini to Politeama (12.2 km from the river mouth).

Leoncini—S. Giovanni alla Vena reach

In this reach water levels at Leoncini and the rating curve at S. Giovanni alla Vena have been taken as boundary conditions.

190

The setting up of the model and the tests carried out involved determination of water levels during flood events at S. Giovanni alla Vena and comparison between the values thus determined and those measured in this section. The calculations were repeated using different values of the roughness coefficient 'n' (the Manning formula has been adopted in both these examples) until the 'n' value was determined which gave the best fit for the calculated wave and the measured one. Figure 4 shows the comparison between an experimental wave and those obtained from calculation using different 'n' values. A sample wave is represented together with experimental waves in Figure 5.

Leoncini—Politeama reach

Water levels at both the extreme sections have been used as boundary conditions. In this case, the best fit between the computed rating curve at S. Giovanni alla Vena and the measured one permits the value of the Manning coefficient 'n' to be determined as shown in Figure 6. The difference between the computed levels at all

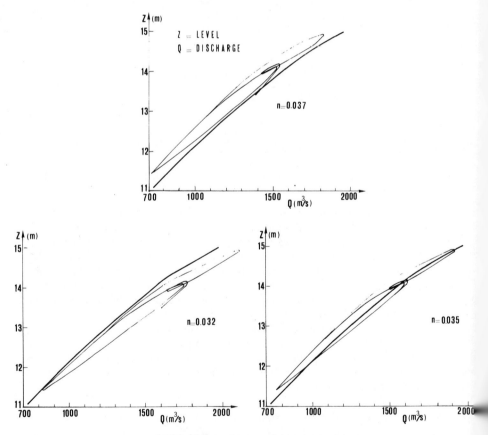

Figure 6. Steady flow rating curve and loop rating curves computed using different values of the roughness coefficient 'n'

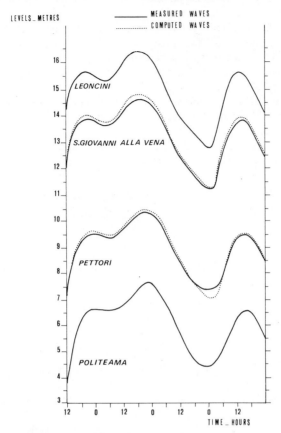

Figure 7. Measured and computed waves at several
stations

the other sections in the reach and the measured ones are small, as shown in
Figure 7.

It should be pointed out that the coefficient 'n' includes all factors which cause
energy losses. Furthermore, besides the friction losses all the other approximations
made in the geometrical description and mathematical formulation of the
phenomenon also affect the value of this parameter; as a result the friction
coefficient has completely lost its original meaning and has become simply a fitting
parameter.

7. Conclusions

On the basis of the results obtained it can be stated that for the numerical solution
of the St Venant equations, the use of an implicit scheme, rather than the
characteristics method or an explicit scheme, is a more efficient approach.

All the experiments demonstrate the validity of the Arno method with regard to efficiency and the storage allocation.

As with all the methods based on the numerical solution of the St Venant equations, the Arno method requires a detailed description of the river bed. Experiments have shown that, to have a sufficient geometrical description, sections about 400 m apart are needed. This geometrical description involves the collection and the management of a large amount of data.

In addition it has to be pointed out that the roughness coefficient has become a fitting parameter. Slight modifications that occur in time in the morphology of the river bed could be taken into account by choosing a new value of the roughness coefficient so as to obtain the best reconstruction of later flood events. By this means it should be possible to avoid frequent new surveys of the river bed.

Appendix. Stability analysis of the adopted numerical scheme

The St Venant equations can be written in the following form:

$$\frac{\partial u}{\partial t} = Mu \tag{23}$$

Bearing in mind the symbology adopted in the text and indicating with

z_0 the river bed elevation

$y = z - z_0$ the water depth

$v = Q/A$ the mean velocity

$S_0 = dz_0/dx$ the bottom slope

$A_x^y = \dfrac{\partial A(x, y)}{\partial x}$ the departure of the bed from prismatic form

the two-dimensional vector u and the 2×2 matrix M are then expressed in the following form:

$$u = \begin{pmatrix} y \\ v \end{pmatrix}, \quad M = \begin{pmatrix} -v\dfrac{\partial}{\partial x} - \dfrac{q}{By} & -\dfrac{A}{B}\dfrac{\partial}{\partial x} - \dfrac{A_x^y}{B} \\ -g\left(\dfrac{\partial}{\partial x} + \dfrac{S_0 - S_f}{y}\right) & -v\dfrac{\partial}{\partial x} \end{pmatrix}$$

For an hyperbolic system, like the St Venant equations, the stability analysis must be made using the heuristic Von Neumann principle. Such a method works only for linear systems, so that the original system must be approximated by a simpler one, obtained by locally linearizing it, that is assuming as constant all the quantities appearing in the expression of M. As a consequence, the stability analysis can be carried out simplifying the matrix M as follows:

$$M_1 = \begin{pmatrix} -v\dfrac{\partial}{\partial x} & -\dfrac{A}{B}\dfrac{\partial}{\partial x} \\[2em] -g\dfrac{\partial}{\partial x} & -v\dfrac{\partial}{\partial x} \end{pmatrix}$$

in which the coefficients of derivatives must be taken as constant. Equation 23 then becomes

$$\frac{\partial u}{\partial t} = M_1 u \tag{24}$$

Using a finite difference approximation for the previous equation, the following expression:

$$\frac{u^{n+1}(x) - u^n(x)}{\Delta t} = L\ [\eta u^{n+1}(x) + (1 - \eta)\ u^n(x)] \tag{25}$$

can be obtained, in which η is a time weighting factor and L a spatial differential operator. After some transformations equation 25 can be written:

$$u^{n+1}(x) = C \cdot u^n(x) \tag{26}$$

in which $u^{n+1}(x)$ is the two-dimensional vector defining the state of the river at the time $(n + 1)\Delta t$ at discrete values of abscissa, and C is expressed in terms of η, Δt and L.

Following the Von Neumann procedure the Fourier expansion of the vector $u(x)$ is considered and the following equation is obtained:

$$\hat{u}(k)^{n+1} = G\hat{u}^n(k) \tag{27}$$

where G, deduced from the matrix C of equation 26, is termed the amplification matrix. The Von Neumann criterion (Richtmyer, 1967) states that the necessary condition for the stability of a linear difference scheme is that the spectral radius of the amplification matrix be less or equal to 1, for any value of k.

We can now analyse, by means of this criterion, the stability of the difference scheme defined by equations 7, 8 and 9 applied to the numerical grid of Figure 2. For simplicity, P_s is here assumed equal to 0.5. Applying this scheme to equation 24, the following expression is obtained for the matrix G:

$$G = \begin{vmatrix} \dfrac{b_1 c_2 - c_1 b_2}{a_1 b_2 - b_1 a_2} & \dfrac{b_1 d_2 - d_1 b_2}{a_1 b_2 - b_1 a_2} \\[4mm] \dfrac{c_1 a_2 - a_1 c_2}{a_1 b_2 - b_1 a_2} & \dfrac{d_1 a_2 - a_1 d_2}{a_1 b_2 - b_1 a_2} \end{vmatrix} \tag{28}$$

where

$$a_1 = 1 + P_t vr \qquad\qquad a_2 = P_t gr$$
$$b_1 = P_t yr \qquad\qquad b_2 = 1 + P_t vr$$
$$c_1 = -1 + (1 - P_t)vr \qquad c_2 = (1 - P_t)\ gr$$
$$d_1 = (1 - P_t)\ yr \qquad\quad d_2 = -1 + (1 - P_t)\ vr$$

and

$$r = i\frac{2\Delta t}{\Delta x}\ tg\ \frac{\Delta x}{2}$$

The two eigenvalues of this matrix are

$$\lambda = \frac{1 + P_t(1 - P_t)\, r^2\,(gy - v^2) - vr + 2P_t vr \pm r\sqrt{(gy)}}{1 + P_t^2 r^2\,(gy - v^2) - 2P_t vr} \tag{29}$$

and its spectral radius is given by the greater module of the two eigenvalues. For simplicity only the three more significative cases are discussed here: $P_t = 0$, $P_t = 1$ and $P_t = 0.5$.

$P_t = 0$ (*Explicit scheme*)

Equation 29 becomes

$$\lambda = 1 - r(v \mp \sqrt{(gy)}) \tag{30}$$

and, as r is a purely imaginary quantity, it follows that $|\lambda| \geqslant 1$, that is the scheme is unstable.

$P_t = 1$ (*Implicit scheme*)

Equation 29 may be written as follows:

$$\lambda = \frac{1 + vr \pm r\sqrt{(gy)}}{(1 + vr)^2 - r^2 gy} = \frac{1}{1 + r(v \mp \sqrt{(gy)})} \tag{31}$$

from which it is seen that $|\lambda| \leqslant 1$ for any value of the quantities, which implies that the scheme is stable in the sense stated by the Von Neumann principle.

$P_t = 0.5$ (*Implicit scheme*)

Equation 29 becomes

$$\lambda = \frac{1 + \dfrac{r^2}{4}\,(gy - v^2) \pm r\sqrt{(gy)}}{1 - \dfrac{r^2}{4}\,(gy - v^2) + rv} \tag{32}$$

from which, noting that r is a purely imaginary quantity, it is easy to see that $|\lambda| = 1$ for any values of the quantities. Thus this scheme also is stable in the sense of the Von Neumann principle.

Unsteady Free-surface Flow Problems

DAVID A. WOOLHISER
US Department of Agriculture, Agricultural Research Service, CSU Foothills
Campus, Fort Collins, Colorado, USA

1. Introduction

Unsteady, free-surface flow as overland or open channel flow is the most dynamic part of the response of a watershed to precipitation. Floods are almost invariably caused by direct surface runoff from rainfall, melting snow or a combination of the two. Therefore, designs for flood control structures or non-structural measures to reduce flood damage must utilize estimates of flood peak rates and frequencies. On the many small agricultural and urban watersheds that have no discharge records the engineer must utilize mathematical models along with rainfall data to make such estimates. In this paper we will consider one important part of hydrologic models — overland flow.

Although the term 'overland flow' is frequently used in reference to very shallow flow over plane surfaces, a less restrictive definition will be used herein. Overland flow will refer to all those flows for which the model discussed in this paper is a useful abstraction. It will include thin sheet flow over plane surfaces and may also include flows over rilled and irregular surfaces or flow in small channels. No precise definition of the boundary between overland flow and channel flow will be given because such a separation is purely operational.

2. The equations of spatially-varied, unsteady flow over a plane

The equations of spatially-varied, unsteady flow over a plane describe many of the important aspects of overland flow. The problem under consideration is shown in Figure 1. A plane of unit width, length L_0 and slope S_0 is receiving rainfall at a rate $i(x,t)$ per unit area. Water is infiltrating at a rate $i_r(x,t)$. The net rate of lateral inflow is

$$q(x,\ t) = i(x,\ t) - i_r(x,\ t) \tag{1}$$

Flow is assumed to be one-dimensional and the dependent variables are the local

Adapted from Chapter 12, *Simulation of Unsteady Flow*, by D. A. Woolhiser, *Unsteady Flow in Open Channels*, Proceedings of Institute on Unsteady Flow in Open Channels, Colorado State University, July 17–28, 1974. Water Resources Publications, For Collins, Colorado.

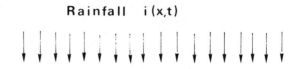

Rainfall i (x,t)

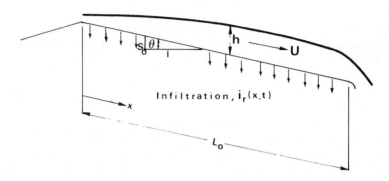

Figure 1. Definition sketch of overland flow on a plane

mean velocity, U, and the local depth, h. The continuity equation is

$$\frac{\partial h}{\partial t} + \frac{\partial (Uh)}{\partial x} = q(x, t) \tag{2}$$

and the momentum equation is

$$\frac{\partial U}{\partial t} + U\frac{\partial U}{\partial x} + g\frac{\partial h}{\partial x} = g(S_0 - S_f) - \frac{U}{h}q(x, t) \tag{3}$$

where S_f is the friction slope. This formulation assumes that over pressure introduced by rainfall is negligible and that the velocity component of the rainfall in the x direction is zero. The obvious assumptions that the sine of the slope angle, θ, is approximately equal to the tangent and that the velocity distribution coefficient β is equal to one, are also included.

To investigate the important properties of this model we will consider a very simple case. We will assume that the plane is impervious and that the rainfall rate is not a function of x or t.

By writing equations 2 and 3 in dimensionless form, the number of parameters can be reduced from five to two with obvious advantages in the graphical portrayal of results.

Experience has shown that the following normalizing quantities are useful.

Normalizing lengths:

L_0 = length of plane

H_0 = normal depth at $x = L_0$ and a flow rate of qL_0.

Normalizing velocity:

$$U_0 = qL_0/H_0 = C\sqrt{(H_0 S_0)} \quad \text{(if the Chézy relationship is used).}$$

Define the following dimensionless variables

$$b^* = \frac{b}{H_0}; \quad U^* = \frac{U}{U_0}; \quad x^* = \frac{x}{L_0}; \quad t^* = \frac{tU_0}{L_0}$$

and $q^* = q/q_0 = 1$, where q_0 is the maximum lateral inflow rate.

By substituting the dimensionless variables into equations 2 and 3 we obtain:

$$\frac{\partial b^*}{\partial t^*} + \frac{\partial(U^* b^*)}{\partial x^*} = 1 \tag{4}$$

$$\frac{\partial U^*}{\partial t^*} + U^* \frac{\partial U^*}{\partial x^*} + \frac{1}{F_0^2}\frac{\partial b^*}{\partial x^*} = \frac{S_0 L_0}{H_0 F_0^2}\left(1 - \frac{U^{*2}}{b^*}\right) - \frac{U^*}{b^*} \tag{5}$$

where

$$F_0 = \frac{U_0}{\sqrt{(gH_0)}} \quad \text{(Froude number)}$$

The dimensionless parameter $S_0 L_0/H_0 F_0^2$ can be interpreted as half the ratio of the total potential energy drop along the plane to the normal energy head at the downstream boundary. Suitable boundary conditions for this problem are the dry initial condition:

$$b^*(x^*, 0) = U^*(x^*, 0) = 0$$

The condition of zero flux at the upper boundary

$$U^*(0, t) = 0 \tag{6}$$

and the critical depth lower boundary condition:

$$U^*(1, t^*) = C^*(1, t^*)$$

if

$$U^*(1 - \Delta x^*, t^*) \leqslant C^*(1 - \Delta x^*, t^*)$$

where $C^* = \sqrt{(b^*)}/F_0$ and $\Delta x^* \to 0$. No lower boundary condition is required if the flow is supercritical.

3. Solutions of overland flow equations

Numerical solutions of equations 4 and 5 reveal interesting properties of the rising hydrograph. As the parameter $S_0 L_0/H_0 F_0^2$, which we shall now denote by k, the kinematic flow number, increases, the solution converges very rapidly toward that for $k = \infty$. The effect of varying the parameter k while holding F_0 constant is shown in Figure 2(a). For $F_0 = 1$ the maximum error between the rising hydrographs for $k = 10$ and $k = \infty$ is of the order of 10%. The effect of varying F_0 while $|k|$ is held constant is shown for three values of k in Figure 2(b), (c) and (d). For $k = 1$, the

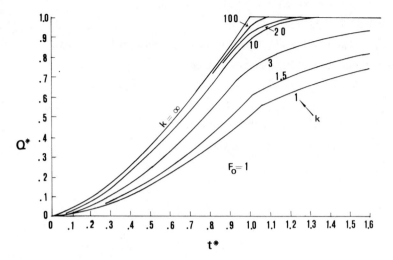

Figure 2(a). The rising hydrograph-variation with k and F_0 : Variation with k. (From Woolhiser and Liggett, 1967)

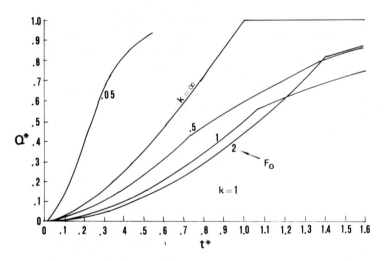

Figure 2(b). The rising hydrograph-variation with k and F_0 : Variation with F_0, $k = 1$

rising hydrographs are very complicated and obviously cannot be represented by a single dimensionless hydrograph. However, as the parameter k increases, the rising hydrographs for different values of F_0 approach the dimensionless hydrograph for $k = \infty$.

The effect of varying k on the steady state celerity and velocity profile is shown in Figure 3. As k increases, both profiles converge on the profile for $k = \infty$.

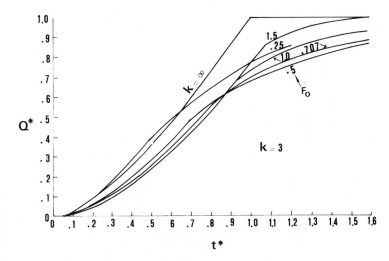

Figure 2(c). The rising hydrograph-variation with k and F_0: Variation with F_0, k = 3

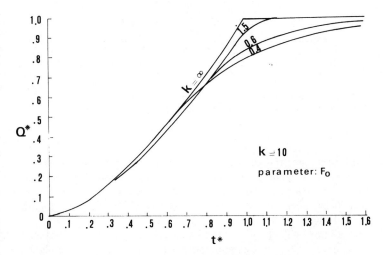

Figure 2(d). The rising hydrograph-variation with k and F_0: Variation with F_0, k = 10

What is the physical significance of the $k = \infty$ case? An examination of equation 5 shows that if all terms in the equation are divided by k, the momentum equation reduces to the following as k approaches infinity

$$b^* = U^{*2} \tag{7}$$

This is the dimensionless Chézy equation. Therefore, there is a unique relationship

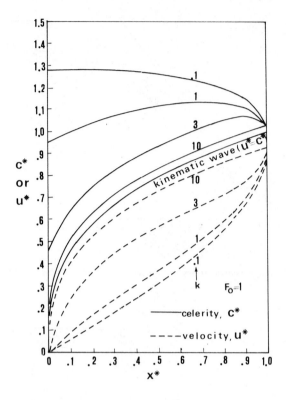

Figure 3. Celerity and velocity profiles: Variation with
k. (From Woolhiser and Liggett, 1967)

between depth and discharge, and the depth is the normal depth for uniform flow
at that discharge. When k is large the solution to equations 4 and 5 can be closely
approximated by the solutions to equations 4 and 7. This is the kinematic wave
approximation which has been described in detail by several investigators (Lighthill
and Whitham, 1955; Iwagaki, 1955).

A few quick calculations will show that the kinematic approximation is excellent
for most cases of overland flow. For example, the parameter k is 7.4 for a plane 20
feet long, with a slope of 0.00025, Manning's n of 0.01 and a lateral inflow rate of
5 inches per hour. A plane this short, flat and smooth would be highly unusual in
hydrologic applications.

4. Kinematic wave solutions for simple watershed geometry

The kinematic wave equations have an important advantage over the shallow water
equations for describing overland flow; analytic solutions are possible for simple
geometries. A great deal of insight into the phenomenon of overland flow can be
gained by studying these solutions.

For overland flow on a plane as shown in Figure 1, the dimensional kinematic wave equations are

$$\frac{\partial h}{\partial t} + \frac{\partial (Uh)}{\partial x} = q(x, t) \tag{8}$$

and

$$S_0 = S_f \tag{9}$$

Equation 9 can be written in the convenient Darcy—Weisbach form

$$U = \sqrt{\left(\frac{8g}{f} S_0 h\right)} \tag{10}$$

where f is a friction factor. In solving for hydrographs from simple watershed geometries we will assume the following parametric relationship

$$U = \alpha h^{m-1} \tag{11}$$

We shall examine appropriate friction relationships and their implications in a later section.

Equation 11 can be substituted into equation 8 to obtain a partial differential equation with one dependent variable

$$\frac{\partial h}{\partial t} + \alpha \frac{\partial h^m}{\partial x} = q(x, t) \tag{12}$$

Equation 12 which is a partial differential equation can be transformed into the characteristic form in the following manner. Along the solution surface the following expression for the total derivative holds:

$$dh = \frac{\partial h}{\partial x} dx + \frac{\partial h}{\partial t} dt \tag{13}$$

Both equations 12 and 13 must hold simultaneously so in matrix notation we have

$$\begin{bmatrix} 1 & \alpha m h^{m-1} \\ dt & dx \end{bmatrix} \cdot \begin{bmatrix} \dfrac{\partial h}{\partial t} \\ \dfrac{\partial h}{\partial x} \end{bmatrix} = \begin{bmatrix} q(x, t) \\ dh \end{bmatrix} \tag{14}$$

By equating the square matrix on the left side to zero we obtain the equation of the characteristic ground curve

$$\frac{dx}{dt} = \alpha m h^{m-1} = mU \tag{15}$$

The compatability condition (which ensures an infinite number of solutions of the simultaneous equations) yields

$$\frac{dh}{dt} = q(x, t) \tag{16}$$

which holds to the direction specified by equation 15.

202

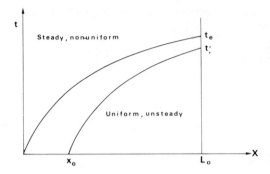

Figure 4. Solution domain

If we consider the simple case of spatially invariant rainfall on an impervious surface beginning at a constant rate, i, at time $t = 0$ and continuing until $t = \infty$, we can solve the above two equations to obtain the solution to the rising hydrograph. Consider the characteristic emanating from $(x_0, 0)$ and intersecting the line $x = L_0$ at time t', as shown in Figure 4. If the plane is initially dry, i.e. $h = 0$ at $t = 0$, integration of equation 16 gives

$$h = it \tag{17}$$

or

$$Q = Uh = \alpha(it)^m \tag{18}$$

The presence of the upstream boundary along which $h = 0$ is not detected at $x = L_0$ until the characteristic originating at $(0,0)$ arrives. This time can be found by solving equation 15. Substituting the expression for h from equation 17 into equation 15

$$\frac{dx}{dt} = \alpha m (it)^{m-1} \tag{19}$$

$$x = \alpha i^{m-1} t^m + C \tag{20}$$

The constant of integration is zero, because when $x = 0$, $t = 0$. Therefore

$$t_e = \left(\frac{L_0}{\alpha i^{m-1}} \right)^{1/m} \tag{21}$$

The equation for the response of a plane to a step input is therefore

$$\left. \begin{array}{l} Q = \alpha(it)^m ; \quad 0 \leqslant t \leqslant \left(\dfrac{L_0}{\alpha i^{m-1}} \right)^{1/m} \\[4mm] Q = iL_0 ; \quad \left(\dfrac{L_0}{\alpha i^{m-1}} \right)^{1/m} < t < \infty \end{array} \right\} \tag{22}$$

The flow in the domain bounded by the limiting characteristic (beginning at $(0,0)$), the line $t = 0$ and the line $x = L_0$ is uniform and unsteady. Outside this area the flow is steady but non-uniform.

The hydrograph of the recession from equilibrium can be found by assuming that at some time, $t_0 > t_e$ the inflow ceases. Solution of equation 16 gives

$$b = b_0 \qquad (23)$$

which is valid along the characteristic

$$x = x_0 + \alpha m b_0^{m-1}(t - t_0) \qquad (24)$$

where b_0 is the equilibrium depth at (x_0, t_0). The expression for the equilibrium depth

$$b_0 = \left(\frac{ix_0}{\alpha}\right)^{1/m} \qquad (25)$$

can be substituted into equation 24 giving

$$x = x_0 + \alpha m \left(\frac{ix_0}{\alpha}\right)^{(m-1)/m}(t - t_0) \qquad (26)$$

On the downstream boundary $x = L_0$ and $Q = \alpha b_0^m = ix_0$. Therefore, the relationship between discharge and time for the recession can be written by substitution into equation 26

$$Q - iL_0 + im\alpha^{1/m} Q^{(m-1)/m}(t - t_0) = 0; \qquad t_0 < t \qquad (27)$$

Rising hydrographs defined by equation 18 and recession hydrographs defined by equation 27 are shown in Figure 5.

When the duration of rainfall is shorter than the equilibrium time, t_e, a 'partial

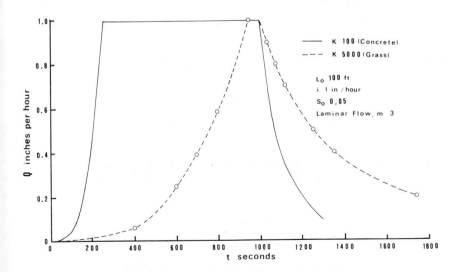

Figure 5. Equilibrium, rising and recession hydrographs

204

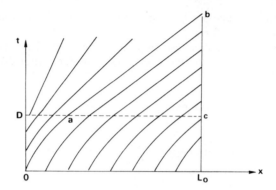

Figure 6. Solution domain — partial equilibrium

equilibrium' hydrograph results. The characteristics of partial equilibrium hydrographs can be readily derived by considering the characteristic shown in Figure 6.

Suppose that rainfall begins at rate i at $t = 0$, and continues until $t = D$. For $t > D$, $i = 0$. Equation 17 is valid along the characteristics beginning at $(0,0)$ described by equation 20 with $C = 0$. At point a and along the line ac, $b = iD$. The equation of the rising segment of the hydrograph from $0 \leqslant t \leqslant D$ is given by equation 18. The outflow rate is a constant in the interval $D \leqslant t \leqslant b$ because $db/dt = 0$ along all characteristics when $t > D$. When $t > b$ the recession hydrograph is identical to a recession from equilibrium beginning at $t = D$ because the depth profile along the line Da is an equilibrium profile.

From equation 20 it can be seen that the distance ac is given by

$$ac = L_0 - \alpha i^{m-1} D^m \tag{28}$$

The slope of the characteristic at point a is

$$\frac{dx}{dt} = \alpha m (iD)^{m-1} \tag{29}$$

The time interval cb is then given by the following equation:

$$cb = \frac{(iD)^{1-m}}{\alpha m} [L_0 - \alpha i^{m-1} D^m] \tag{30}$$

$$= \frac{L_0 (iD)^{1-m}}{\alpha m} - \frac{D}{m}$$

The equation for the partial equilibrium hydrograph for a rain of duration $D < t_e$ can thus be written as:

$$\left.\begin{array}{l} Q = \alpha (it)^m; \quad 0 \leqslant t \leqslant D \\[2mm] Q = \alpha (iD)^m; \quad D \leqslant t \leqslant D + \dfrac{L_0 (iD)^{1-m}}{\alpha m} - \dfrac{D}{m} \\[3mm] Q - iL_0 + im\alpha^{1/m} Q^{(m-1)/m} (t - D) = 0; \quad D + \dfrac{L_0 (iD)^{1-m}}{\alpha m} - \dfrac{D}{m} < t \end{array}\right\} \tag{31}$$

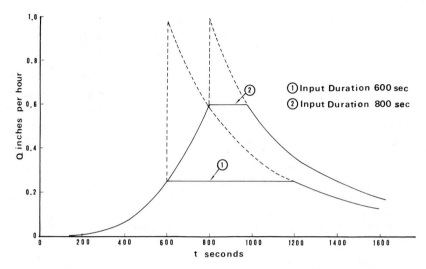

Figure 7. Partial equilibrium hydrographs. $K = 5000$, $L_0 = 100$ ft, $i = 1$ inch per hour, $S_0 = 0.05$, $m = 3$

A family of partial equilibrium hydrographs is shown in Figure 7. The flat top is a characteristic of the partial equilibrium hydrograph from a plane. The hydrograph has a sharp peak when $D = t_e$ and again has a flat top when $D > t_\epsilon$.

5. Hydraulic resistance in overland flow

Resistance to rainfall-induced overland flow over natural and man-made surfaces may be influenced by several factors. Boundary roughness is frequently much greater than that encountered in ordinary hydraulic structures. At low rates of flow the roughness elements protrude through the free water surface, and at high rates of flow the boundary geometry may change in time and distance because of erosion or because the vegetation is bent over by the flowing water. The impact of raindrops may also have an important effect. On vegetated surfaces the plant leaves and stems may offer more resistance to flow than the soil roughness.

In the past 30 years there have been many laboratory and field investigations aimed at finding the relative importance of the above factors or the appropriate resistance formulae and methods of parameter estimation.

In laboratory studies the most popular approach has been to assume that the Darcy–Weisbach resistance law (equation 10) is appropriate and then to estimate the friction factor, f, using measurements of the depth, discharge and slope.

For laminar flow over a smooth surface the theoretical relationship between the friction factor and Reynolds number is

$$f = 24/R_e \tag{32}$$

For laminar flow over rough surfaces a similar relation has been observed:

$$f = K/R_e; \quad K > 24 \tag{33}$$

where K is a parameter related to the characteristics of the surface and can become very large (40 000) for dense turf. With raindrop impact it appears that the parameter K can be approximated by

$$K = K_0 + Ai^b \tag{34}$$

where K_0 is the parameter without rainfall and A and b are empirical parameters. When i is in inches per hour, the coefficient A is of the order of 10 and the exponent b is approximately unity. Obviously if the surface is smooth ($K_0 = 24$) the raindrop impact effect is important. However, it becomes insignificant for vegetated surfaces.

Transition to an apparently turbulent regime has been reported at Reynolds numbers ranging from 100 to 1000. The higher transition Reynolds numbers, R_T, were usually associated with smooth surfaces. The most frequently cited R_T values are in the range $300 < R_T < 500$.

A number of resistance laws have been used for turbulent flow. The Manning formula

$$U = \frac{1.49}{n} S^{1/2} b^{2/3} \tag{35}$$

has been used most frequently.

Another frequently used relation is the Chézy formula

$$U = C\sqrt{(bs)}$$
$$f = 8g/C^2 \tag{36}$$

where C is the Chézy resistance coefficient.

It is not feasible to measure directly the depth of flow over very rough surfaces or in field studies. Therefore, the friction factor must be obtained by inference from the steady state detention storage, from analysis of the rising hydrograph or by optimization techniques utilizing some function of the difference between observed and computed hydrographs for the objective function.

The steady state detention storage can be measured experimentally by integrating the measured recession hydrograph. The analytical expression is obtained by integrating equation 25. The mean detention depth $\bar{b}$, is then given by

$$\bar{b} = \int_0^{L_0} \frac{b(x)dx}{L_0} = \frac{1}{L_0} \int_0^{L_0} \left(\frac{ix}{\alpha}\right)^{1/m} dx \tag{37}$$

$$\bar{b} = \left(\frac{i}{\alpha}\right)^{1/m} \left(\frac{m}{m+1}\right) L_0^{1/m} \tag{38}$$

For laminar flow, $m = 3$ and $\alpha = 8gs/K\nu$ where K is the parameter defined in equation 33. Substituting these identities into equation 38 and solving for K we obtain

$$K = \left(\frac{4}{3}\right)^3 \frac{8gs}{\nu L_0 i} \bar{b}^3 \tag{39}$$

where $\bar{b}$ is the measured detention depth.

This method of experimentally finding the value of K_0 requires that the flow be laminar for all $x < L_0$. Raindrop impact effect will also be included. The parameters A and b in equation 34 can be estimated by performing experiments with several rainfall intensities.

The exponent m and the parameter K can also be estimated from the rising hydrograph from a plane surface. For laminar flow the equation for the rising hydrograph is

$$Q = \frac{8gS_0}{K\nu} i^m t^m \tag{40}$$

Let

$$Q' = \frac{Q\nu}{8gS_0 i^m}$$

then

$$\log Q' = m \log t - \log K \tag{41}$$

If Q' and t obtained from experimental data are plotted on logarithmic graph paper, m and K can be obtained graphically. Examples of similar plots (Q versus t) are shown in Figure 8(a) and (b) for experiments on an asphalt and a turf covered plane. The change in slope of the logarithmic hydrograph may indicate a change in the flow regime for the turf plane whereas it appears that the flow on the asphalt plane was essentially laminar for these runs.

For experimental watersheds or plots that have geometries other than a plane or under natural rainfall the rising hydrograph and the equilibrium detention are very complex; therefore optimization techniques must be utilized for parameter

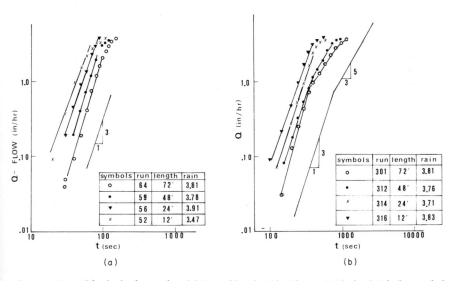

Figure 8. Logarithmic hydrographs. (a) Run 64, 59, 56, 52; $s = 0.01$, $i = 3.8$ in/hr; asphalt plane. (b) Run 301, 312, 314, 316; $s = 0.01$, $i = 3.8$ in/hr; turf plane. (After Morgali, 1970)

estimation. In this method the form of the friction law is assumed and starting parameter values are estimated. Equation 8 is then solved numerically and an objective function is evaluated. The parameters are then adjusted by some optimization scheme until the objective function is minimized. One objective function that is frequently used and is appropriate for parameter estimation for single events is

$$F(K, A, b) = \sum_{i=1}^{n} [Q_0(i\Delta t) - Q_c(i\Delta t)]^2 \qquad (42)$$

where the subscripts o and c refer to observed and computed discharge respectively and Δt is a fixed time increment. If a set of N runoff events is available for analysis the objective function could incorporate the sum of squares of deviation between observed and computed peak rates.

Table 1. Resistance parameters for overland flow

Surface	Laminar flow K_0	Turbulent flow	
		Manning n	Chézy C
Concrete or asphalt	24–108	0.01 –0.013	73–38
Bare sand	30–120	0.01 –0.016	65–33
Gravelled surface	90–400	0.012–0.03	38–18
Bare clay–loam soil (eroded)	100–500	0.012–0.033	36–16
Sparse vegetation	1000–4000	0.053–0.13	11–5
Short grass prairie	3000–10 000	0.10 –0.20	6.5–3.6
Bluegrass sod	7000–40 000	0.17 –0.48	4.2–1.8

Values of the laminar resistance parameter K_0 and of Manning's n and Chézy's C for typical surfaces are shown in Table 1. The tabulated values are ranges found in the literature and were obtained by the techniques described above, utilizing data from controlled experiments or from small experimental watersheds. The Chézy C values were obtained by equating laminar and turbulent friction factors at a transition Reynolds number of 500. Manning's n was estimated in the same way for all but the concrete and asphalt surfaces. The slope was taken as 0.05 and the kinematic viscosity was 1.2×10^{-5}. Most of these values were obtained for small areas such as plots or very small watersheds and are undoubtedly biased. One might expect that lower friction factors would be found for larger watersheds with the same vegetative cover because of a greater concentration of runoff in rills and small channels.

Raindrop disturbance parameters A and b from Equation 34 found in the literature are shown in Table 2.

Table 2. Rainfall disturbance parameters

A	b	Source
5.67	4/3	Izzard (1944)
27.2	0.4	Li (1972)
10.0	1.0	Fawkes (1972)

6. Numerical methods for solving kinematic equations for overland flow

Although the kinematic wave equations can be solved analytically unless shocks are present, numerical solutions are more convenient when lateral inflow rates change with time, distance or both. Three finite difference schemes for these equations are shown in Table 3.

All of these methods have been used successfully. The single-step Lax–Wendroff method has second order accuracy and will have the smallest errors of approximation for a given Δx and Δt. The four-point implicit method is unconditionally stable so may save some computation time if larger time steps are used. However, the finite difference equation is non-linear in h_j^{i+1} and must be solved by an iterative technique. If convergence of this iterative scheme is slow the advantage of unconditional stability may be only apparent.

7. Hydrologic applications

Numerical models based upon the shallow water equations or the kinematic wave approximation can be used to calculate runoff hydrographs resulting from rainfall on urban or agricultural watersheds. The kinematic wave approximation is certainly adequate for overland flow and is preferred to the shallow water equations because of its inherent simplicity. Care must be used if the kinematic approximation is to be used for channel flow because it cannot account for backwater effects. Either model has advantages over the unit hydrograph approach for predicting runoff for ungauged watersheds because the model structure and resistance parameters can be estimated without prior rainfall and runoff records.

The first step in applying these models is to decide upon the model geometry. Two approaches have been used. The first attempts to maintain a close geometric similarity between the prototype watershed and the idealized network or cascade of planes and channels that specify the model geometry (Harley, Perkins and Eagleson, 1970). The second approach represents all watersheds, regardless of their complexity, by simple geometric elements such as a combination of two planes and a channel or a linearly converging section (Wooding, 1966).

An example of the geometric simplification involved in the first approach is shown in Figure 9. In this example a parking lot is represented by six overland flow planes that contribute lateral inflow to three swale (channel) flow elements. If the kinematic wave equations are used, the hydrographs for each of the planes can be computed first, then the hydrographs at the downstream boundary of each channel could be computed with the time varying outflow of the planes treated as lateral

Table 3. Rectangular grid finite difference schemes*

Method	Finite difference equation	Order of approximation	Linear stability criterion
Single-step Lax–Wendroff	$b_j^{i+1} = b_j^i - \alpha\Delta t \left[\dfrac{(b_{j+1}^{im} - b_{j-1}^{im})}{2\Delta x} - \dfrac{1}{2}\alpha(q_{j+1}^i + q_{j-1}^i) \right] + \dfrac{\Delta t^2 m}{4\Delta x}\alpha \left\{ (b_{j+1}^{im-1} + b_j^{im-1}) \left[\alpha\dfrac{(b_{j+1}^{im} - b_j^{im})}{\Delta x} - \dfrac{1}{2}(q_{j+1}^i + q_j^i) \right] - (b_j^{im-1} + b_{j-1}^{im-1}) \left[\alpha\dfrac{(b_j^{im} - b_{j-1}^{im})}{\Delta x} - \dfrac{1}{2}(q_j^i + q_{j-1}^i) \right] + \dfrac{2\Delta x}{\alpha m\Delta t}(q_j^{i+1} - q_j^i) \right\}$	$0(\Delta x)^2$	$\dfrac{\Delta t}{\Delta x} \leqslant \dfrac{1}{\alpha m h^{m-1}}$
Upstream differencing	$b_j^{i+1} = b_j^i + m\alpha\dfrac{\Delta t}{\Delta x}(b_j^{im} - b_{j-1}^{im}) + q_j^i\,\Delta t$	$0(\Delta x)$	$\dfrac{\Delta t}{\Delta x} \leqslant \dfrac{1}{2.75\alpha m b^{m-1}}$
Brakensiek's four-point implicit	$\dfrac{b_j^{i+1} - b_j^i + b_{j-1}^{i+1} - b_{j-1}^i}{2\Delta t} + \dfrac{\alpha}{\Delta x}(b_j^{i+1m} - b_{j-1}^{i+1m}) - 1/4(q_{j-1}^{i+1} + q_j^{i+1} + q_{j-1}^i + q_j^i) = 0$	$0(\Delta x)$	Unconditionally stable

* Adapted from Kibler and Woolhiser, 1970.

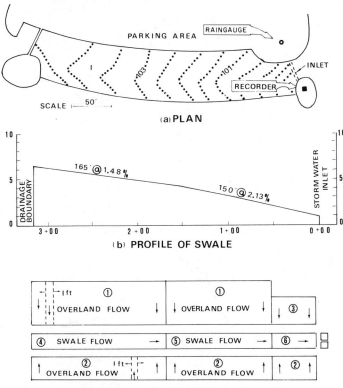

(a) PLAN

(b) PROFILE OF SWALE

(c) SCHEMATIC REPRESENTATION OF DRAINAGE PLAN

Component	Length (ft)	Width or Dia (ft)	Slope (ft/ft)	Side Slope	Inflow to Component	
					Lateral inflow	Upstream inflow
①	36	1	.019	—	Rainfall	—
②	20	1	.0167	—	Rainfall	—
③	25	1	.019	—	Rainfall	—
④	165	—	.0148	113 : 1	① and ②	—
⑤	100	—	.0213	113 : 1	① and ②	④
⑥	50	—	.0213	113 : 1	② and ③	⑤

(d) PHYSICAL CHARACTERISTICS OF COMPONENTS IN THE SCHEMATIC REPRESENTATION

Figure 9. Geometric characteristics of small urban area (after Schaake, 1965)

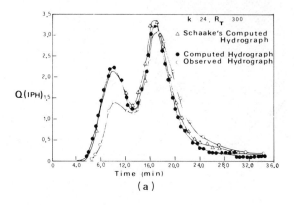

(a)

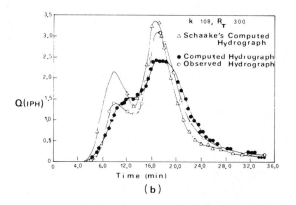

(b)

Figure 10. Comparison of measured and synthesized run-off hydrographs — urban area

inflow to the channel and with the discharge from the upstream channel section as the upstream boundary condition. Appropriate resistance parameters can be selected from Table 1. Hydrographs obtained by an explicit numerical solution of the kinematic wave equations are shown in Figure 10. The friction parameters were chosen as the extremes for paved surfaces shown in Table 1. The transition Reynolds number, R_T, was 500. The observed peak discharge lies between the discharges computed for the extreme values of the friction factor. Schaake obtained his hydrograph by solving the 'complete' equations numerically. The close agreement between Schaak's solution and the kinematic hydrograph reinforces the conclusion that the kinematic model is adequate for overland flow.

An example of the representation of an agricultural watershed by cascades of planes and channels is shown in Figure 11.

Simple kinematic models of overland flow are now being used in hydrologic practice. These models will be especially useful in design situations where they can

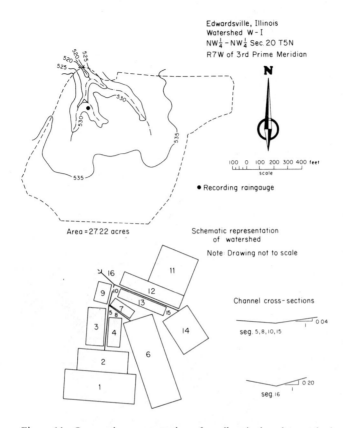

Figure 11. Geometric representation of small agricultural watershed

be used to determine the effect of detention storage or drainage design on peak discharge rates from urban watersheds. In rural areas they will be useful in evaluating the hydrologic effects of terraces, diversions and detention structures and in predicting peak runoff rates where no data are available for identifying simpler models or for developing regionalized information.

WMO Project on Intercomparison of Conceptual Models used in Operational Hydrological Forecasting

WORLD METEOROLOGICAL ORGANIZATION (WMO)
United Nations, Geneva, Switzerland

1. Introduction

The possibility of assembling various physical concepts of the elements of the hydrological cycle in connected phases of the runoff process, and eventually in a simulation of catchment behaviour using a conceptual model, can result in significant improvement in hydrological forecasting and prediction. The rapid development of this approach, in its various forms, has resulted in a great number of different types of models which are described in the various publications. National services in charge of hydrological forecasting, unless they develop a suitable model themselves, face the difficulty of ascertaining the relative advantages and disadvantages of the many models proposed for operational use. Model testing is taking place in several countries of the world, but only large services with sufficient logistic support in manpower, software and hardware are in a position to conduct such tests extensively.

In view of this, and in order to meet several other related needs, WMO initiated a project for an internationally co-ordinated intercomparison of the use of conceptual models for operational hydrological forecasting. The Co-ordinating Council of the International Hydrological Decade supported the idea of this project, which was implemented in response to a recommendation of the third session of the WMO Commission for Hydrology, as approved by the Executive Committee of WMO.

2. Aim of the project

The aim of the project was defined as follows:

— to proceed with an intercomparison of conceptual hydrological models which use electronic computers to provide short-term forecasts of streamflow;
— to provide information and guidance on the use of such models in various forecasting situations, with regard to specific conditions and accuracy requirements.

Published by WMO as *Operational Hydrology Report No. 7*, WMO No. 429, Geneva, 1975.

It is to be emphasized that the objective of the project was not to find the model which fits best in all circumstances.

3. Implementation plan

The implementation plan of the project was divided into three phases, the preliminary phase, the intercomparison phase and the reporting phase.

4. The preliminary phase

The plan of action of the project was formulated on the basis of three informal study group meetings covering all geographical areas of the world and including experts directly involved in the subject. These meetings were held in Washington, D.C., Paris and Tokyo. A detailed description of the project and the plans that have been drawn up is given in a WMO report entitled 'Intercomparison of Conceptual Models for Purposes of Hydrological Forecasting—Background Report and Plan of Implementation' which was circulated, together with a 'Questionnaire on Operational Conceptual Models for use in Short-Term Hydrological Forecasting', to all WMO Member countries concerned in 1971. In reply to this questionnaire 21 models were submitted by nine Member countries.

5. The intercomparison phase

A 'Meeting of Experts' (Geneva, October, 1972) proposed 19 of the submitted models for inclusion in the intercomparison. For various reasons, only ten models were actually tested in the project. The tested models as well as the standard data sets tested on them are given in Table 1.

Following the recommendations of the meeting of experts, 13 river basin data sets were collected by the WMO Secretariat from seven countries. These sets were sent to each model owner who identified and ranked, in order of preference, the data sets which could be tested on his model. On the basis of the answers received, six standard data sets from climatologically and geographically varied basins in six countries were chosen to be tested, as a maximum, on the participating models. These were the Bird Creek (Oklahoma, USA, 2344 km^2), the Bikin River (coastal region, USSR, 13 100 km^2), the Wollombi Brook (Australia, 1580 km^2), the Kizu River (Kiuki region, Japan, 1445 km^2), the Sanaga River (at Edea, Cameroun, 131 500 km^2) and the Nam Mune River (above Ubol, Thailand, 104 000 km^2).

As proposed by the meeting of experts several graphical and statistical verification criteria were used in the evaluation and intercomparison of the simulations produced by the participating models. The graphical criteria included linear scale plots of simulated and observed hydrographs, double mass plots of simulated versus observed monthly discharge volumes, flow duration curves of both simulated and observed daily discharges and scatter diagrams of simulated versus observed monthly maximum discharges. The statistical verification criteria comprised the computation of the coefficient of variation of residual of errors, the ratio of relative and absolute error to the mean, the arithmetic mean, the phasing coefficient and the coefficient of persistence. These statistical coefficients were

Model name (and abbreviation)	Name and address of model developer	Standard data sets tested on the model					
		Bird Creek	Bikin River	Wollombi Brook	Kizu River	Sanaga River	Nam Mune River
Commonwealth Bureau of Meteorology Model (CBM)	Commonwealth Bureau of Meteorology P.O. Box 1289 K, *Melbourne*, Vic. 3001, Australia	X	X	X	X		
GIRARD 1	ORSTOM, 19 rue E. Carrière, 75018 *Paris*, France	X	X				
Serial Storage Type Model (Tank I)	National Research Center for Disaster Prevention, 1 Ginza Higasi 6, Chuo-ku, *Tokyo*, Japan	X	X	X	X	X	X
Serial Storage Type Model (Tank II)	ditto	X		X			
The Flood Forecasting Model (IMH2-SSVP)	Institute of Meteorology and Hydrology, Sos. Bucaresti-Ploiesti 97, *Bucarest*, Romania	X	X				
Streamflow Synthesis and Reservoir Regulation (SSARR)	Corps of Engineers, *Portland*, Oregon, USA	X	X		X	X	X
National Weather Service Hydrologic (NWSH) Model	National Weather Service, *Silver Spring*, Maryland, USA	X		X	X	X	
Sacramento River Forecast Centre Hydrologic Model (SRFCH)	National Weather Service River Forecast Center, *Sacramento*, California, USA	X		X	X	X	
Rainfall Runoff Model of the Hydrometeorological Research Centre of the USSR (HMC)	Hydrometeorological Center of the USSR, Bolsevistskaja 13, *Moscow* 123376, USSR	X	X	X			
Constrained Linear Systems (CLS)	IBM Scientific Center, Via S. Marie 67, *Pisa*, Italy, and Hydraulic Institute of Pavia University, Piazza Leonardo da Vinci, *Pavia*, Italy	X	X	X	X	X	X

indicated for mean daily discharge, maximum monthly discharge, monthly volumes of flow and mean daily discharge for low flow days.

6. The reporting phase

A restricted technical conference, attended by representatives of agencies partici-pating in the project and also several invited experts, was organized by WMO in Geneva from 8 to 12 July, 1974. The Conference considered the results of the project and prepared conclusions and recommendations to national authorities in need of guidance on this subject.

The results of the project, including the proceedings of the technical conference and its conclusions and recommendations, will be published by WMO in the form of a technical report for circulation to all concerned.

The main conclusions and recommendations adopted by the Conference are given below.

7. Evaluation and comparison of the performance of the models submitted for intercomparison and conclusions on the use of models in various forecasting situations

The models submitted for intercomparison were divided into three groups displaying the following characteristics:

(a) Explicit moisture accounting.
(b) Implicit moisture accounting.
(c) Systems approach with the use of indices.

The modellers classified their models, in accordance with the above characteristics, as follows:

(i) Explicit moisture accounting: NWS, SSARR, SRFCH, HMC, GIRARD.
(ii) Implicit moisture accounting: TANK.
(iii) Index (systems approach): CLS, IMH, CBM.

The selection of a model for a specific forecasting situation should be guided by the following criteria:

(a) General and specific purpose and benefits of the forecast (e.g. continuous hydrograph of discharges, floods, water quality, water resources management, etc.).
(b) Climatic and physiographic characteristics of the basin.
(c) Length of record of the different types of input data.
(d) Quality of data field, both in time and space.
(e) The availability and size of computers, for both development and operation of the model, as well as the possibility of the use of the models, by relatively non-expert hydrological forecasting personnel.
(f) The possible need for transposing model parameters from smaller catchments to large catchments, usually downstream, where sufficient data for development is not available, and the possible application of models to large river systems with important human interference (man-made structures).

(g) The ability of the model to be conveniently up-dated on the basis of current hydrometeorological conditions.

With respect to climatic and physiographic characteristics of the basin, a prospective user of a model does not need to be highly discriminative in the selection of models if the basin for which the model is selected is climatically humid and a large supply of moisture is available throughout the forecasting and development period. In climatically humid basins simple models may perform equally as well as complex, sophisticated models. For basins in semi-arid and arid regions the prospective user of the model will have to be highly discriminative in the selection of the model, as indicated below.

In general, explicit moisture accounting models are better equipped to simulate river response during and after a long dry spell. The tendency to underestimate individual large flow events (peaks) demonstrated by the explicit moisture accounting models can be alleviated in actual operational forecasting procedures by objectively modifying reported precipitation input values.

In the presence of high noise in the data field available for model development, implicit moisture accounting models and in particular index (systems approach) models have a better capacity to filter this noise and therefore may give better forecasting results that explicit moisture accounting models.

The implicit moisture accounting models, such as the TANK, are very adaptable and flexible with respect to the size and climatic and physiographic characteristics of the basin. In the TANK model, for example, by introducing additional reservoirs (tanks) stream channel elements and areal distribution of soil moisture may be simulated if such components are predominant in the runoff process.

The Conference made the following recommendations concerning development of models, optimization techniques and verification criteria for possible further use in intercomparison of models in general (not only in connection with the WMO project):

(a) When several models are being compared on several data sets the results are greatly improved if all the models are tested on all the data sets. Provision should therefore be made for all the data sets to satisfy the requirements of all the models.
(b) As far as possible, a combination of manual and automatic procedures should be used in model calibration.
(c) As one of the many factors involved in model selection, it would be advantageous if verification and intercomparison of models in general could be done in accordance with at least some generally accepted verification criteria. The numerical verification criteria for such general use should, as far as possible, be selected from among those used in this project.

8. Conclusions and recommendations for future activities, of WMO in particular, in this field

All the data sets used in this project should be cleaned up and retained in the WMO Secretariat for possible use upon request by any interested model owner, providing that the results of the testing will be communicated to the international community through WMO. An up-dating of the final report of the project with new tests performed may be considered.

The feasibility of conducting a similar intercomparison project for models of the snowmelt process and runoff from the snowmelt should be studied. It is evident that this project will have to start with an inquiry into the availability of data.

WMO should continue all efforts in order to encourage national authorities in improvement and standardization of instruments and methods of observation for those elements of the hydrological cycle required as inputs in models. In this respect specific requirements of modelling should be borne in mind when the installation of data collection systems is being planned.

It will be the role of an international organization, WMO being the most suitable one, to develop, in cooperation with national agencies, a model which would contain alternative subroutines proven as best by this intercomparison project, in particular to be used in specific forecasting situations and conditions. The simulation package developed in this way may prove particularly useful in areas prone to large floods such as tropical cyclone areas and other severe weather circumstances.

Future efforts in developing hydrological forecasting models should be directed to the development of an 'on-the-line model' which would combine in one system a data collection, transmission and processing function, as well as the forecasting model. The results of the intercomparison project, particularly with respect to the quality of data used for the intercomparison, indicate that the ultimate solution of the forecasting problem is dependent on the development of such systems. It is obvious that such a system may, in addition to functions performed for hydrological forecasting, serve other fields of economic activities, in particular for water resources management, agriculture, forestry, protection of the environment (water quality), etc.

Capable agencies should be encouraged to provide opportunities for training of specialists in hydrological forecasting models in particular within the framework of WMO training programmes.

Part 3

COMPUTER PROGRAMS

MALSAK: Markov and Least Squares ARMA Kernels

GIOVANNA FINZI
Electrotechnics and Electronics Institute, Milan Polytechnic, Italy

EZIO TODINI
IBM Scientific Center, Pisa, Italy

JAMES R. WALLIS
IBM Scientific Center, Pisa (while on leave from IBM Research Center, Yorktown Heights, New York, USA)

1 Introduction

MALSAK is a computer program developed at the IBM Pisa Scientific Center for fitting lag-one Markov and ARMA(1, 1) processes to observed univariate hydrologic sequences. After the Markov and ARMA(1, 1) driving parameters have been estimated, MALSAK generates synthetic hydrologic sequences and compares some of their correlation properties to those of the observed sequences. Comparisons between observed and synthetic sequences are based upon correlogram and spectral analysis, means, standard deviations and skewness.

Square root and logarithmic transformation options are available for the input data, but no explicit formulation for preserving the skewness of the original sequences is attempted by MALSAK. The package is designed for, and has been tested under, CP-CMS operated on an IBM 360-67, and this guide presupposes on the part of the user a working knowledge of CP-CMS and some familiarity with the concepts of synthetic hydrology.

2.1 General description of MALSAK

MALSAK is written in FORTRAN IV and is designed for use under CP-CMS on an IBM 360-67. The program accepts data from only one site at a time but allows for up to 12 seasons per year (monthly values). Input flow vectors must be complete and from 3 to 500 years in length.

The program calculates the first three moments (means, standard deviations, skew coefficients) for each season as well as an overall estimate of the average annual moments. Correlograms and power spectra of actual flows and seasonally standardized flows are computed and plotted.

The generating processes used by MALSAK are either a lag-one Markov (Thomas and Fiering, 1962) or an ARMA(1, 1) process (Box and Jenkins, 1970; O'Connell, 1974).

MALSAK attempts to avoid negative simulated flows by optimal square root or logarithmic transformations of the raw data with subsequent convolution back into untransformed sample space.

Initialization of problem parameters is done by the user at a remote terminal (IBM 2741) in response to program generated queries.

2.2 Purpose and objectives of MALSAK

The evaluation of proposed complex multi-reservoir water resource systems is analytically intractable. In 1962 the Harvard water program (Maass *et al.*, 1962) demonstrated that optimum or near optimum system designs might result from the use of simulation using very long records. As long records are not available at many hydrologic sites they advocated the use of synthetic traces generated by a lag-one Markov model at each site. Much recent literature has suggested that a lag-one Markov model may fail to preserve the observed persistence (Mandelbrot, 1965; Matalas and Wallis, 1971; O'Connell, 1974).

It is the purpose and objective of this program to provide an easy mechanism for evaluating whether or not a lag-one Markov generating process is sufficient to represent the observed phenomenon or whether or not an ARMA(1, 1) process would be more appropriate for the users' modelling effort.

2.3 Extent of program coverage

MALSAK processes only one sequence at a time and no attempt at a multisite evaluation by Markov or ARMA(1, 1) processes is made. No data fill-in mechanism is provided by MALSAK and all input sequences must be complete and continuous. The use of segmented periods joined so as to appear continuous should be avoided as such patching has a differential effect upon the Markov and ARMA processes.

2.4 List of input—output files

MALSAK is designed to work under CP-CMS time sharing. The following input and output files are used

FT01F001 Reads the input flow data. These data must have been previously stored in the user's CMS library under name and type, where name is DATI and type the river gauging station name (up to 8 BCD characters).

FT05F001 Reads terminal input in response to MALSAK generated queries.

FT06F001 Writes terminal output (minimal).

FT08F001 Writes complete output file of problem definition, input and output statistics. If only one repetitive sequence of synthetic numbers is requested they will also be printed on this file.

FT04F001 Temporary storage for simulated sequences. To prevent P-disk full messages occurring during the processing of large jobs this file is rewound at the end of each repetitive synthetic sequence. Note: this is equivalent to preserving only the last generated sequence.

3.1 Useful pointers for CP-CMS MALSAK user

MALSAK is initialized by the user at a remote computer terminal by responding to MALSAK generated demands. These queries in order of their appearance are:

(a) NAME OF GAUGING STATION DATA SET (———): Response should be up to 8 characters of BCD (left justified).
(b) INITIAL SEED FOR PSEUDO RANDOM NUMBER GENERATION (———): Response should be a string of integer numbers, IRPAT, (right justified) if IRPAT = 0 program terminates before simulations.
(c) THE SUGGESTED TRANSFORMATION IS (———). SELECT WHICH TRANSFORMATION YOU PREFER, NONE = 1, LOG10 = 2, SQRT = 3 (———):
Response is an integer variable.
If the 'no transformation' option is selected by the user the additional query appears:
(d) DO YOU WISH TO HAVE NEGATIVE SIMULATED FLOWS SET TO ZERO? (———):
Response should be 'yes' or 'no' (left justified).
(e) After plotting the required transformed and seasonally standardized flow correlogram, MALSAK asks:
DO YOU WISH TO TRY ANOTHER TRANSFORMATION? (———):
Response should be 'yes' or 'no'. If 'yes' MALSAK returns to query (c); otherwise:
(f) WHICH GENERATING MECHANISM DO YOU WISH? (———):
Response is an integer variable, MARKOV = 0, ARMA(1, 1) = 1.
(g) LENGTH OF SIMULATED SEQUENCES IN YEARS (———):
Response should be a three character integer, LSIM, where $3 \leqslant LSIM \leqslant 500$ (right justified).
(h) NUMBER OF SIMULATED SEQUENCES (———):
Response should be a three character integer, LOOP (right justified).
(i) After plotting and printing the average simulated correlogram and the average correlogram plus or minus one standard deviation, MALSAK asks:
DO YOU WISH TO USE THE OTHER STOCHASTIC PROCESS? (———):
Response is 'yes' or 'no'; if 'yes' MALSAK reiterates to query (g); otherwise:
(j) DO YOU WISH TO PROCESS A DIFFERENT DATA SET? (———):
Response is 'yes' or 'no'; if 'yes' MALSAK reiterates to query (b); otherwise STOP.

3.2 Formulae

X_{ijk} Flow at station i, year j and season k
L Length of record in years
M Number of seasons
N Number of sites

Statistic estimates

$$\bar{X}_{ik} = \frac{1}{L} \sum_{j=1}^{L} X_{ijk} \quad \text{Station season mean}$$

$$\bar{Y}_i = \frac{1}{L \cdot M} \sum_{k=1}^{M} \sum_{j=1}^{L} X_{ijk} \quad \text{Annual station mean}$$

$$S_{ik}^2 = \frac{1}{L-1} \cdot \sum_{j=1}^{L} X_{ijk}^2 - \frac{L}{L-1} \cdot \bar{X}_{ik}^2 \quad \text{Station season variance}$$

$$\bar{S}_i^2 = \frac{1}{M \cdot L - 1} \sum_{k=1}^{M} \sum_{j=1}^{L} X_{ijk}^2 - \frac{M \cdot L}{M \cdot L - 1} \bar{Y}_i^2 \quad \text{Annual station variance}$$

$$G_{ik} = \left[\sum_{j=1}^{L} X_{ijk}^3 - 3 \cdot (L-1) \cdot \bar{X}_{ik} \cdot S_{ik}^2 + 2 \cdot L \cdot \bar{X}_{ik}^3 \right] \frac{L}{(L-1)(L-2) \cdot S_{ik}^3}$$

Station season skewness

$$\bar{G}_i = \left[\sum_{k=1}^{M} \sum_{j=1}^{L} X_{ijk}^3 - 3 \cdot (M \cdot L - 1)\bar{Y}_i \cdot \bar{S}_i^2 + 2 \cdot L \cdot M \cdot \bar{Y}_i^3 \right]$$

$$\frac{L \cdot M}{(L \cdot M - 1)(L \cdot M - 2) \cdot S_i^3} \quad \text{Annual station skewness}$$

$$Z_{ijk} = \frac{X_{ijk} - \bar{X}_{ik}}{S_{ik}} \quad \text{Standardized flows}$$

$$t = (J-1) \cdot M + K$$

$$Z_{it} = Z_{ijk}$$

$$C_i(LAG) = \frac{\sum_{t=1+LAG}^{L \cdot M} Z_{it} \cdot Z_{i(t-LAG)}}{L \cdot M - LAG} \quad \text{Lag } LAG \text{ covariance at station } i$$

$$R_i(LAG) = C_i(LAG)/C_i(0) \quad \text{Lag } LAG \text{ correlation at station } i$$

$$MLAG = MIN(60, L \cdot M/6) \quad \text{Maximum considered lag}$$

$$f_\tau = \frac{1}{2\pi} (C(0) + 2 \sum_{LAG=1}^{MLAG-1} C(LAG) \cos \pi\tau \, LAG$$

$$+ C(MLAG) \cos \pi\tau) \quad \text{Power spectrum estimate}$$

$$\begin{cases} \hat{f}_0 = \tfrac{1}{2}(f_0 + f_1) \\ \hat{f}_{MLAG} = \tfrac{1}{2}(f_{MLAG} + f_{MLAG-1}) \\ \hat{f} = \tfrac{1}{4} f_{\tau-1} + \tfrac{1}{2} f_\tau + \tfrac{1}{4} f_{\tau+1} \quad 1 \leqslant \tau \leqslant MLAG - 1 \quad \text{Tuckey's smoothing procedure} \end{cases}$$

ARMA(1,1) driving parameters φ and θ are estimated as follows:

φ is estimated imposing $\rho_1 = R(1)$ and minimizing

$$J(\varphi) = \sum_{LAG=2}^{MLAG} (R(LAG) - \varphi^{LAG-1}\rho_1)^2$$

θ is then computed as:

$$\hat{\theta} = \frac{(1 - 2\hat{\varphi}\rho_1 + \hat{\varphi}^2) - \sqrt{(1 - 2\hat{\varphi}\rho_1 + \hat{\varphi}^2)^2 - 4(\hat{\varphi} - \rho_1)^2}}{2(\hat{\varphi} - \rho_1)}$$

4. Glossary of Italian terms for the following program

NOME DEL PROGETTO
project name

INIZIAL. DELLA VAR. CASUALE
initial seed for the pseudo random number generation

CORRELOGRAMMA
correlogram

VALORI MEDI DEL COEFF. DI ASIMMETRIA
mean values of the skewness coefficient

TRASFORMAZIONE
transformation

NESSUNA
none

COEFF. ASIMM.
skewness coefficient

IL COEFF. DI ASIMMETRIA E'MINIMO QUANDO SI USA COME
TRASFORMAZIONE . . .
the skewness coefficient is minimum when . . . transformation is used

QUALE TRASFORMAZIONE SI DESIDERA?
the suggested transformation is

SI DESIDERA CHE I FLUSSI NEGATIVI VENGANO MESSI A ZERO?
do you wish to have negative simulated flows set to zero?

CORRELOGRAMMA DEI DATI STORICI TRASFORMATI E
STANDARDIZZATI
correlogram of transformed and standardized data

SI VUOLE SCEGLIERE UN'ALTRA TRASFORMAZIONE?
do you wish to try another transformation?

METODO
method

NUMERI DI ANNI DA SIMULARE
number of years to be simulated

NUMERO DI SIMULAZIONI
number of simulations

CORRELOGRAMMA E LIMITI DI CONFIDENZA (±SIGMA) DEI DATI
   SIMULATI TRASFORMATI E STANDARDIZZATI
correlogram and confidence interval (±sigma) of transformed and standardized
   simulated data

SI VUOLE L'ALTRO PROCESSO STOCASTICO?
do you wish another generating mechanism?

NUMERO DI ANNI DA SIMULARE
number of years to be simulated

NUMERO DI SIMULAZIONI
number of simulations

SI VUOLE PASSARE AD UN ALTRO PROBLEMA?
do you wish to process a different data set?

PROGETTO
project

SERIE STORICHE E LORO ANALISI STATISTICA
time series and their statistics

ANNI
years

STAGIONI
seasons

STAZIONE
gauging station

DEFLUSSI STORICI
time series

STATISTICHE STAGIONALI
seasonal statistics

PORTATE MINORI O UGUALI A ZERO
discharges less or equal to zero

PORTATE MASSIME
maximum discharges

VALORI MEDI
mean values

SCARTI QUADRATICI MEDI
standard deviations

COEFF. DI ASIMMETRIA
skewness coefficients

COEFF. DI VARIAZIONE
variance coefficients

STATISTICHE DELLA SERIE
time series statistics

PASSO
step

VALORE
value

GRAFICO
diagram

SI USA COME TRASFORMAZIONE: NESSUNA
no transformation is used

SPETTRO DI POTENZA DEI DATI TRASFORMATI E STANDARDIZZATI
power spectrum of transformed and standardized data

FREQ.
frequency

PROCESSO DI GENERAZIONE TIPO MARKOV-LAG1
Markov-lag1 generation process

VALORI MEDI DELLE STATISTICHE DELLE SERIE SIMULATE
mean values of statistics of the simulated time series

SCARTI QUADR. MEDI DELLE STATISTICHE DELLE SERIE SIMULATE
mean standard deviations of statistics of the simulated time series

4.1 Sample problem input

```
TEVERE
    22   12    1    1
ROMA
(2X,I4,2X,12F6.0)
    1937  0247.00302.00597.00468.00292.00199.00176.00157.00221.00341.00456.01015.0
    1938  0422.00310.00234.00201.00340.00221.00165.00159.00171.00214.00249.00423.0
    1939  0369.00265.00343.00262.00338.00360.00185.00166.00205.00262.00373.00368.0
    1940  0386.00539.00265.00253.00171.00287.00214.00167.00164.00337.00396.00303.0
    1941  0571.00990.00588.00418.00534.00315.00228.00197.00212.00208.00337.00247.0
    1942  0262.00546.00355.00327.00322.00189.00164.00150.00171.00170.00207.00289.0
    1947  0219.00913.00436.00324.00178.00154.00142.00139.00177.00160.00158.00301.0
    1948  0510.00394.00214.00198.00197.00171.00137.00129.00135.00192.00168.00167.0
    1949  0171.00118.00137.00113.00114.00112.00102.00083.80094.40010.70228.00212.0
    1950  0210.00229.00210.00201.00153.00110.00111.00111.00135.00160.00183.00357.0
    1951  0451.00576.00544.00325.00347.00187.00149.00130.00144.00145.00283.00208.0
    1952  0335.00333.00170.00163.00137.00117.00110.00105.00133.00134.00180.00435.0
    1953  0395.00330.00186.00171.00158.00246.00137.00126.00121.00175.00135.00148.0
    1954  0176.00331.00285.00168.00298.00187.00123.00107.00103.00104.00116.00120.0
    1955  0136.00244.00408.00173.00122.00094.20091.10082.90099.40107.00164.00197.0
    1956  0262.00256.00354.00286.00332.00154.00113.00096.10099.00101.00183.00147.0
    1957  0182.00268.00195.00263.00183.00152.00098.70092.80095.50108.00108.00138.0
    1958  0170.00149.00284.00501.00190.00140.00110.00097.10100.00108.00150.00298.0
    1959  0243.00213.00164.00233.00178.00130.00096.00100.00112.00137.00226.00732.0
    1960  0433.00521.00535.00387.00305.00188.00151.00126.00224.00334.00337.00631.0
    1961  0604.00284.00219.00198.00194.00180.00135.00129.00150.00204.00361.00282.0
    1962  0268.00286.00414.00279.00188.00148.00131.00116.00136.00151.00459.00321.0
```

230

4.2 Sample problem terminal sheet

```
$ malsak
EXECUTION BEGINS...


        NOME DEL PROGETTO =( roma    )

        INIZIAL. DELLA VAR. CASUALE= (    77553)


CORRELOGRAMMA
```

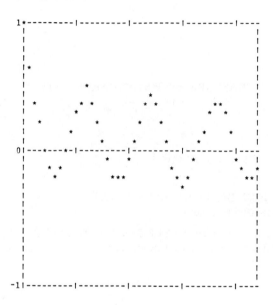

```
        VALORI MEDI DEL COEFF. DI ASIMMETRIA

        TRASFORMAZIONE :-      NESSUNA       LOG10         SQRT

        COEFF. ASIMM.         4.577        -0.283        2.386

        IL COEFF. DI ASIMMETRIA E' MINIMO QUANDO SI USA COME TRASFORMAZIONE:  LOG10

        QUALE TRASFORMAZIONE SI DESIDERA? ( NESSUNA=1 - LOG10=2 - SQRT=3 ) : (1)

        SI DESIDERA CHE I FLUSSI NEGATIVI VENGANO MESSI A ZERO? ( SI - NO ) : (no)
```

CORRELOGRAMMA DEI DATI TRASFORMATI E STANDARDIZZATI

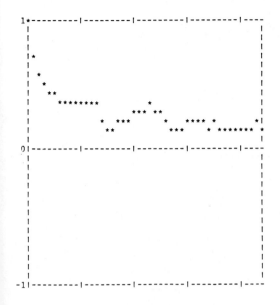

SI VUOLE SCEGLIERE UN'ALTRA TRASFORMAZIONE? (SI - NO) : (no)

METODO - MARKOV (0) , ARIMA (1) - (0)

NUMERO DI ANNI DA SIMULARE = (22)

NUMERO DI SIMULAZIONI   = (20)

RO1 = .67842   FI = .94450   THETA = .58489

232

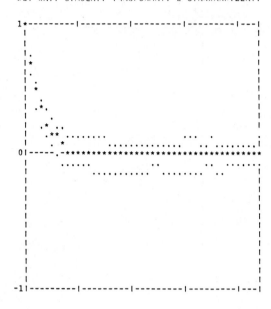

CORRELOGRAMMA E LIMITI DI CONFIDENZA (± SIGMA)
DEI DATI SIMULATI TRASFORMATI E STANDARDIZZATI

SI VUOLE L' ALTRO PROCESSO STOCASTICO (SI-NO) :(si)

NUMERO DI ANNI DA SIMULARE = (22)

NUMERO DI SIMULAZIONI   = (20)

CORRELOGRAMMA E LIMITI DI CONFIDENZA (± SIGMA)
DEI DATI SIMULATI TRASFORMATI E STANDARDIZZATI

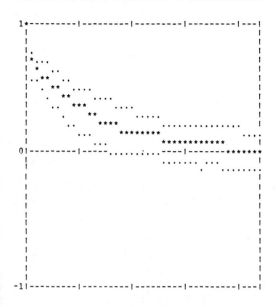

SI VUOLE L' ALTRO PROCESSO STOCASTICO (SI-NO) :(no)

SI VUOLE PASSARE AD UN ALTRO PROBLEMA? (SI-NO) :(no)
R;

4.3 Sample problem offline print

PROGETTO: TIVERE

SERIE STORICHE F ICFC ANALISI STATISTICA

ANNI   : 22

STAGIONI : 12

SERIE STORICHE E LORO ANALISI STATISTICA

STAZIONE:ROMA

DEFLUSSI STORICI

ANNO	GEN.	FEB.	MAR.	APR.	MAG.	GIU.	LUG.	AGO.	SET.	OTT.	NOV.	DIC.
1937	247.00	302.00	597.00	468.00	292.00	199.00	176.00	157.00	221.00	341.00	456.00	1015.00
1938	422.00	310.00	234.00	201.00	340.00	221.00	165.00	159.00	171.00	214.00	249.00	423.00
1939	369.00	265.00	343.00	262.00	338.00	360.00	185.00	166.00	205.00	262.00	373.00	368.00
1940	386.00	539.00	265.00	253.00	171.00	287.00	214.00	167.00	164.00	337.00	396.00	303.00
1941	571.00	990.00	588.00	418.00	534.00	315.00	228.00	197.00	212.00	208.00	237.00	247.00
1942	262.00	546.00	355.00	327.00	322.00	180.00	164.00	150.00	171.00	170.00	207.00	289.00
1947	219.00	913.00	436.00	324.00	178.00	154.00	142.00	139.00	177.00	160.00	158.00	301.00
1948	510.00	394.00	214.00	198.00	197.00	171.00	137.00	129.00	135.00	192.00	168.00	167.00
1949	171.00	118.00	137.00	113.00	114.00	112.00	102.00	83.80	94.40	10.70	228.00	212.00
1950	210.00	229.00	210.00	201.00	153.00	167.00	111.00	111.00	135.00	160.00	183.00	357.00
1951	451.00	576.00	544.00	325.00	347.00	187.00	149.00	130.00	144.00	145.00	283.00	278.00
1952	335.00	333.00	170.00	163.00	137.00	117.00	110.00	105.00	133.00	134.00	180.00	435.00
1953	395.00	330.00	186.00	171.00	158.00	246.00	137.00	126.00	121.00	175.00	135.00	148.00
1954	176.00	331.00	285.00	168.00	298.00	187.00	123.00	107.00	103.00	104.00	116.00	120.00
1955	136.00	244.00	408.00	173.00	122.00	94.20	91.10	82.90	99.40	107.00	164.00	197.00
1956	262.00	256.00	354.00	286.00	332.00	154.00	98.70	96.10	95.50	101.00	183.00	147.00
1957	182.00	268.00	195.00	263.00	183.00	152.00	110.00	92.80	100.00	108.00	108.00	138.00
1958	170.00	149.00	284.00	501.00	190.00	140.00	96.00	97.10	112.00	108.00	150.00	298.00
1959	243.00	213.00	164.00	233.00	178.00	130.00	151.00	100.00	224.00	137.00	226.00	732.00
1960	433.00	521.00	535.00	387.00	305.00	188.00	135.00	126.00	150.00	334.00	337.00	631.00
1961	604.00	284.00	219.00	198.00	194.00	180.00	131.00	129.00	204.00	204.00	361.00	282.00
1962	268.00	286.00	414.00	279.00	188.00	148.00	131.00	116.00	136.00	151.00	459.00	321.00

STATISTICHE STAGIONALI

PORTATE MINORI O UGUALI A ZERO

0.0%	0.0%	0.0%	0.0%	0.0%	0.0%	0.0%	0.0%	0.0%	0.0%	0.0%	0.0%

PORTATE MASSIME

604.00	990.00	597.00	501.00	534.00	360.00	228.00	197.00	224.00	341.00	459.00	1015.00

VALORI MEDI

319.18	381.68	324.41	268.73	239.59	183.69	139.49	125.76	145.56	175.58	248.04	333.59

SCARTI QUADRATICI MEDI

136.98	222.11	144.40	103.52	102.94	67.83	37.29	30.41	42.51	83.54	109.49	215.72

COEFF. DI ASIMMETRIA

0.61	1.64	0.64	0.79	1.12	1.17	0.88	0.57	0.54	0.64	0.65	1.91

COEFF. DI VARIAZIONE

0.43	0.58	0.45	0.39	0.43	0.37	0.27	0.24	0.29	0.48	0.44	0.65

STATISTICHE DELLA SERIE

VALOR MEDIO :   240.44
SCARTO QUADR. MEDIO: 147.08
COEFF. DI ASIMMETRIA : 2.09
COEFF. DI VARIAZIONE : 0.61

SERIE STORICHE E LORO ANALISI STATISTICA

STAZIONE:ROMA
CORRELOGRAMMA:

GRAFICO

PASSO	VALORE
0:	1.
1:	0.6144
2:	0.3595
3:	-0.1699
4:	-0.0194
5:	-0.1296
6:	-0.1725
7:	-0.1215
8:	0.0169
9:	0.1620
10:	0.2659
11:	0.3636
12:	0.4728
13:	0.3536
14:	0.1899
15:	0.0694
16:	-0.0956
17:	-0.1731
18:	-0.2083
19:	-0.1813
20:	-0.0385
21:	0.0970
22:	0.2120
23:	0.3462
24:	0.3876
25:	0.3153
26:	0.2010
27:	0.0395
28:	-0.1269
29:	-0.2298
30:	-0.2399
31:	-0.1935
32:	-0.0615
33:	-0.0549
34:	0.1518
35:	0.2774
36:	0.3022
37:	0.3021
38:	0.2609
39:	0.1035
40:	-0.0651
41:	-0.1665
42:	-0.2310
43:	-0.1870
44:	-0.1150

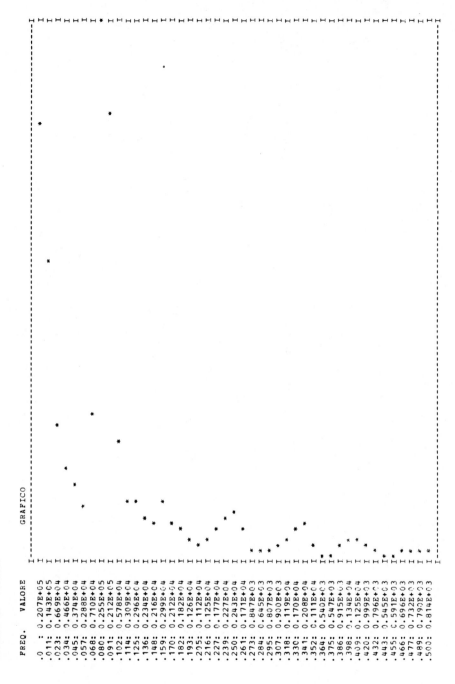

SPETTRO DI POTENZA:

GRAFICO

FREQ.   VALORE

FREQ.	VALORE
.0	0.207E+05
.011	0.143E+05
.023	0.669E+04
.034	0.466E+04
.045	0.374E+04
.057	0.288E+04
.068	0.710E+04
.080	0.255E+05
.091	0.212E+05
.102	0.578E+04
.114	0.309E+04
.125	0.296E+04
.136	0.234E+04
.148	0.216E+04
.159	0.299E+04
.170	0.212E+04
.182	0.182E+04
.193	0.126E+04
.205	0.112E+04
.216	0.125E+04
.227	0.177E+04
.239	0.227E+04
.250	0.243E+04
.261	0.171E+04
.273	0.847E+03
.284	0.645E+03
.295	0.807E+03
.307	0.900E+03
.318	0.119E+04
.330	0.170E+04
.341	0.208E+04
.352	0.111E+04
.364	0.540E+03
.375	0.547E+03
.386	0.915E+03
.398	0.134E+04
.409	0.125E+04
.420	0.999E+03
.432	0.796E+03
.443	0.545E+03
.455	0.591E+03
.466	0.696E+03
.477	0.732E+03
.489	0.792E+03
.500	0.814E+03

SERIE STORICHE E LORO ANALISI STATISTICA

VALORI MEDI DEL COEFF. DI ASIMETRIA

TRASFORMAZIONE :-   NESSUNA   LOG10   SQRT

COEFF. ASIMM.   4.577   -0.283   2.386

IL COEFF. DI ASIMETRIA E' MINIMO QUANDO SI USA COME TRASFORMAZIONE: LOG10

SI USA COME TRASFORMAZIONE : NESSUNA

STAZIONE :ROMA

CORRELOGRAMMA DEI DATI TRASFORMATI E STANDARDIZZATI

PASSO   VALORE   GRAFICO

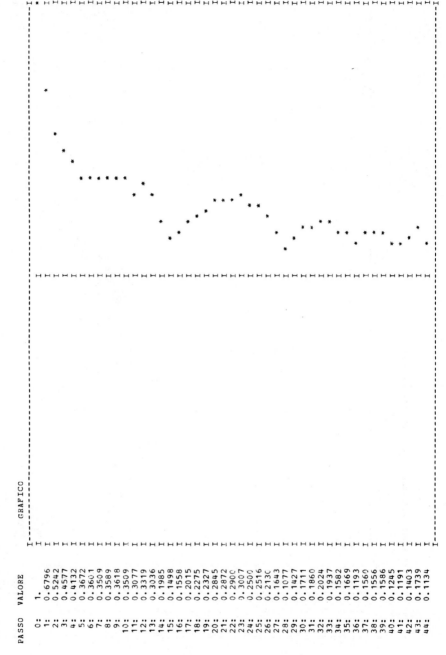

PASSO	VALORE
0:	1.
1:	0.6796
2:	0.5242
3:	0.4577
4:	0.4132
5:	0.3672
6:	0.3601
7:	0.3509
8:	0.3589
9:	0.3618
10:	0.3509
11:	0.3077
12:	0.3319
13:	0.3036
14:	0.1985
15:	0.1498
16:	0.1558
17:	0.2015
18:	0.2275
19:	0.2327
20:	0.2845
21:	0.2872
22:	0.2900
23:	0.3007
24:	0.2500
25:	0.2516
26:	0.2130
27:	0.1643
28:	0.1077
29:	0.1427
30:	0.1711
31:	0.1860
32:	0.2024
33:	0.1937
34:	0.1582
35:	0.1669
36:	0.1193
37:	0.1560
38:	0.1556
39:	0.1586
40:	0.1245
41:	0.1191
42:	0.1403
43:	0.1739
44:	0.1134

SPETTRO DI POTENZA DEI DATI TRASFORMATI E STANDARDIZZATI:

FREQ.	VALORE	GRAFICO
.0 :	0.233E+01	*
.011:	0.142E+01	*
.023:	0.529E+00	*
.034:	0.378E+00	*
.045:	0.304E+00	*
.057:	0.151E+00	*
.068:	0.695E-01	*
.080:	0.189E+00	*
.091:	0.304E+00	*
.102:	0.217E+00	*
.114:	0.118E+00	*
.125:	0.994E-01	*
.136:	0.750E-01	*
.148:	0.939E-01	*
.159:	0.134E+00	*
.170:	0.993E-01	*
.182:	0.676E-01	*
.193:	0.506E-01	*
.205:	0.439E-01	*
.216:	0.641E-01	*
.227:	0.101E+00	*
.239:	0.101E+00	*
.250:	0.610E-01	*
.261:	0.441E-01	*
.273:	0.338E-01	*
.284:	0.388E-01	*
.295:	0.576E-01	*
.307:	0.743E-01	*
.318:	0.567E-01	*
.330:	0.455E-01	*
.341:	0.491E-01	*
.352:	0.375E-01	*
.364:	0.207E-01	*
.375:	0.273E-01	*
.386:	0.369E-01	*
.398:	0.525E-01	*
.409:	0.380E-01	*
.420:	0.211E-01	*
.432:	0.265E-01	*
.443:	0.315E-01	*
.455:	0.283E-01	*
.466:	0.277E-01	*
.477:	0.377E-01	*
.489:	0.443E-01	*
.500:	0.307E-01	*

PROCESSO DI GENERAZIONE TIPO MARKOV-LAG1
****

VALORI MEDI DELLE STATISTICHE DELLE SERIE SIMULATE
****

ANNI   : 22

STAGIONI   : 12

NUMERO SIMULAZIONI : 20

VALORI MEDI DELLE STATISTICHE DELLE SERIE SIMULATE
NESSUNA TRASFORMAZIONE - CON FLUSSI NEGATIVI - ANNI SIMULATI : 22 - NUMERO DI SIMULAZIONI : 20

STAZIONE:ROMA

STATISTICHE STAGIONALI

PORTATE MINORI O UGUALI A ZERO

1.14% 4.55% 1.36% 0.45% 1.36% 0.45% 0.0 % 0.0 % 0.0 % 0.0 % 1.82% 1.82% 6.59%

PORTATE MASSIME

581.14 799.68 602.79 451.97 417.60 312.75 208.39 187.38 226.82 344.69 462.08 716.46

VALORI MEDI

319.70 387.57 330.49 267.06 231.03 182.26 136.30 123.86 142.98 172.83 244.55 333.32

SCARTI QUADRATICI MEDI

138.83 228.74 145.07 103.38 103.25 67.35 37.30 29.78 43.42 85.11 111.74 205.95

COEFF. DI ASIMMETRIA

-0.12 -0.13 -0.19 -0.22 -0.11 -0.04 0.03 0.17 0.05 0.14 -0.05 -0.18

COEFF. DI VARIAZIONE

0.43 0.59 0.44 0.39 0.45 0.37 0.27 0.24 0.30 0.49 0.46 0.62

STATISTICHE DELLA SERIE

VALOR MEDIO :   239.33
SCARTO QUADR. MEDIO: 150.80
COEFF. DI ASIMMETRIA : 0.93
COEFF. DI VARIAZIONE : 0.63

VALORI MEDI DELLE STATISTICHE DELLE SERIE SIMULATE
NESSUNA TRASFORMAZIONE - CON FLUSSI NEGATIVI - ANNI SIMULATI : 22 - NUMERO DI SIMULAZIONI : 20

STAZIONE:ROMA

CORRELOGRAMMA E LIMITI DI CONFIDENZA (+ SIGMA)

DEI DATI SIMULATI TRASFORMATI E STANDARDIZZATI

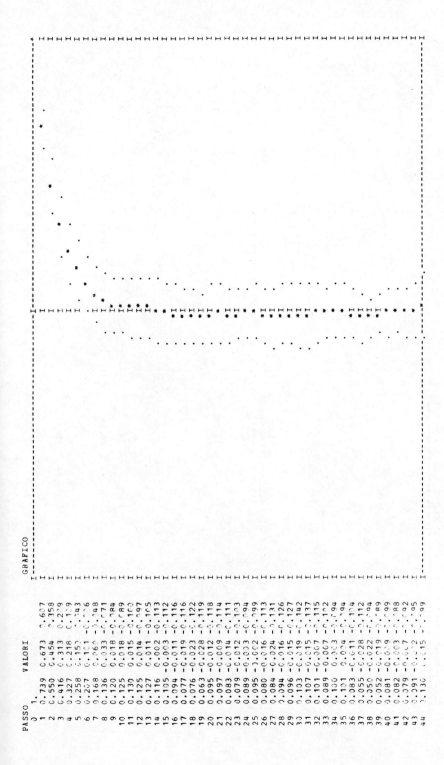

GRAFICO

PASSO	VALORI	
0	1.	.607
1	0.673	.358
2	0.550	.289
3	0.416	.259
4	0.327	.199
5	0.258	.743
6	0.207	.101 -.726
7	0.168	.260 -.248
8	0.136	.033 -.284
9	0.120	.018 -.071
10	0.125	.015 -.089
11	0.130	.014 -.160
12	0.127	.014 -.097
13	0.127	.011 -.165
14	0.116	.002 -.113
15	0.105	-0.003 -.112
16	0.094	-0.011 -.116
17	0.077	-0.019 -.116
18	0.076	-0.023 -.122
19	0.063	-0.028 -.119
20	0.095	-0.012 -.118
21	0.097	-0.009 -.114
22	0.083	-0.012 -.111
23	0.079	-0.012 -.103
24	0.089	-0.003 -.094
25	0.095	-0.002 -.099
26	0.080	-0.016 -.113
27	0.084	-0.024 -.131
28	0.094	-0.016 -.126
29	0.096	-0.015 -.127
30	0.103	-0.019 -.142
31	0.107	-0.015 -.137
32	0.101	-0.007 -.115
33	0.089	-0.003 -.102
34	0.100	-0.003 -.094
35	0.101	-0.004 -.094
36	0.083	-0.011 -.104
37	0.055	-0.028 -.112
38	0.050	-0.022 -.094
39	0.052	-0.019 -.99
40	0.081	-0.009 -.88
41	0.082	-0.011 -.94
42	0.079	-0.007 -.92
43	0.091	-0.002 -.95
44	0.130	-0.015 -.99

SCARTI QUADR. MEDI DELLE STATISTICHE DELLE SERIE SIMULATE
****

    ANNI   :   22

    STAGICNI   :   12

    NUMERO SIMULAZICNI   :   2?

SCARTI QUADR. MEDI DELLE STATISTICHE DELLE SERIE SIMULATE
NESSUNA TRASFORMAZIONE - CON FLUSSI NEGATIVI - ANNI SIMULATI : 22 - NUMERO DI SIMULAZIONI : 2?

STAZIONE: ROMA

STATISTICHE STAGIONALI

PORTATE MASSIME

72.18	115.27	57.78	47.09	37.45	33.60	15.14	15.63	27.44	54.28	67.15	112.43

VALORI MEDI

35.71	53.44	29.79	24.81	25.84	17.31	8.98	7.34	8.69	21.75	25.25	48.96

SCARTI QUADRATICI MEDI

22.82	31.26	18.87	14.90	15.23	11.37	6.53	4.92	7.96	18.42	14.51	34.12

COEFF. DI ASIMMETRIA

0.44	0.45	0.53	0.48	0.47	0.53	0.46	0.49	0.51	0.42	0.59	0.5?

COEFF. DI VARIAZIONE

0.64   0.59   0.63   0.60   0.59   0.65   0.73   0.67   0.92   0.85   0.57   0.76

STATISTICHE DELLA SERIE

VALOR MEDIO :   17.11
SCARTO QUADR. MEDIO: 14.19
COEFF. DI ASIMMETRIA :   0.27
COEFF. DI VARIAZIONE :   0.83

PROCESSO DI GENERAZIONE TIPO ARIMA(1,0,1) - FI = 0.94450 THETA = 0.58489
****

VALORI MEDI DELLE STATISTICHE DELLE SERIE SIMULATE
****

     ANNI   : 22

     STAGIONI   : 12

     NUMERO SIMULAZIONI : 20

VALORI MEDI DELLE STATISTICHE DELLE SERIE SIMULATE - ANNI SIMULATI : 22 - NUMERO DI SIMULAZIONI : 20
NESSUNA TRASFORMAZIONE - CON FLUSSI NEGATIVI - ANNI SIMULATI : 22 - NUMERO DI SIMULAZIONI : 20

     STAZIONE:ROMA

STATISTICHE STAGIONALI

PORTATE MINORI O UGUALI A ZERO

1.59%	5.68%	1.36%	1.14%	2.73%	0.23%	0.0 %	0.0 %	0.23%	3.18%	2.73%	8.64%

PORTATE MASSIME

562.82	759.85	580.08	464.15	437.22	296.75	202.23	185.01	226.65	329.32	434.14	745.75

VALORI MEDI

310.21	374.13	311.63	263.27	233.31	178.21	135.46	124.63	145.16	173.54	238.11	323.42

SCARTI QUADRATICI MEDI

138.35	217.75	137.97	102.53	105.10	68.18	37.21	31.28	43.39	84.54	108.02	215.74

COEFF. DI ASIMMETRIA

-0.04	-0.14	-0.04	0.08	-0.01	-0.09	-0.03	-0.03	-0.16	-0.22	-0.02	0.03

COEFF. DI VARIAZIONE

0.45	0.58	0.44	0.39	0.45	0.38	0.27	0.25	0.30	0.49	0.45	0.67

STATISTICHE DELLA SERIE

VALOR MEDIO : 234.25
SCARTO QUADR. MEDIO: 147.21
COEFF. DI ASIMMETRIA : 0.98
COEFF. DI VARIAZIONE : 0.63

NESSUNA TRASFORMAZIONE - CON FLUSSI NEGATIVI - ANNI SIMULATI : 22 - NUMERO DI SIMULAZIONI : 20

STAZIONE:ROMA

CORRELOGRAMMA E LIMITI DI CONFIDENZA (+ SIGMA)

DEI DATI SIMULATI TRASFORMATI E STANDARDIZZATI

GRAFICO

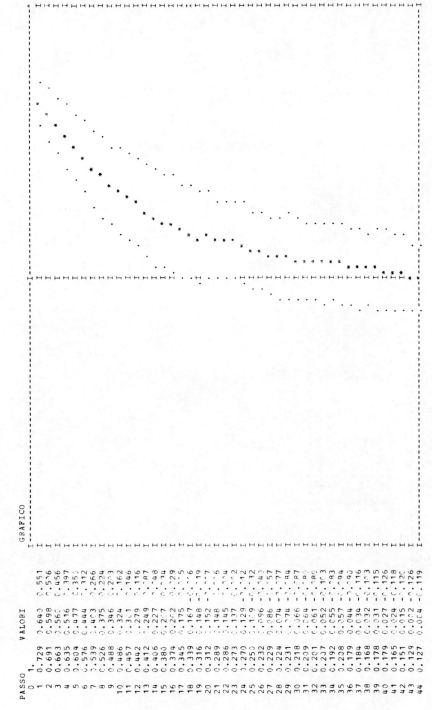

PASSO	VALORI		
0	1.		0.551
1	0.729	0.640	0.576
2	0.691	0.598	0.456
3	0.663	0.560	0.397
4	0.635	0.516	.35
5	0.604	0.477	.312
6	0.576	0.444	.266
7	0.539	0.403	.224
8	0.526	0.375	.203
9	0.488	0.346	.162
10	0.486	0.324	.146
11	0.457	0.301	.116
12	0.442	0.279	.087
13	0.412	0.249	.048
14	0.406	0.227	.034
15	0.380	0.207	.029
16	0.374	0.202	.005
17	0.345	0.175	-.006
18	0.339	0.167	-.19
19	0.316	0.148	-.19
20	0.312	0.137	-.07
21	0.289	0.148	-.6
22	0.286	0.145	-.04
23	0.273	0.137	-.12
24	0.270	0.129	-.12
25	0.250	0.119	-.32
26	0.232	0.096	-.40
27	0.229	0.086	-.57
28	0.224	0.074	-.777
29	0.231	0.074	-.84
30	0.218	0.066	-.87
31	0.209	0.064	-.89
32	0.207	0.061	-.103
33	0.237	0.052	-.83
34	0.192	0.055	-.94
35	0.208	0.044	-.90
36	0.179	0.044	-.116
37	0.184	0.034	-.103
38	0.168	0.032	-.103
39	0.178	0.031	-.115
40	0.179	0.027	-.126
41	0.165	0.024	-.118
42	0.151	0.015	-.120
43	0.129	0.002	-.126
44	0.127	0.004	-.119

SCARTI QUADR. MEDI DELLE STATISTICHE DELLE SERIE SIMULATE
****

ANNI   : 22

STAGICNI   : 12

NUMERO SIMULAZICNI : 20

SCARTI QUADR. MEDI DELLE STATISTICHE DELLE SERIE SIMULATE
NESSUNA TRASFORMAZIONE - CON FLUSSI NEGATIVI - ANNI SIMULATI : 22 - NUMERO DI SIMULAZIONI : 20

STAZIONE:ROMA

STATISTICHE STAGIONALI

PORTATE MASSIME

| 70.36 | 138.59 | 80.90 | 65.61 | 67.17 | 31.21 | 16.22 | 17.50 | 27.84 | 47.07 | 44.83 | 119.64 |

VALORI MEDI

| 57.34 | 73.35 | 50.09 | 40.96 | 38.14 | 25.34 | 15.53 | 11.67 | 15.65 | 32.41 | 46.39 | 86.71 |

SCARTI QUADRATICI MEDI

| 24.33 | 39.30 | 21.56 | 20.62 | 17.59 | 9.17 | 5.30 | 5.48 | 6.72 | 16.02 | 20.72 | 33.97 |

COEFF. DI ASIMMETRIA

| 0.42 | 0.49 | 0.41 | 0.61 | 0.56 | 0.39 | 0.35 | 0.52 | 0.53 | 0.56 | 0.41 | 0.34 |

COEFF. DI VARIAZIONE

| 0.42 | 0.54 | 0.43 | 0.50 | 0.46 | 0.36 | 0.34 | 0.47 | 0.43 | 0.49 | 0.45 | 0.39 |

STATISTICHE DELLA SERIE

VALOR MEDIO :   39.16

SCARTO QUADR. MEDIO: 16.59

COEFF. DI ASIMMETRIA : 0.29

COEFF. DI VARIAZIONE : 0.42

SPUMA: Simulation Package using Matalas Algorithm

GIOVANNA FINZI
Electrotechnics and Electronics Institute, Milan Polytechnic, Italy

EZIO TODINI
IBM Scientific Center, Pisa, Italy

JAMES R. WALLIS
IBM Scientific Center, Pisa (while on leave from IBM Research Center, Yorktown Heights, New York, USA)

1 Introduction

SPUMA is a FORTRAN IV simulation package developed at the IBM Pisa Scientific Center for generating synthetic hydrologic flows at one or more sites and for one or more seasons.

The generating process for the synthetic flows is a lag-one Markov process and, following the Matalas algorithm, the means, variances, lag-zero and lag-one correlation and cross-correlations are preserved. Square root and logarithmic transformation options are available for the input data, but no explicit formulation for preserving the skewness of the original sequences is attempted by SPUMA. The package is designed for, and has been tested under, CP-CMS operated on an IBM 360—67, and this guide presupposes on the part of the user a working knowledge of CP-CMS and some familiarity with the concepts of synthetic hydrology.

2.1 General description of SPUMA

SPUMA is written in FORTRAN IV and is designed for use under CP-CMS on an IBM 360-67. The program accepts data from up to 10 sites and for each site allows for up to 12 seasons (monthly values). Input flow vectors must be complete and contemporaneous and from 3 to 500 years in length.

The program calculates the first three moments (means, standard deviation, and skew coefficients) for each season and site as well as an overall estimate of the average monthly moments. Lag-one and lag-zero correlation and cross-correlation matrices are estimated after standardization by the appropriate monthly means and standard deviation. The generating process for the synthetic flows used by SPUMA is lag-one Markov (Matalas, 1967), and the resulting flows will preserve the observed means, standard deviations, and lag-one and lag-zero correlations and cross-correlations for an infinite sample. The Matalas algorithm expects normally distributed input flows and, if highly skewed flows are used it is to be expected that negative simulated flows would be generated. SPUMA attempts to avoid negative simulated flows by optional square-root or logarithmic transformation of the row data with subsequent convolution back into the untransformed sample space.

SPUMA is operational under the CP-CMS time sharing system. Initialization of problem parameters is done by the user at a remote terminal (IBM 2741) in response to program generated queries.

2.2 Purpose and objective of SPUMA

The evaluation of proposed complex multi-reservoir water resource systems is analytically intractable. In 1962 the Harvard water program (Maass *et al.*, 1962) demonstrated that optimum or near-optimum system designs might result from the use of simulation using very long records. As long records are not available at many hydrologic sites they advocated the use of synthetic traces generated by a lag-one Markov model at each site. Matalas (1967) generalized the original lag-one algorithm to include the lag-one and lag-zero cross-correlations, and Young and Pisano, (1968) attempted to produce a computer code, NMP, to implement the Matalas algorithm.

O'Connell (1973) documented a major error in the source coding of NMP and suggested the program could be corrected fairly simply. Finzi, Todini and Wallis (herein) analysed the code more completely and detected other major coding errors, which led to the corrected and altered code referred to hereafter as SPUMA.

The objectives behind the development of SPUMA were, first, to generate an operationally useful, easy to use Markovian multivariate synthetic hydrology program operable in a time sharing environment; and, second, to produce a program which would allow for easy investigation into the nature of multivariate Markov small sample and transformation biases. Small sample biases may be introduced into the synthetic traces which are always finite, and hence less than the infinite required by the algorithm for the preservation of the sample statistics. Small sample and transformation introduced biases may be considerable, and may lead to serious distortions in the subsequent reservoir design simulations. SPUMA allows the user to estimate the size of these biases both in transformed and untransformed sample space by maintaining the cumulative sums and sums of squares of the statistics for simulated sequences. After the final simulated sequence has been generated and preserved the mean standard deviation of each of the statistics is printed out for user comparison with those of the original data. The user may then observe that not all statistics have been adequately preserved, at which point it becomes necessary for the user to consider whether or not these biases are sufficiently large to have an appreciable effect on the subsequent optimization simulation.

2.3 Extent of program coverage

To apply SPUMA correctly it is necessary to assume that the observed streamflow is multivariate normal and weakly stationary and that the generating mechanism of historic streamflow can be adequately represented by a lag-one Markov process. Given the above assumptions the Matalas (1967) algorithm will correctly preserve the observed means, standard deviations, lag-zero and lag-one correlations and cross-correlations in an infinite synthetic sequence.

As hydrologic data is rarely multivariate normal, SPUMA has some optional transformations that can be applied in an attempt to make the application of the algorithm more nearly theoretically correct. The use of these transformations does not guarantee that the resulting sequences will be multivariate normal and deviations can lead to anomalies and biases in the expected results (Finzi, Todini and Wallis (herein)). If the correlation structure of the observed sequences is non-Markovian, that is

$$\rho_k \neq \rho_1^k \qquad (1)$$

then it appears difficult to justify the use of SPUMA generated synthetic traces. However, if equation 1 can be regarded as an equality then SPUMA may be used, and synthetic sequences generated.

In addition to the above conceptual restrictions on the use of SPUMA there are a number of other limits, the most important of which are:

(1) No data fill-in mechanism is provided by SPUMA and all input sequences must be complete and contemporaneous.
(2) No more than ten sites may be processed at any one time.
(3) No more than 12 seasons (months) per year may be specified.
(4) Observed and synthetic sequences must be specified in the range 3 to 500 years in length.

2.4 List of input—output files

SPUMA is designed to work under CP-CMS time sharing. The following input and output files are used

FT01F001 Reads the input flow data. These data must have been previously stored in the user's CMS library under name and type, where name is DATI and type the river basin name (up to 8 BCD characters).

FT05F001 Reads terminal input in response to SPUMA generated queries.

FT06F001 Writes terminal output (minimal).

FT08F001 Writes complete output file of problem definition, input and output statistics. If only one repetitive sequence of synthetic numbers is requested they will also be printed on this file.

FT04F001 Temporary storage for simulated sequences. To prevent P-disk full messages occurring during the procession of large jobs this file is rewound at the end of each repetitive synthetic sequence. Note: this is equivalent to preserving only the last generated sequence. (If the user requires to preserve more of the generated synthetic sequences he should mount a tape on logical unit 4 and remove the intermediate rewinds.)

3.1 Useful pointers for CP-CMS SPUMA user

SPUMA is initialized by the user at a remote computer terminal by responding to SPUMA generated demands. These queries in order of their appearance are:

(a) NAME OF THE RIVER BASIN DATA SET (− − −):
Response should be up to 8 characters of BCD (left justified).
(b) INITIAL SEED FOR PSEUDO RANDOM NUMBER GENERATION (− − −):
Response should be a string of integer numbers, IRPAT, (right justified) if IRPAT = 0 program terminates before simulations.
(c) LENGTH OF SIMULATED SEQUENCES IN YEARS (− − −):
Response should be a three-character integer, LSIM, where $3 \leqslant LSIM \leqslant 500$ (right justified).
(d) NUMBER OF SIMULATED SEQUENCES (− − −):
(e) THE SUGGESTED TRANSFORMATION IS (− − −). SELECT WHICH TRANSFORMATION YOU PREFER, NONE = 1, LOG10 = 2, SQRT = 3 (− − −):
Response is an integer variable.
If the 'no transformation' option is selected by the user the additional query appears:
(f) DO YOU WISH TO HAVE NEGATIVE SIMULATED FLOWS SET TO ZERO? (− − −):
Response should be 'yes' or 'no' (left justified)
After the simulation has been completed, SPUMA generates a further series of demands; these start with an iteration of query (c). SPUMA recognizes three different types of replies; these are LSIM = 0, new LSIM = old LSIM, and new LSIM ≠ old LSIM.

new LSIM = 0

(g) DO YOU WISH A DIFFERENT TRANSFORMATION? (− − −):
Response is either 'yes' or 'no'. If 'yes' SPUMA iterates queries from (b), if 'no' SPUMA proceeds with:
(h) DO YOU WISH TO PROCESS A DIFFERENT PROBLEM? (− − −):
Response is either 'yes' or 'no'. If 'yes' SPUMA iterates from (a); if 'no' execution terminates.

new LSIM = old LSIM

SPUMA repeats query (d). If new LOOP > old LOOP the simulation statistics are argumented until new LOOP simulations have been completed. If new LOOP ≤ old LOOP SPUMA sets accumulated statistics to zero and restarts an identical problem to the one previously selected by using an updated value for IRPAT.

new LSIM ≠ old LSIM

SPUMA repeats the previously defined problem only using an up-dated initial value of IRPAT and the new value of LSIM.

3.2 Formulae

X_{ijk} Flow at station i, year j and season k
L Length of record in years
M Number of seasons
N Number of sites

Statistic estimates

$$\bar{X}_{ik} = \frac{1}{L} \sum_{j=1}^{L} X_{ijk} \quad \text{Station season mean}$$

$$\bar{Y}_i = \frac{1}{L \cdot M} \sum_{k=1}^{M} \sum_{j=1}^{L} X_{ijk} \quad \text{Annual station mean}$$

$$S_{ik}^2 = \frac{1}{L-1} \cdot \sum_{j=1}^{L} X_{ijk}^2 - \frac{L}{L-1} \cdot \bar{X}_{ik}^2 \quad \text{Station season variance}$$

$$\bar{S}_{ik}^2 = \frac{1}{M \cdot L - 1} \sum_{k=1}^{M} \sum_{j=1}^{L} X_{ijk}^2 - \frac{M \cdot L}{M \cdot L - 1} \bar{Y}_i^2 \quad \text{Annual station variance}$$

$$G_{ik} = \left[\sum_{j=1}^{L} X_{ijk}^3 - 3 \cdot (L-1) \cdot \bar{X}_{ik} \cdot Z_{ik}^2 + 2 \cdot L \cdot \bar{X}_{ik}^3 \right] \frac{L}{(L-1)(L-2) \cdot S_{ik}^3}$$

Station season skewness

where: $Z_{ik}^2 = \sum_{j=1}^{L} X_{ijk}^2$

$$\bar{G}_i = \left[\sum_{k=1}^{M} \sum_{j=1}^{L} X_{ijk}^3 - 3 \cdot (M \cdot L - 1)\bar{Y}_i \cdot \bar{Z}_i^2 + 2 \cdot L \cdot M \cdot \bar{Y}_i^3 \right]$$

$$\frac{L \cdot M}{(L \cdot M - 1)(L \cdot M - 2) \cdot S_i^3} \quad \text{Annual station skewness}$$

where: $\bar{Z}_i^2 = \sum_{k=1}^{M} \sum_{j=1}^{L} X_{ijk}^2$

$$Z_{ijk} = \frac{X_{ijk} - \bar{X}_{ik}}{S_{ik}} \quad \text{Standardized flows}$$

$$t = (J-1) \cdot M + K$$

$$Z_{it} \equiv Z_{ijk}$$

$$r_{pq}(0) = \frac{\sum\limits_{t=1}^{L \cdot M} Z_{pt} \cdot Z_{qt}}{\sqrt{\sum\limits_{t=1}^{L \cdot M} Z_{pt}^2 \cdot \sum\limits_{t=1}^{L \cdot M} Z_{qt}^2}}$$ Lag-zero cross-correlation between stations p and q

$$r_{pq}(1) = \frac{\sum\limits_{t=2}^{L \cdot M} Z_{pt} \cdot Z_{q(t=1)}}{\sqrt{\sum\limits_{t=1}^{L \cdot M} Z_{pt}^2 \cdot \sum\limits_{t=1}^{L \cdot M} Z_{qt}^2}} \cdot \frac{L \cdot M - 1}{L \cdot M - 2}$$ Lag-one cross-correlation between stations p and q

$$\rho_p(1) = \frac{\sum\limits_{t=2}^{L \cdot M} Z_{pt} \cdot Z_{p(t-1)}}{\sum\limits_{t=1}^{L \cdot M} Z_{pt}^2} \cdot \frac{L \cdot M - 1}{L \cdot M - 2}$$ Lag-one correlation at station p

$$M_0 = \begin{bmatrix} 1 & & \\ & 1 & r_{qp}(0) \\ r_{pq}(0) & \cdots & \\ & & 1 \end{bmatrix}$$ Lag-zero cross-correlation matrix: the matrix is symmetric

$$M_1 = \begin{bmatrix} \rho_1(1) & & & r_{qp}(1) \\ & \rho_2(1) & & \\ & & \cdots & \\ r_{pq}(1) & & & \rho_N(1) \end{bmatrix}$$ Lag-one correlation at station p

Generating algorithm

Lag-one Markov process

$$z_t = Az_{t-1} + B_{et}$$

where

$$z_t = \begin{bmatrix} z_{1t} \\ z_{2t} \\ \vdots \\ z_{Nt} \end{bmatrix} \qquad \epsilon_t = \begin{bmatrix} \epsilon_{1t} \\ \epsilon_{2t} \\ \vdots \\ \epsilon_{Nt} \end{bmatrix}$$

with ϵ_t a NIP $(0,1)$.

Matrices A and B are matrices to be estimated following Matalas (1967) as:

$$A = M_1 M_0^{-1}$$

$$BB^T = M_0 - M_1 M_0^{-1} M_1^T$$

on the hypothesis of B lower triangular (Young, 1968) and the condition of BB^T symmetrical positive definite (Slack, 1973).

3.3 Flow chart of SPUMA

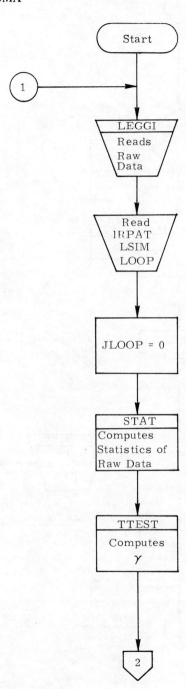

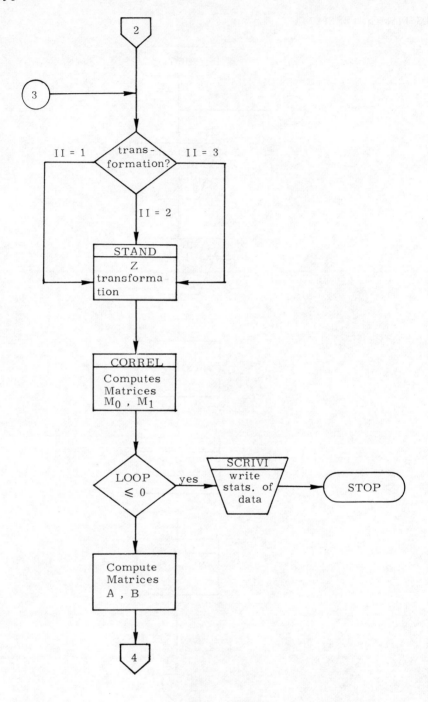

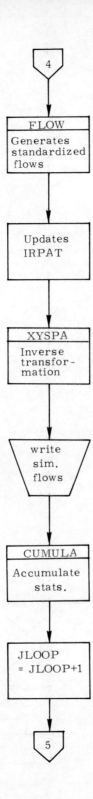

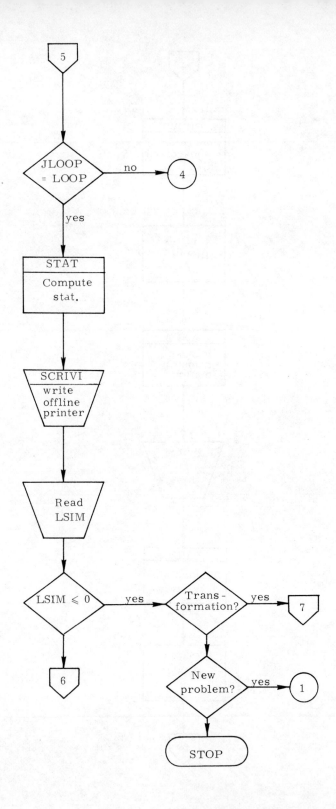

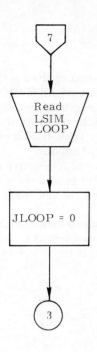

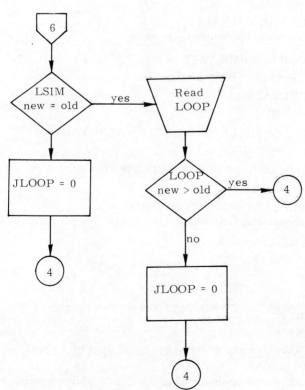

3.4 Timing

We have not yet devised an accurate algorithm for estimating the amount of CPU time that the user can expect to incur when processing a typical SPUMA problem. Variables that would have to be considered by such an algorithm would be: number of sites, number of seasons, length of historic records, length of simulated records and number of repetitive simulated records; although it is only the last two of these variables which become critical during most user terminal sessions.

An example of a large job was the 5-site, 12-season, 29-year record for the Arno river data, which took 6 seconds of CPU time to process the historic data. Simulating 100 sequences each of 29 years in length took an additional 328 seconds of CPU time (IBM 360-67 operated under CP-CMS).

It is suggested that large jobs should not be attempted until the user becomes familiar with the program and that intially the user should restrict his jobs to those with synthetic sequences equal to or less than 100 years in length and with no more than 5 or 10 repetitions.

4. Glossary of Italian terms for the following program

NOME DEL PROGETTO
project name

INIZIAL. DELLA VAR. CASUALE
initial seed of pseudo random number generation

NUMERO DI ANNI DA SIMULARE
number of years to be simulated

NUMERO DI SIMULAZIONI
number of simulations

MATRICE DELLE CORRELAZIONI INCROCIATE DI LAG 0
lag-0 cross correlation matrix

MATRICE DELLE CORRELAZIONI INCROCIATE DI LAG 1
lag-1 cross correlation matrix

VALORI MEDI DEL COEFF. DI ASIMMETRIA
mean values of the skewness coefficient

TRASFORMAZIONE
transformation

NESSUNA
none

COEFF. ASIMM.
skewness coefficient

IL COEFF. DI ASIMMETRIA E' MINIMO QUANDO SI USA COME
    TRASFORMAZIONE: . . .
the skewness coefficient is minimum when . . . transformation is used

QUALE TRASFORMAZIONE SI DESIDERA?
the suggested transformation is

SI DESIDERA CHE I FLUSSI VENGANO MESSI A ZERO?
do you wish to have negative simulated flows set to zero?

SI, NO
yes, no

VALORI MEDI DELLE CORRELAZIONI DI LAG 0
mean values of lag-0 correlations

VALORI MEDI DELLE CORRELAZIONI DI LAG 1
mean values of lag-1 correlations

SCARTI QUADR. MEDI DELLE CORRELAZIONI DI LAG 0
standard deviations of lag-0 correlations

SCARTI QUADRATICI MEDI DELLE CORRELAZIONI DI LAG 1
standard deviations of lag-1 correlations

NUMERO DI ANNI DA SIMULARE
number of years to be simulated

SI VUOLE UN'ALTRA TRASFORMAZIONE SUGLI STESSI DATI?
do you wish a different transformation?

SI VUOLE PASSARE AD UN ALTRO PROBLEMA?
do you wish to process a different problem?

PROGETTO
project

SERIE STORICHE E LORO ANALISI STATISTICA
time series and their statistics

STAZIONI
gauging stations

ANNI
years

STAGIONI
seasons

DEFLUSSI STORICI
time series

STATISTICHE STAGIONALI
seasonal statistics

PORTATE MINORI O UGUALI A ZERO
discharges less or equal to zero

PORTATE MASSIME
maximum discharges

VALORI MEDI
mean values

SCARTI QUADRATICI MEDI
standard deviations

COEFF. DI ASIMMETRIA
skewness coefficients

COEFF. DI VARIAZIONE
variance coefficients

STATISTICHE DELLA SERIE
time series statistics

SI USA COME TRASFORMAZIONE: NESSUNA
transformation used: none

MATRICE . . .
matrix . . .

VALORI MEDI DELLE STATISTICHE DELLE SERIE SIMULATE
mean values of time series statistics

NESSUNA TRASFORMAZIONE
no transformation

CON FLUSSI NEGATIVI
with negative simulated flows

4.1 Sample problem input

```
TEVERE
  22    12     2      1
ROMA
(2X,I4,2X,12F6.0)
   1937   0247.00302.00597.00468.00292.00190.00176.00157.00221.00341.00456.01015.0
   1938   0422.00310.00234.00201.00340.00221.00165.00159.00171.00214.00249.00423.0
   1939   0369.00265.00343.00262.00338.00360.00185.00166.00205.00262.00373.00368.0
   1940   0386.00539.00265.00253.00171.00287.00214.00167.00164.00337.00396.00303.0
   1941   0571.00990.00588.00418.00534.00315.00228.00197.00212.00208.00337.00247.0
   1942   0262.00546.00355.00327.00322.00189.00164.00150.00171.00170.00207.00289.0
   1947   0219.00913.00436.00324.00178.00154.00142.00139.00177.00160.00158.00301.0
   1948   0510.00394.00214.00198.00197.00171.00137.00129.00135.00192.00168.00167.0
   1949   0171.00118.00137.00113.00114.00112.00102.00083.80094.40010.70228.00212.0
   1950   0210.00229.00210.00201.00153.00110.00111.00111.00135.00169.00183.00357.0
   1951   0451.00576.00544.00325.00347.00187.00149.00130.00144.00145.00283.00208.0
   1952   0335.00333.00170.00163.00137.00117.00110.00105.00133.00134.00189.00435.0
   1953   0395.00330.00186.00171.00158.00246.00137.00126.00121.00175.00135.00148.0
   1954   0176.00331.00285.00168.00298.00187.00123.00107.00103.00104.00116.00120.0
   1955   0136.00244.00408.00173.00122.00094.20091.10082.90009.40107.00164.00197.0
   1956   0262.00256.00354.00286.00332.00154.00113.00096.10099.00101.00183.00147.0
   1957   0182.00268.00195.00263.00183.00152.00098.70092.80095.50108.00108.00138.0
   1958   0170.00149.00284.00501.00190.00140.00110.00097.10100.00108.00150.00298.0
   1959   0243.00213.00164.00233.00178.00130.00096.00100.00112.00137.00226.00732.0
   1960   0433.00521.00535.00387.00305.00188.00151.00126.00224.00334.00337.00631.0
   1961   0604.00284.00219.00198.00194.00180.00135.00129.00150.00204.00361.00282.0
   1962   0268.00286.00414.00279.00188.00148.00131.00116.00136.00151.00459.00321.0


BASCHI
(2X,I4,2X,12F6.0)
   1937   0090.50085.50244.00151.00062.90017.50018.90010.20041.30136.00176.00357.0
   1938   0123.00086.50040.00030.20098.40040.70012.70013.70020.00050.80155.80147.0
   1939   0146.00065.60121.00083.30146.00087.60014.20012.10043.40084.60148.00152.0
   1940   0153.00235.00060.00080.80082.20097.80051.80019.40018.30122.00152.00099.9
   1941   0219.00435.00224.00109.00193.00064.20025.70017.00018.20022.10107.00039.4
   1942   0043.60211.00117.00081.90091.40027.50020.40012.40016.80015.90066.40084.7
   1947   0081.20524.00235.00123.00029.40019.80008.70013.90036.70026.20040.70106.0
   1948   0294.00178.00051.90053.00062.80039.10015.70008.40009.10047.60021.40011.9
   1949   0049.50014.90037.40014.70016.90028.30006.20003.00006.00014.60094.70072.0
   1950   0063.40090.60060.60087.50035.00008.40003.40006.50017.80027.40044.60160.0
   1951   0231.00320.00284.00128.00142.00032.40011.40007.70028.20022.40144.00070.6
   1952   0176.00151.00040.10027.50022.30010.30009.60006.00019.20022.50059.50205.0
   1953   0170.00144.00046.40038.60031.80083.80021.00019.60011.60051.50025.20048.9
   1954   0058.50050.80131.00049.70195.00068.40018.90010.00009.70010.70024.50022.2
   1955   0029.70134.00222.00045.70015.20006.40007.20005.60011.60020.30060.40084.0
   1956   0155.00114.00165.00147.00114.00032.90013.70005.70006.60008.50048.70035.1
   1957   0055.70116.00067.50130.00058.60037.30006.90005.60006.60016.50015.00027.8
   1958   0051.90052.70171.00253.00046.10021.00006.50005.20006.50013.50061.80125.0
   1959   0119.00108.00074.10104.00061.60026.20009.50012.60022.60032.00087.50401.0
   1960   0228.00318.00313.00153.00085.80027.00016.40006.30096.70218.00169.00324.0
   1961   0279.00078.70036.70060.30059.10050.70011.10007.50012.30057.90172.00127.0
   1962   0088.10115.00206.00100.00045.80025.60017.70012.20014.50022.30174.00101.0

FINE

R;
```

264

4.2 Sample problem terminal sheet

```
$ spuma
EXECUTION BEGINS...



        NOME DEL PROGETTO =(example )

        INIZIAL. DELLA VAR. CASUALE= (     56799)

        NUMERO DI ANNI DA SIMULARE = ( 22)

        NUMERO DI SIMULAZIONI      = (  5)

        MATRICE DELLE CORRELAZIONI INCROCIATE DI LAG 0


          1.00000  0.85474
          0.85474  1.00000



        MATRICE DELLE CORRELAZIONI INCROCIATE DI LAG 1


          0.67966  0.53737
          0.46354  0.49391



        VALORI MEDI DEL COEFF. DI ASIMMETRIA
        TRASFORMAZIONE :-      NESSUNA       LOG10         SQRT
        COEFF. ASIMM.         4.411        -0.316         2.072


        IL COEFF. DI ASIMMETRIA E' MINIMO QUANDO SI USA COME TRASFORMAZIONE:   LOG10

        QUALE TRASFORMAZIONE SI DESIDERA? ( NESSUNA=1 - LOG10=2 - SQRT=3 ) : (1)
        SI DESIDERA CHE I FLUSSI NEGATIVI VENGANO MESSI A ZERO? ( SI - NO ) : (no)

        VALORI MEDI DELLE CORRELAZIONI DI LAG 0


          1.00000  0.85735
          0.85735  1.00000

        VALORI MEDI DELLE CORRELAZIONI DI LAG 1


          0.70846  0.56143
          0.51256  0.53271
```

SCARTI QUADR. MEDI DELLE CORRELAZIONI DI LAG 0

0.0   0.00929
0.00929 0.0

SCARTI QUADR. MEDI DELLE CORRELAZIONI DI LAG 1

0.01462 0.02257
0.02313 0.02453

NUMERO DI ANNI DA SIMULARE = (0   )

SI VUOLE UN'ALTRA TRASFORMAZIONE SUGLI STESSI DATI? (SI-NO) :(no)

SI VUOLE PASSARE AD UN ALTRO PROBLEMA? (SI-NO) :(no)

R;

4.3 Sample problem offline print

PROGETTO: TEVERE

SERIE STORICHE E ICRC ANALISI STATISTICA

STAZIONI DI MISURA : 2

ANNI   : 22

STAGIONI   : 12

SERIE STORICHE E ICRC ANALISI STATISTICA

STAZIONE:ROMA

DEFLUSSI STORICI

ANNO	GEN.	FEB.	MAR.	APR.	MAG.	GIU.	LUG.	AGO.	SET.	OTT.	NOV.	DIC.
1937	247.00	302.00	597.00	468.00	292.00	199.00	176.00	157.00	221.00	341.00	456.00	1015.00
1938	422.00	310.00	234.00	201.00	340.00	221.00	165.00	159.00	171.00	214.00	249.00	423.00
1939	369.00	265.00	343.00	262.00	338.00	360.00	185.00	166.00	205.00	262.00	373.00	368.00
1940	386.00	539.00	265.00	253.00	171.00	287.00	214.00	167.00	164.00	337.00	396.00	303.00
1941	571.00	990.00	588.00	418.00	534.00	315.00	228.00	197.00	212.00	337.00	337.00	247.00
1942	262.00	546.00	355.00	327.00	322.00	189.00	164.00	150.00	171.00	170.00	207.00	289.00
1947	219.00	913.00	436.00	324.00	178.00	154.00	142.00	139.00	177.00	160.00	158.00	301.00
1948	510.00	394.00	214.00	198.00	197.00	171.00	137.00	129.00	135.00	192.00	168.00	167.00
1949	171.00	118.00	137.00	113.00	114.00	112.00	102.00	83.80	94.40	10.70	228.00	212.00
1950	210.00	229.00	210.00	201.00	153.00	187.00	111.00	111.00	135.00	160.00	183.00	357.00
1951	451.00	576.00	544.00	325.00	347.00	187.00	149.00	130.00	144.00	145.00	283.00	208.00
1952	335.00	333.00	170.00	163.00	137.00	177.00	110.00	105.00	133.00	134.00	180.00	435.00
1953	395.00	330.00	186.00	171.00	158.00	246.00	137.00	126.00	121.00	175.00	135.00	148.00
1954	176.00	331.00	285.00	168.00	298.00	187.00	123.00	107.00	103.00	104.00	116.00	120.00
1955	136.00	244.00	408.00	173.00	122.00	94.20	91.10	82.90	99.40	107.00	164.00	197.00
1956	262.00	256.00	354.00	286.00	332.00	154.00	113.00	96.10	99.50	101.00	183.00	147.00
1957	182.00	268.00	195.00	263.00	183.00	152.00	98.70	92.80	95.50	108.00	108.00	138.00
1958	170.00	149.00	284.00	501.00	190.00	140.00	110.00	97.10	100.00	108.00	150.00	298.00
1959	243.00	213.00	164.00	233.00	178.00	130.00	96.00	100.00	112.00	137.00	226.00	732.00
1960	433.00	521.00	535.00	387.00	305.00	188.00	151.00	126.00	224.00	334.00	337.00	631.00
1961	604.00	284.00	219.00	198.00	194.00	180.00	135.00	129.00	150.00	204.00	361.00	282.00
1962	268.00	246.00	414.00	279.00	188.00	149.00	131.00	116.00	136.00	151.00	459.00	321.00

STATISTICHE STAGIONALI

PORTATE MINORI O UGUALI A ZERO

0.0 %	0.0 %	0.0 %	0.0 %	0.0 %	0.0 %	0.0 %	0.0 %	0.0 %	0.0 %	0.0 %	0.0 %

PORTATE MASSIME

604.00	990.00	597.00	501.00	534.00	360.00	228.00	197.00	224.00	341.00	459.00	1015.00

VALORI MEDI

319.18	281.68	324.41	268.73	239.59	165.69	135.49	125.76	145.56	175.58	248.04	333.59

SCARTI QUADRATICI MEDI

136.98	222.11	144.40	103.52	102.94	67.83	37.29	30.41	42.51	83.54	109.49	215.72

COEFF. DI ASIMMETRIA

0.61	1.64	0.64	0.79	1.12	1.17	0.88	0.57	0.54	0.64	0.65	1.91

COEFF. DI VARIAZIONE

0.43	0.58	0.45	0.39	0.43	0.47	0.27	0.24	0.29	0.48	0.44	0.65

STATISTICHE DELLA SERIE

VALOR MEDIO :   240.44
SCARTO QUADR. MEDIO: 147.08
COEFF. DI ASIMMETRIA : 2.09
COEFF. DI VARIAZIONE : 0.61

SERIE STORICHE E LORO ANALISI STATISTICA

STAZIONE:BASCHI

DEFLUSSI STORICI

ANNO	GEN.	FEB.	MAR.	AFR.	MAG.	GIU.	LUG.	AGO.	SET.	OTT.	NOV.	DIC.
1937	90.50	95.50	244.00	151.00	62.00	17.50	18.90	10.20	41.30	136.00	176.00	357.00
1938	123.00	86.50	40.00	30.20	58.40	40.70	12.70	13.70	20.00	50.80	155.80	142.00
1939	146.00	65.60	121.00	83.30	146.00	87.60	14.20	12.10	43.40	84.60	148.00	152.00
1940	153.00	235.00	60.00	80.80	82.70	67.30	51.80	19.40	18.30	122.00	152.00	99.90
1941	219.00	435.00	224.00	109.00	193.00	64.20	25.70	17.00	18.20	122.10	107.00	39.40
1942	43.60	211.00	117.00	81.90	61.40	27.50	20.40	12.40	16.80	15.90	66.40	84.70
1943	81.20	524.00	235.00	123.00	29.40	10.80	8.70	13.90	36.70	26.20	40.70	106.00
1948	294.00	172.00	51.90	53.00	62.80	30.10	15.70	8.40	9.10	47.60	21.40	11.90
1949	49.50	14.90	37.40	14.70	16.50	28.10	6.20	3.00	6.00	14.60	94.70	72.00
1950	63.40	90.60	60.60	87.50	35.00	8.40	3.40	6.50	17.80	27.40	44.60	160.00
1951	231.00	320.00	234.00	128.00	142.00	32.40	11.40	7.70	28.20	22.40	144.00	160.00
1952	176.00	151.00	40.10	27.50	22.30	10.30	9.40	6.00	19.20	22.50	59.50	205.00
1953	170.00	144.00	46.40	38.60	31.80	83.80	21.00	19.60	11.60	51.50	25.20	48.90
1954	58.50	50.80	131.00	49.70	195.00	68.40	18.90	10.00	9.70	10.70	24.50	22.20
1955	29.70	134.00	222.00	45.70	15.00	6.40	7.20	5.60	11.60	20.30	60.40	84.00
1956	155.00	114.00	165.00	147.00	114.00	32.90	13.70	5.70	6.60	8.50	48.70	35.10
1957	55.70	114.00	67.50	130.00	58.10	37.20	6.90	5.60	6.60	16.60	15.00	27.80
1958	51.90	52.70	171.00	253.00	46.10	21.00	6.50	5.20	6.50	13.50	61.80	125.00
1959	119.00	108.00	74.10	104.00	61.60	26.20	9.50	12.60	22.60	32.00	87.50	401.00
1960	228.00	219.00	313.00	153.00	85.80	27.00	16.40	6.30	96.70	218.00	169.00	324.00
1961	279.00	78.70	36.70	60.30	59.10	50.70	11.10	7.50	12.30	57.90	172.00	127.00
1962	88.10	115.00	206.00	100.00	45.80	35.60	17.70	12.20	14.50	22.30	174.00	101.00

STATISTICHE STAGIONALI

PORTATE MINORI O UGUALI A ZERO

0.0 %	0.0 %	0.0 %	0.0 %	0.0 %	0.0 %	0.0 %	0.0 %	0.0 %	0.0 %	0.0 %	0.0 %

PORTATE MASSIME

294.00	524.00	313.00	253.00	195.00	67.80	51.80	19.60	96.70	218.00	176.00	401.00

VALORI MEDI

132.05	164.92	133.99	93.24	77.06	36.77	14.89	10.03	21.53	47.43	93.10	127.34

SCARTI QUADRATICI MEDI

| 79.55 | 129.52 | 90.08 | 55.16 | 52.66 | 26.06 | 10.05 | 4.71 | 20.00 | 51.36 | 57.80 | 107.56 |

COEFF. DI ASIMMETRIA

| 0.60 | 1.54 | 0.52 | 1.03 | 1.04 | 1.01 | 2.47 | 0.65 | 2.79 | 2.23 | 0.23 | 1.45 |

COEFF. DI VARIAZIONE

| 0.60 | 0.79 | 0.67 | 0.59 | 0.68 | 0.67 | 0.67 | 0.47 | 0.93 | 1.08 | 0.62 | 0.84 |

STATISTICHE DELLA SERIE

VALOR MEDIO :   79.53
SCARTO QUADR. MEDIO: 83.82
COEFF. DI ASIMMETRIA : 1.94
COEFF. DI VARIAZIONE : 1.05

SERIE STORICHE E LORO ANALISI STATISTICA

MATRICE DELLE CORRELAZIONI INCROCIATE DI LAG 0

1.00000 0.85474
0.85474 1.00000

MATRICE DELLE CORRELAZIONI INCROCIATE DI LAG 1

0.67966 0.53737
0.46354 0.49391

SERIE STORICHE E LORO ANALISI STATISTICA

VALORI MEDI DEL COEFF. DI ASIMMETRIA

TRASFORMAZIONE :-	NESSUNA	LOG10	SQRT
COEFF. ASIMM.	4.411	-0.316	2.072

IL COEFF. DI ASIMMETRIA E' MINIMO QUANDO SI USA COME TRASFORMAZIONE: LOG10

SI USA COME TRASFORMAZIONE : NESSUNA

MATRICE A

0.818   -0.162
0.154   0.363

MATRICE BB'

0.531   0.555
0.555   0.750

MATRICE B

0.729
0.762   0.411

VALORI MEDI DELLE STATISTICHE DELLE SERIE SIMULATE
****

    STAZIONI DI MISURA : 2

    ANNI   : 22

    STAGIONI   : 12

    NUMERO SIMULAZIONI : 5

VALORI MEDI DELLE STATISTICHE DELLE SERIE SIMULATE
NESSUNA TRASFORMAZIONE - CON FLUSSI NEGATIVI - ANNI SIMULATI : 22 - NUMERO DI SIMULAZIONI : 5
STAZIONE=ROMA

STATISTICHE STAGIONALI

PORTATE MINORI O UGUALI A ZERO

0.0%	5.45%	3.64%	0.0%	0.0%	0.0%	0.0%	0.0%	0.0%	1.82%	4.55%	8.18%

PORTATE MASSIME

605.14	784.95	591.32	433.91	413.21	316.41	229.80	188.46	218.37	346.17	422.23	775.78

VALORI MEDI

314.72	371.10	291.09	249.27	228.02	178.84	135.88	125.27	143.63	177.56	230.50	313.45

SCARTI QUADRATICI MEDI

143.44	229.63	160.02	95.63	100.00	70.79	44.71	32.33	45.16	84.08	116.37	219.97

COEFF. DI ASIMMETRIA

0.05	-0.09	-0.02	0.16	-0.07	0.03	0.32	-0.11	-0.45	0.03	-0.30	0.16

COEFF. DI VARIAZIONE

| 0.46 | 0.62 | 0.55 | 0.38 | 0.44 | 0.40 | 0.33 | 0.26 | 0.31 | 0.47 | 0.50 | 0.70 |

STATISTICHE DELLA SERIE

VALOR MEDIO : 229.94
SCARTO QUADR. MEDIO: 149.59
COEFF. DI ASIMMETRIA : 1.06
COEFF. DI VARIAZIONE : 0.65

VALORI MEDI DELLE STATISTICHE DELLE SERIE SIMULATE
NESSUNA TRASFORMAZIONE - CON FLUSSI NEGATIVI - ANNI SIMULATI : 22 - NUMERO DI SIMULAZIONI : 5
STAZIONE:BASCHI

STATISTICHE STAGIONALI

PORTATE MINORI O UGUALI A ZERO

| 6.36% | 8.18% | 7.77% | 3.64% | 5.45% | 6.36% | 9.09% | 2.73% | 13.64% | 15.45% | 10.91% | 12.73% |

PORTATE MASSIME

| 298.26 | 295.08 | 308.03 | 188.68 | 164.86 | 90.24 | 36.53 | 19.21 | 56.80 | 138.97 | 201.22 | 354.74 |

VALORI MEDI

| 137.23 | 171.21 | 119.74 | 89.97 | 79.65 | 40.34 | 14.90 | 10.29 | 21.33 | 50.36 | 85.56 | 126.96 |

SCARTI QUADRATICI MEDI

| 87.94 | 129.77 | 89.48 | 49.72 | 48.62 | 35.56 | 10.89 | 4.70 | 20.10 | 48.23 | 68.62 | 116.46 |

COEFF. DI ASIMMETRIA

| -0.20 | -0.23 | 0.17 | 0.02 | -0.33 | -0.17 | 0.20 | -0.01 | -0.11 | 0.10 | -0.41 | 0.15 |

COEFF. DI VARIAZIONE

| 0.64 | 0.76 | 0.75 | 0.55 | 0.61 | 0.64 | 0.73 | 0.46 | 0.94 | 0.96 | 0.80 | 0.92 |

STATISTICHE DELLA SERIE

VALOR MEDIO :   78.88
SCARTO QUADR. MEDIO: 86.22
COEFF. DI ASIMMETRIA :   1.05
COEFF. DI VARIAZIONE :   1.09

VALORI MEDI DELLE STATISTICHE DELLE SERIE SIMULATE - ANNI SIMULATI : 22 - NUMERO DI SIMULAZIONI : 5
NESSUNA TRASFORMAZIONE - CON FLUSSI NEGATIVI

MATRICE DELLE CORRELAZIONI INCROCIATE DI LAG 0

1.00000 0.85735
0.85735 1.00000

MATRICE DELLE CORRELAZIONI INCROCIATE DI LAG 1

0.70846 0.56143
0.51256 0.53271

SCARTI QUADR. MEDI DELLE STATISTICHE DELLE SERIE SIMULATE
****

          STAZIONI DI MISURA :   2

          ANNI   :   22

          STAGIONI   :   12

          NUMERO SIMULAZIONI :   5

SCARTI QUADR. MEDI DELLE STATISTICHE DELLE SERIE SIMULATE
NESSUNA TRASFORMAZIONE - CON FLUSSI NEGATIVI - ANNI SIMULATI : 22 - NUMERO DI SIMULAZIONI :   5
    STAZIONE:ROMA

          STATISTICHE STAGIONALI

          PORTATE MASSIME
          45.57   26.85   113.75   44.13   57.12   36.63   18.42   19.34   26.92   28.02   61.49   59.57

          VALORI MEDI
          21.51   48.61   26.47   16.83   14.38   6.38   5.67   10.93   9.22   24.72   32.56   61.68

          SCARTI QUADRATICI MEDI
          23.78   19.43   8.27   12.06   18.09   12.54   5.75   3.73   5.97   10.47   11.17   12.94

          COEFF. DI ASIMMETRIA
          0.41   0.21   0.59   0.43   0.46   0.64   0.29   0.53   0.64   0.43   0.53   0.48

          COEFF. DI VARIAZIONE
          1.11   0.40   0.31   0.72   1.26   1.50   0.96   0.34   0.65   0.42   0.34   0.21

STATISTICHE DELLA SERIE

VALOR MEDIO :   20.19
SCARTO QUADR. MEDIO: 4.04
COEFF. DI ASIMMETRIA : 0.24
COEFF. DI VARIAZIONE : 0.20

SCARTI QUADR. MEDI DELLE STATISTICHE DELLE SERIE SIMULATE
NESSUNA TRASFORMAZIONE - CON FLUSSI NEGATIVI - ANNI SIMULATI : 22 - NUMERO DI SIMULAZIONI : 5

STAZIONE:BASCHI

STATISTICHE STAGIONALI

PORTATE MASSIME
46.82 38.17 53.67 19.08 18.11 17.50 4.22 1.92 9.57 17.35 29.17 52.32

VALORI MEDI
13.37 18.48 10.41 5.28 3.09 1.73 0.95 1.50 3.59 9.18 12.04 22.05

SCARTI QUADRATICI MEDI
22.12 28.53 3.58 5.15 5.16 3.70 1.94 0.88 3.09 9.24 4.60 14.99

COEFF. DI ASIMMETRIA
0.37 0.55 0.58 0.24 0.44 0.55 0.48 0.45 0.89 0.50 0.66 0.50

COEFF. DI VARIAZIONE
1.65 1.54 0.34 0.97 1.67 2.14 2.04 0.58 0.86 1.01 0.38 0.68

STATISTICHE DELLA SERIE

VALOR MEDIO :   5.31

SCARTO QUADR. MEDIO: 5.08

COEFF. DI ASIMMETRIA :   0.21

COEFF. DI VARIAZIONE :   0.96

SCARTI QUADR. MEDI DELLE STATISTICHE DELLE SERIE SIMULATE
NESSUNA TRASFORMAZIONE - CON FLUSSI NEGATIVI - ANNI SIMULATI : 22 - NUMERO DI SIMULAZICNI : 5

MATRICE DELLE CORRELAZIONI INCROCIATE DI LAG 0

0.0   0.C0929

0.00929 0.0

MATRICE DELLE CORRELAZICNI INCROCIATE DI LAG 1

0.01462 0.02257

0.02313 0.02453

PICOMO: A Program for the Identification of Conceptual Models

JAMES C. I. DOOGE
Department of Civil Engineering, University College, Dublin, Ireland

J. P. J. O'KANE
Department of Civil Engineering, University College, Dublin, Ireland

1. Introduction

This paper is a companion to 'Problems and methods of rainfall—runoff modelling' by James C. I. Dooge (herein). The paper consists of three different levels of description of the computer program PICOMO and its use.

Level 1 describes the program in broad terms under the headings: input data, output data and data processing. Level 2 expands these headings with sufficient detail to allow someone else to run the program. Level 3 describes the way in which the program can be used as an aid in hydrological research. This is illustrated with two markedly different sets of data as originally presented at the IBM Workshop on Mathematical Models in Hydrology held in Pisa, December 1974. Readers who have read the paper cited above may prefer to start at Level 3 in order to maintain continuity.

Copies of the program may be obtained on request from the authors.

2. Level 1 description

Input data on cards

The program requires as input successive sets of rainfall—runoff pairs in any units, whether intensities or volumes. Each set of rainfall—runoff pairs must be preceded by a header-card identifying the set and a card specifying (a) the number of *active* rainfall ordinates, (b) the number of runoff ordinates and (c) the number of subdivisions of the time interval between ordinates to be used during numerical integration. Rainfall ordinates which occur after the prescribed active number of ordinates are assumed to contribute nothing to subsequent runoff values.

Output data on line printer

The input data is echo-checked immediately. This is followed in separate sections by

(a) Normalized active-rainfall/runoff pairs and the normalizing constants. The RMS difference between normalized active-rainfall and runoff. The moments of (i) normalized active-rainfall, (ii) normalized runoff and (iii) the unit hydrograph which links (i) and (ii). The shape factors of this catchment unit hydrograph.

(b) The parameter values for the seventeen models included in the program which are found by moment matching. The predicted shape factors not fixed by the matching and the differences between them and the shape factors of the catchment unit hydrograph.

(c) For each model, for which feasible parameter values have been found, a tableau of six columns is printed which lists successive values in time of (i) normalized active-rainfall (ii) the unit pulse response for the stated model, (iii) normalized runoff predicted by the stated model, (iv) normalized runoff, (v) prediction error, (vi) time interval.

Finally the RMS error of the prediction and the sum of the ordinates of the pulse response are printed at the bottom of each tableau. Should the parameter values, which have been identified for a given model, be physically unrealistic, then the tableau for that model is skipped.

Sections (a), (b) and (c) of the output are repeated for each successive set of rainfall-runoff pairs.

Data processing

The structure of the program is shown in Figure 1. It consists of a main program divided into three activities, three subroutines and one function sub-program. Communication between the sub-programs is by argument list only. There is no COMMON storage area.

Main program: Activity 1

Activity 1 in the main program reads the input data described above. The rainfall—runoff pairs, whether they be given as intensities or volumes, are normalized to give *volumes* of active-rain and runoff in successive *unit* time intervals which *sum to unity*. The program is therefore 'units-free' and works in volumes. The normalizing constants are available to convert to any preferred system of units. Activity 1 then calculates and outputs the data denoted by (a) in Output data above. The first three moments (the second and third are about the mean) of the unit hydrograph, which is assumed to link the normalized rainfall and runoff data, are calculated using the theorem of moments and then passed to Activity 2.

Main program: Activity 2

Activity 2 identifies the parameter values of each model by solving a set of equations. Models with only one parameter yield one equation in that parameter on

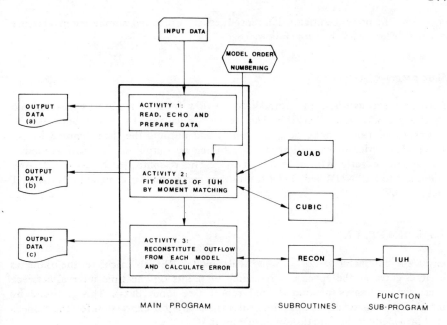

Figure 1. The structure of PICOMO

equating the first moment of the catchment unit hydrograph derived from the data
with the first moment of the model IUH. Multi-parameter models require as many
moment equations as there are parameters. In general these simultaneous equations
are non-linear in the parameter values.

However, the simultaneous equations arising from the two- and three-parameter
models currently in PICOMO can be reduced to a single quadratic or cubic equation
by elimination. The subroutines QUAD and CUBIC solve these equations explicitly.
Imaginary roots, when they appear for any model, cause Activity 3 to be skipped.
This test is carried out in QUAD and CUBIC. Additional tests on the parameters are
carried out in Activity 2 to ensure that they are physically meaningful. For
example, a negative real value for a storage delay time implies undamped
exponentials in the model IUH and is therefore skipped.

When the model parameters have been fixed, the lowest order shape-factor not
used in matching, is predicted. For one-parameter models, S_2 is predicted; for
two-parameter models, S_3 is predicted. S_4 is not calculated. The difference is then
found between the shape-factor predicted by the model and that derived from the
catchment unit hydrograph. The data listed in (b) under Output data above is
printed for each model in turn.

The internal ordering and numbering of the models in the program does not
necessarily correspond to that shown on output. The order in which the models are
executed is controlled by SWITCH 1 at the start of the activity. Both the order of
execution and numbering of the models on output can be altered by changing the
initial values of the arrays ORDER (17) and REFNUM (17) in lines 4 and 5 of the

program. The present initialization reproduces the order and numbering in reference (1) and differs from the program ordering.

Main program: Activity 3

Activity 3 reconstitutes the normalized outflow from each model by calling and executing subroutine RECON. The activity calculates the error between the reconstituted runoff and the given runoff and outputs the data denoted by (c) above. The order of execution and numbering on output of the various models corresponds exactly with that in Activity 2 and is controlled by Switch 2. Any alteration to REFNUM and ORDER produces corresponding changes in Activities 1 and 2.

Subroutine RECON

Given the parameter values for a particular model, RECON calculates the ordinates of its S-curve at the specified frequency of points on the time interval between successive ordinates of rainfall and runoff (see input data). This is found by integrating numerically (trapezoidal rule) the analytical expression for the Model's IUH provided by the function sub-program IUH.

The S-curve is then differenced to give the ordinates of the unit pulse response. Numerical integration (trapezoidal rule) is again used to convert the sampled representation of the unit pulse response to volumes of runoff in successive intervals of time in correspondence with the rainfall and runoff data. This is called 'model DUH' on output.

Finally the normalized active rainfall is convoluted with the model DUH to produce the outflow from the model.

Function sub-program IUH

IUH contains the analytical expression for the IUH of all the models considered. IUH returns to RECON the value of the IUH at a specified point in time for a given model. The model order in IUH corresponds exactly with the internal order in Activity 2. A switch at the beginning of the sub-program selects the correct IUH for the given model.

3. Level 2 description

Input description

Medium: Punched cards, one record per card.
Volume: For each data set, the number of rainfall—runoff pairs plus 2.

Record Description

Record identifi- cation number	Program line	Field name(s)	Name table ref.	Format
1	10	—	1	'—80 cols.—' of text
2	15	NX, NY, NDELT	2, 3 5	3I4
3	19	X(I), Y(I)	8, 9	2F10.4

Record sequence: 1, 2 and 3 the latter repeated on I, NY times. This pattern is repeated for each data set and is terminated by the JCL card /* indicating no further data.

Validation of input: None

Dimension restrictions: $NX < 150$, $NY < 150$, $NY * NDELT < 1000$.

Instruction modification: Lines 5 and 6 of the main program. The internal order, number and title of the 17 models is

1. One linear reservoir
2. Scalene triangle, peak at $\frac{1}{3}$ the base
3. Two equal linear reservoirs
4. Single channel
5. Routed rectangle
6. Routed triangle
7. Channel and reservoir/lag and route
8. Cascade (2 E.L.R.S.) with lateral inflow
9. N equal linear reservoirs, upstream inflow
10. Cascade of two unequal reservoirs, upstream inflow
11. Lagged cascade of N equal linear reservoirs
12. Isosceles triangle
13. Rectangle
14. Diffusion reach
15. Convective diffusion reach
20. Cascade of 3 reservoirs
21. Two reservoirs with lateral inflow

(Note the gap 16—19 inclusive.)

The order of execution is specified by the index vector ORDER initialized in line 5 of the program as

INTEGER ORDER (17) /4, 13, 2, 1, 3, 14, 12, 7, 5, 6, 9, 10, 8, 15, 11, 20, 21/

The reference numbers which are attached to each model in the order of execution are contained in the index vector REFNUM. There is a 1:1 correspondence between the elements of ORDER and REFNUM.

REFNUM is initialized in line 6 of the program as

INTEGER REFNUM (17) /1, 2, 4, 5, 6, 9, 11, 12, 13, 14, 16, 17, 19, 20, 22, 23, 24/

These initial values are in accordance with Dooge (herein).

REFNUM may be initialized with any set of numbers satisfying the output field I2. ORDER may be initialized with any permutation of the integers 1 to 15 (inclusive), 20 and 21. Should it be desired to execute only $S(1 \leqslant S \leqslant 17)$ of the models then

(a) the first S element of ORDER must contain a subset of the numbers 1 to 15 (inclusive), 20 and 21, and
(b) the remaining elements of ORDER must *not* be members of that set of numbers.

For example, suppose we wish to execute '14. Diffusion reach' and '15. Convective diffusion reach', only, and to number them 1. and 2. on output. Then ORDER and REFNUM should be changed to read

ORDER (17) /14, 15, 0, 0, . . . , 0/

REFNUM (17) /1, 2, 0, 0, . . . , 0/

Array size modification. The dimension restrictions on NX, NY and NDELT can be relaxed by increasing the size of (a) arrays X(150), DUH(150) and PY(150) in the main program and (b) arrays X(150), S(1000), SDUH(1000), DUH(150) and PY(150) in subroutine RECON. The current version of the program, when run under the G compiler (IBM 360), required 58K of store.

Output description

    Medium: Line printer
    Volume: Each section (a, b, c) begins on a new page. See Figure 1.
              Section (a), 2 lines for each rainfall/runoff pair plus 50 lines.
              Section (b), 14 lines for each model.
              Section (c), for each model executed, 11 lines plus one for each rainfall/runoff pair.
              Sections (a), (b) and (c) are repeated for each data set presented for processing.

Data processing description

This has not been included in the present text but may be obtained on request from the authors. It is designed to facilitate the alteration and extension of the program.

The net total CPU time used for processing the two data sets discussed in Level 3 was 1 min 49 sec under the G compiler (IBM 360).

Table 1. Name table

1.	One record of 80 characters of text.
2.	NX the number of active rainfall ordinates.
3.	NY the number of runoff ordinates.
4.	DUR the duration of the time interval between successive rainfall/runoff ordinates. This is always set equal to 1. in the program.
5.	NDELT the number of subdivisions of the unit time interval to be used in numerical integration.
6.	NINT = NY * NDELT the number of ordinates used in numerical integration.
7.	DT = 1/NDELT length of sub-intervals in numerical integration.
8.	X(150) the vector of (normalized active) rainfall ordinates.
9.	Y(150) the vector of (normalized) runoff ordinates.
10.	ORDER(17) the vector of internal model numbers in the order in which they are to be executed.
11.	REFNUM(17) the reference numbers to be associated with each model on output.
12.	DUH(150) ordinates of the unit pulse response of a model as volumes in successive unit intervals of time.
13.	PY(150) normalized outflow from a model: the predicted runoff as volumes in successive unit intervals of time.
14.	S(1000) values of the S-curve for a model sampled at intervals of DT.
15.	SDUH(1000) values of the unit pulse response for a model sampled at intervals of DT.

Table 2. The test data sets

Data set	A	B
Sampling time interval	1 day	3 hrs
Catchment area	753 sq. miles	248 sq. miles
Rainfall	ins	cusecs
Runoff	cusecs	cusecs

4. Level 3 description: Program use

Test data

The program was tested on two markedly different sets of data taken from Dooge (1973) where they are attributed to Sherman (1932) (test data set A) and to Nash (1958) (test data set B). Set A represents a complex storm and has been preprocessed to remove (a) losses from the rainfall and (b) groundwater recessions from the runoff. Set B on the other hand represents a near single event storm. In addition the storm resolution is considerably better in set B since its ratio of lag time to sampling interval is approximately 8 whereas it is only about 3 for A. The units for the data are shown in Table 2. Figures 2(a) and 2(b) show the echo-check and normalization of data sets A and B.

The family of models tested

The program attempts to fit 17 of the 24 one-, two- and three-parameter models presented in Dooge (herein). The models form a family the structure of which can

TEST DATA SET A

NUMBER OF ACTIVE RAIN ORDINATES = 16

NUMBER OF RUNOFF ORDINATES = 22

NUMBER OF SUBDIVISIONS OF TIME INTERVAL = 4

RAINFALL AND RUNOFF DATA

0.0680	132.0000
0.0	176.0000
0.0	229.0000
0.0	263.0000
0.0370	312.0000
0.0	264.0000
0.0270	167.0000
0.1020	553.0000
0.0800	665.0000
0.4400	1615.0000
0.0830	2116.0000
0.8800	4201.0000
0.6900	6168.0000
0.8200	8570.0000
0.4230	10229.0000
0.5000	11461.0000
0.0	10924.0000
0.0400	9375.0000
0.1300	7355.0000
0.0330	5146.0000
0.0740	3500.0000
0.0250	2377.0000

NORMALISED

RAINFALL AND RUNOFF DATA

0.0164	0.0015
0.0	0.0020
0.0	0.0027
0.0	0.0031
0.0089	0.0036
0.0	0.0031
0.0065	0.0019
0.0246	0.0064
0.0193	0.0078
0.1060	0.0188
0.0200	0.0246
0.2120	0.0489
0.1663	0.0720
0.1976	0.0999
0.1019	0.1191
0.1205	0.1337
0.0	0.1272
0.0	0.1091
0.0	0.0856
0.0	0.0605
0.0	0.0407
0.0	0.0277

NORMALISING CONSTANTS: VX = 4.1500   VY = 85899.0000

RMS DIFFERENCE BETWEEN X AND Y = 0.0659

Figure 2(a). Echo-check and normalization of data set A

be presented by the directed graph, Kaufmann (1968), shown in Figure 3. Each vertex X_i corresponds to a model. Pairs of vertices X_i and X_j are connected by arcs (X_i, X_j) in order to indicate the relation that the model at the terminal extremity of an arc X_j contains as a special case the model at the initial extremity X_i. For example, model 22 the 'lagged cascade of n equal reservoirs', contains model 12: 'lag and route', and model 16: 'Nash cascade' as special cases. Hence we define the arcs (X_{12}, X_{22}) and (X_{16}, X_{22}) in order to represent this inclusion. Models 12 and

TEST DATA SET B

NUMBER OF ACTIVE RAIN ORDINATES =   3
NUMBER OF RUNOFF ORDINATES =   38
NUMBER OF SUBDIVISIONS OF TIME INTERVAL =   5

RAINFALL AND RUNOFF DATA

```
 1829.0000        0.0
 3530.0000       30.0000
 8330.0000       34.0000
    0.0          90.0000
    0.0         130.0000
    0.0         120.0000
    0.0         120.0000
    0.0         110.0000
    0.0         104.0000
    0.0          91.0000
    0.0          74.0000
    0.0          68.0000
    0.0          57.0000
    0.0          47.0000
    0.0          39.0000
    0.0          33.0000
    0.0          29.0000
    0.0          24.0000
    0.0          21.0000
    0.0          17.0000
    0.0          15.5000
    0.0          13.5000
    0.0          11.5000
    0.0          10.0000
    0.0           8.5000
    0.0           7.0000
    0.0           6.5000
    0.0           6.0000
    0.0           5.5000
    0.0           5.0000
    0.0          45.0000
    0.0          40.0000
    0.0          35.0000
    0.0          30.0000
    0.0          25.0000
    0.0          15.0000
    0.0           5.0000
    0.0           0.0
```

NORMALISED

RAINFALL AND RUNOFF DATA

```
   0.1336        0.0
   0.2579        0.0023
   0.6085        0.0026
   0.0           0.0738
   0.0           0.0994
   0.0           0.0971
   0.0           0.0964
   0.0           0.0874
   0.0           0.0783
   0.0           0.0685
   0.0           0.0595
   0.0           0.0512
   0.0           0.0437
   0.0           0.0361
   0.0           0.0294
   0.0           0.0241
   0.0           0.0211
   0.0           0.0181
   0.0           0.0158
   0.0           0.0136
   0.0           0.0117
   0.0           0.0102
   0.0           0.0087
   0.0           0.0075
   0.0           0.0064
```

Figure 2(b). Echo-check and normalization of data set B

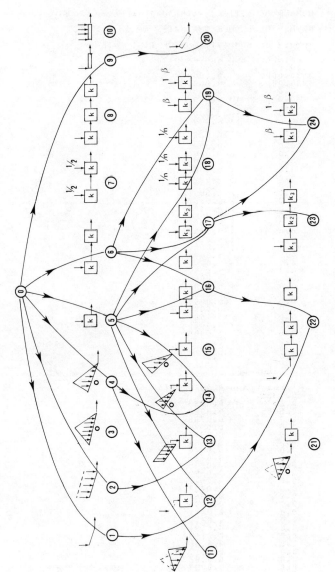

Figure 3. Model inclusion graph

16, in their turn, contain models 1, 5 and 6 as special cases. Hence, we define the arcs (X_1, X_{12}), (X_5, X_{12}), (X_5, X_{16}), (X_6, X_{16}), and so on.

The binary relation of model inclusion is

(a) strictly anti-symmetric, i.e. if X_j includes X_i as a special case then X_i cannot include X_j as a special case; and
(b) transitive, i.e. if model X_j includes X_i, and X_k includes X_j, then X_k also includes X_i as a special case.

Hence the relation of model inclusion always defines a strict ordering of the models and the graph showing this will have no circuits. The ordering is partial not total since models with the same number of parameters cannot be related by inclusion.

The strict ordering of the models by inclusion is not shown in its entirety in Figure 3, e.g. (X_{22}, X_5) is not shown since it is implied by (X_{22}, X_{16}) and (X_{16}, X_5). This is done for clarity. In addition only those arcs which relate the 17 models in the program are shown. Hence Figure 3 is a partial graph obtained by deleting arcs from the full graph which represents the strict-order relation defined by model inclusion on the 24 models in Dooge (herein). Model 0 is the model whose outflow is equal to its inflow and has no non-zero parameters. Since it is included as a special case in every other model and has no special case itself, its vertex X_0 is the minorant of the graph in Figure 3.

This strict ordering will be used subsequently to display (a) the consistency of measures of goodness of fit other than moments and (b) the improvement in measures of fit with increasing numbers of parameters. One can then attempt to trade extra parameters against greater model accuracy.

Shape factor plot

Figures 4(a) and 4(b) show the moments and shape-factors calculated by the program for data sets A and B. Figures 5(a) and 5(b) show a portion of the output from the parameter identification on sets A and B. Figure 6 shows a plot of S_3 versus S_2 for one parameter models. S_1 is fixed by the moment matching. The model whose (S_3, S_2) point lies closest to that for a particular data set is best in the sense that it reproduces the dimensionless second and third moments of the

```
        ACTIVE-RAINFALL MOMENTS
    U3X =   -30.9907     U2X =    0.9244     UP1X =    12.0858
            RUNOFF  MOMENTS
    U3Y =   -29.8477     U2Y =   10.8895     UP1Y =    15.9304
        MOMENTS OF THE IUH
    UP1H =       3.2446   U2H =    3.9651     U3H =      1.1431
        SHAPE FACTORS OF THE IUH


     S1 =       1.0000   S2 =    0.3766     S3 =      0.0335
```

Figure 4(a). Moments and shape-factors for data set A

288

```
ACTIVE-RAINFALL MOMENTS
U3X =   -0.3682    U2X =    0.5166   UP1X =    2.4749
       RUNOFF   MOMENTS
U3Y = 343.2402    U2Y =   37.7861   UP1Y =   10.6986
   MOMENTS OF THE IUH
UP1H =     8.2237  U2H =     37.2695  U3H =     343.6084
   SHAPE FACTORS OF THE IUH
  S1 =    1.0000  S2 =     0.5511  S3 =      0.6178
```

Figure 4(b). Moments and shape-factors for data set B

```
13. ROUTED RECTANGLE
BASE OF RECTANGLE =    2.8669
STORAGE DELAY TIME =    1.8111
MODEL SHAPE FACTOR S3 =    0.3478
DIFFERENCE IN S3: DATA - MODEL =   -0.3144


14. ROUTED TRIANGLE
BASE OF TRIANGLE =    2.6573
STORAGE DELAY TIME =    1.9160
MODEL SHAPE FACTOR S3 =    0.4118
DIFFERENCE IN S3: DATA - MODEL =   -0.3784


16. N EQUAL LINEAR RESERVOIRS
NUMBER OF RESERVOIRS IN CASCADE =    2.6550
STORAGE DELAY TIME FOR EACH RES. =    1.2221
MODEL SHAPE FACTOR S3 =    0.2837
DIFFERENCE IN S3: DATA - MODEL =   -0.2503


17. CASCADE OF TWO UNEQUAL RESERVOIRS
DELAY TIME FOR RESERVOIR 1 =    2.5151
DELAY TIME FOR RESERVOIR 2 =    0.7295
MODEL SHAPE FACTOR S3 =    0.9543
DIFFERENCE IN S3: DATA - MODEL =   -0.9208


19. CASCADE (2) WITH LATERAL INFLOW
DELAY TIME FOR THE RESERVOIRS =    1.4332
FRACTION OF INFLOW INTO FIRST RESERVOIR =    1.2639
MODEL SHAPE FACTOR S3 =    0.3479
DIFFERENCE IN S3: DATA - MODEL =   -0.3144
```

Figure 5(a). Parameters for set A

```
13. ROUTED RECTANGLE
BASE OF RECTANGLE =      4.5198
STORAGE DELAY TIME =     5.9638
MODEL SHAPE FACTOR S3 =    0.7628
DIFFERENCE IN S3: DATA - MODEL =    -0.1450


14. ROUTED TRIANGLE
BASE OF TRIANGLE =     4.3686
STORAGE DELAY TIME =     6.0394
MODEL SHAPE FACTOR S3 =    0.7922
DIFFERENCE IN S3: DATA - MODEL =    -0.1743


16. N EQUAL LINEAR RESERVOIRS
NUMBER OF RESERVOIRS IN CASCADE =      1.8146
STORAGE DELAY TIME FOR EACH RES. =      4.5320
MODEL SHAPE FACTOR S3 =    0.6074
DIFFERENCE IN S3: DATA - MODEL =    0.0104


17. CASCADE OF TWO UNEQUAL RESERVOIRS
DELAY TIME FOR RESERVOIR 1 =     7.6461
DELAY TIME FOR RESERVOIR 2 =     0.5776
MODEL SHAPE FACTOR S3 =    1.6082
DIFFERENCE IN S3: DATA - MODEL =    -0.9904


19. CASCADE (2) WITH LATERAL INFLOW
DELAY TIME FOR THE RESERVOIRS =     4.3276
FRACTION OF INFLOW INTO FIRST RESERVOIR =      0.9003
MODEL SHAPE FACTOR S3 =    0.5826
DIFFERENCE IN S3: DATA - MODEL =    0.0352
```

Figure 5(b). Parameters for set B

catchment unit hydrograph better than any other one parameter model in the program. See Dooge (1973) and Dooge (herein).

The RMS criterion of fit

Even though the models have been fitted by moments we can compare their performance on the basis of other criteria of fit, e.g. RMS error in the model output and time to peak. Figures 7(a) and 7(b) show typical output from the program for doing this. Tables 3 and 4 summarise the results from the test data sets.

Figures 8(a) 8(b) display the RMS error for the two data sets. If ability to match moments were a perfect predictor of RMS error, which it is not, then a plot of RMS

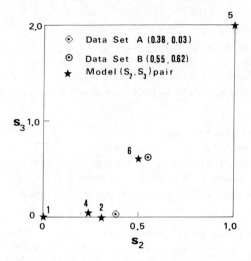

Figure 6. S_3/S_2 plot for one-parameter models

RAINFALL	DUH-MODEL 20	PREDICTED Y	RUNOFF (Y)	ERROR	TIME
0.0163855	0.0069803	0.0001144	0.0015367	0.0014223	1
0.0	0.1457294	0.0023879	0.0020489	-0.0003389	2
0.0	0.2806438	0.0045985	0.0026659	-0.0019326	3
0.0	0.2235674	0.0036633	0.0030617	-0.0006015	4
0.0089157	0.1408759	0.0023706	0.0036322	0.0012616	5
0.0	0.0835208	0.0026678	0.0030734	0.0004056	6
0.0065060	0.0487885	0.0033470	0.0019441	-0.0014028	7
0.0245783	0.0284938	0.0035798	0.0064378	0.0028580	8
0.0192771	0.0167211	0.0070722	0.0077533	0.0006811	9
0.1060241	0.0098752	0.0128081	0.0188011	0.0059931	10
0.0200000	0.0058710	0.0279431	0.0246336	-0.0033095	11
0.2120483	0.0035129	0.0427770	0.0489063	0.0061293	12
0.1662651	0.0021144	0.0666482	0.0720381	0.0053898	13
0.1975904	0.0012797	0.1076301	0.0998847	-0.0077454	14
0.1019278	0.0007784	0.1370620	0.1190817	-0.0179803	15
0.1204820	0.0004756	0.1460980	0.1336569	-0.0124410	16
0.0	0.0002917	0.1360947	0.1271726	-0.0089221	17
0.0	0.0001796	0.1113826	0.1091398	-0.0022428	18
0.0	0.0001110	0.0735552	0.0856238	0.0120686	19
0.0	0.0000687	0.0443628	0.0604896	0.0161269	20
0.0	0.0000428	0.0261104	0.0407455	0.0146352	21
0.0	0.0000266	0.0153166	0.0276720	0.0123555	22

DUH TOTAL =0.9999   RMS ERROR = 0.0083321

THE 22 TH MODEL HAS BEEN SKIPPED
DUE TO ILLEGAL PARAMETER VALUES.

THE 23 TH MODEL HAS BEEN SKIPPED
DUE TO ILLEGAL PARAMETER VALUES.

THE 24 TH MODEL HAS BEEN SKIPPED
DUE TO ILLEGAL PARAMETER VALUES.

Figure 7(a). Tableau output for set A

RAINFALL	DUH-MODEL 22	PREDICTED Y	RUNOFF(Y)	ERROR	TIME
0.1336109	0.0099544	0.0013300	0.0	-0.0013300	1
0.2578713	0.0520494	0.0095213	0.0022592	-0.0072621	2
0.6085178	0.0781502	0.0299212	0.0025604	-0.0273608	3
0.0	0.0877559	0.0635508	0.0738007	0.0102499	4
0.0	0.0888768	0.0820604	0.0994051	0.0173447	5
0.0	0.0852808	0.0877143	0.0971459	0.0094316	6
0.0	0.0791471	0.0866495	0.0963928	0.0097433	7
0.0	0.0718084	0.0818990	0.0873550	0.0054570	8
0.0	0.0640890	0.0752427	0.0783191	0.0030764	9
0.0	0.0564917	0.0677713	0.0685292	0.0007580	10
0.0	0.0493111	0.0601554	0.0594924	-0.0006629	11
0.0	0.0427059	0.0527981	0.0512087	-0.0015894	12
0.0	0.0367470	0.0459291	0.0436780	-0.0022511	13
0.0	0.0314486	0.0396652	0.0361473	-0.0035179	14
0.0	0.0267906	0.0340504	0.0293697	-0.0046807	15
0.0	0.0227324	0.0290829	0.0240982	-0.0049847	16
0.0	0.0192226	0.0247329	0.0210859	-0.0036470	17
0.0	0.0162056	0.0209552	0.0180736	-0.0028816	18
0.0	0.0136259	0.0176968	0.0158144	-0.0018824	19
0.0	0.0114295	0.0149022	0.0135552	-0.0013470	20
0.0	0.0095667	0.0125171	0.0116726	-0.0008446	21
0.0	0.0079922	0.0104899	0.0101664	-0.0003235	22
0.0	0.0066652	0.0087730	0.0086603	-0.0001127	23
0.0	0.0055497	0.0073236	0.0075307	0.0002071	24
0.0	0.0046142	0.0061035	0.0064011	0.0002976	25
0.0	0.0038312	0.0050788	0.0052715	0.0001926	26
0.0	0.0031773	0.0042203	0.0048949	0.0006746	27
0.0	0.0026320	0.0035024	0.0045184	0.0010160	28
0.0	0.0021780	0.0029032	0.0041419	0.0012387	29
0.0	0.0018005	0.0024038	0.0037653	0.0013615	30
0.0	0.0014871	0.0019883	0.0033888	0.0014005	31
0.0	0.0012273	0.0016431	0.0030123	0.0013692	32
0.0	0.0010119	0.0013566	0.0026357	0.0012791	33
0.0	0.0008338	0.0011192	0.0022592	0.0011401	34
0.0	0.0006865	0.0009225	0.0018827	0.0009602	35
0.0	0.0005649	0.0007599	0.0011296	0.0003697	36
0.0	0.0004645	0.0006255	0.0003765	-0.0002489	37
0.0	0.0003818	0.0005145	0.0	-0.0005145	38

DUH TOTAL =0.9985   RMS ERROR = 0.0063678

Figure 7(b). Tableau output for set B

Table 3. Results for data set A

Model no.	Shape-factors		Predicted output		
	S_2	S_3	RMS error	q_p	t_p
0	0.3776	0.0335	0.0659	0.1337	16
1	0.0000	0.0000	0.0279	0.1897	17
2	0.3333	0.0000	0.0037	0.1301	16
4	0.2188	0.0312	0.0086	0.1469	16
5	1.0000	2.0000	0.0135	0.1245	15
6	0.5000	0.5000	0.0062	0.1341	16
9	∞	∞	0.0447	0.0418	18
11	0.3766	0.1260	0.0036	0.1318	16
12	0.3766	0.4623	0.0085	0.1412	16
13	0.3766	0.3478	0.0070	0.1435	16
14	0.3766	0.4118	0.0083	0.1464	16
16	0.3766	0.2837	0.0061	0.1405	16
17	0.3766	0.9543	0.0086	0.1305	15
19	0.3766	0.3479	0.0074	0.1407	16
20	0.3766	0.4256	0.0083	0.1461	16
22	—	—	—	—	—
23	—	—	—	—	—
24	—	—	—	—	—

Table 4. Results for data set B

Model no.	Shape-factors		Predicted output		
	S_2	S_3	RMS error	q_p	t_p
0	0.5511	0.6178	0.1165	0.0994	5
1	0.0000	0.0000	0.0904	0.5384	11
2	0.3333	0.0000	0.0192	0.0608	14—16
4	0.2188	0.0312	0.0183	0.1006	9
5	1.0000	2.0000	0.0164	0.1015	4
6	0.5000	0.5000	0.0069	0.0876	7
9	∞	∞	0.0285	0.0304	8
11	0.5511	0.1998	—	—	—
12	0.5511	0.8182	0.0089	0.1303	6
13	0.5511	0.7628	0.0071	0.1052	7
14	0.5511	0.7922	0.0072	0.1113	7
16	0.5511	0.6074	0.0068	0.0864	6
17	0.5511	1.6082	0.0113	0.0985	5
19	0.5511	0.5826	0.0078	0.0835	6
20	0.5511	0.9111	0.0082	0.1117	7
22	0.5511	0.6178	0.0064	0.0877	6
23	—	—	—	—	—
24	0.5511	0.6178	0.0071	0.0858	7

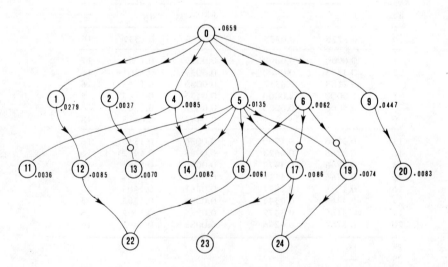

Figure 8(a). RMS error for data set A on the model inclusion graph

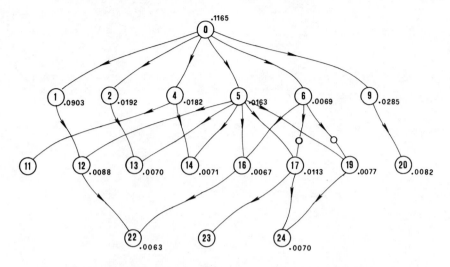

Figure 8(b). RMS error for data set B on the model inclusion graph

error on the model inclusion graph would show a strict ordering of the models with respect to RMS error. In data set A the symbols on the arcs show that there are three violations of this order. In data set B there are two direct violations and one indirect; the arc (X_6, X_{24}) is not shown. By and large the strict ordering of the models is reproduced. Clearly, this type of systematic analysis can be repeated for any other measure of fit, e.g. time to peak.

The model inclusion graph only displays a partial though strict ordering of the models. Hence a further comparison of RMS error between models with the same number of parameters is necessary in order to attempt a total ordering of the models. This in turn can be represented by another graph. In data set A the best one-parameter model: 2. Rectangle, is better than all two-parameter models with the exception of model: 11. Scalene triangle. None of the three-parameter models produced realistic parameters. The sensitivity of these results to changes in the number of active rainfall ordinates has not been investigated. In data set B, model: 6. Two equal reservoirs with upstream inflow, is the best one-parameter model and is surpassed only by the two-parameter model: 16. Nash cascade, and by the three-parameter model: 22. The lagged Nash cascade.

In both cases a law of diminishing returns appears to hold for the models considered. The RMS of the zero model is merely the RMS difference between inflow and outflow. The inclusion of an appropriate one-parameter model reduces this by at least an order of magnitude. However, the addition of further parameters produces a marginal decrease in RMS error. In addition physically unrealistic values of the parameters occur more frequently.

CLS: Constrained Linear Systems

SERGIO MARTELLI
IBM Scientific Center, Pisa, Italy

EZIO TODINI
IBM Scientific Center, Pisa, Italy

JAMES R. WALLIS
IBM Scientific Center, Pisa, (while on leave from IBM Research Center, Yorktown Heights, New York, USA)

1.1 Introduction

CLS is a fast, easy to use computer program written in FORTRAN IV for operation under the CP-CMS. CLS solves the discrete time linear system in N inputs:

$$q = Hu + \epsilon$$

either as an unconstrained least squares or as a constrained linear system with $u \geqslant 0$ and $Gu = 1$.

The optional constraints of CLS are felt to be of particular usefulness to hydrologists, especially in those area where data is sparse or bad, or where budget or time constraints prevent other more complex methods from being used.

1.2 General description of CLS

We may define a discrete time linear system in N inputs as

$$q = Hu + \epsilon \tag{1}$$

where u is a vector of Nk impulse responses, k being the length of each individual impulse response, q a vector of discrete outputs for the time interval Δt, H a partitioned matrix of discrete time inputs, and ϵ an error vector (Natale and Todini, 1974). In hydrology there are many systems that are linear or can be thought of as linear and the resolution of the impulse response vector u, given H, q and some assumption about the nature of ϵ, is a common problem in hydrologic analysis.

The constrained linear systems program package (CLS) was developed at the IBM Pisa Scientific Center for the solution of hydrologic linear systems with multiple inputs and a single output. If the constrained option is invoked then the solution finds:

$$\min. J(\epsilon'\epsilon) = \tfrac{1}{2}u'H'Hu - u'H'q \tag{2}$$

$$u \geqslant 0$$

subject to:

$$\mathbf{Gu} = 1$$

where $\mathbf{G}$ is a matrix of coefficients which definition can be found in 3.1.

It is also possible to run the CLS program without constraints (unconstrained ordinary least squares method), but the $\hat{\mathbf{u}}$ are much more unstable, and likely to appear unsatisfactory to most users.

1.3 Source language

CLS is written in FORTRAN IV and is a fully interactive program package designed for use under CP-67/CMS on an IBM 360–67 computer.

2.1 Purpose and objectives

Usually the estimate of $\mathbf{u}$ in the linear system represented by equation 1 is obtained via the inversion of the matrix $(\mathbf{H}' \mathbf{V}_\epsilon^{-1} \mathbf{H})$, with $\mathbf{V}_\epsilon = 1$ the variance of the errors, assumed Gaussian and independently distributed. The matrix $(\mathbf{H}' \mathbf{V}_\epsilon^{-1} \mathbf{H})$ is frequently ill-conditioned (Abadie, 1970), and in addition when $N > 1$ the level of the errors due to the inversion becomes comparable to the values of the parameters that are to be estimated.

However, for linear hydrologic systems we possess *a priori* information about the nature of the parameter $\mathbf{u}$ and it seems reasonable that the estimating technique for $\mathbf{u}$ should incorporate all of the available knowledge and hence reduce the field of choice for $\hat{\mathbf{u}}$. For instance, it seems reasonable to hypothesize that $\mathbf{u} \geqslant 0$, which is equivalent to saying that water does not flow up the stream channel. In addition, if channel flow is regarded as a stationary process than conservation of mass should allow us $\sum_{i=1}^{k} u_i = 1$ or at least equality to same constant Φ (runoff coefficient).

CLS was designed to facilitate the solution of constrained linear hydrologic systems with multiple inputs. We wanted a program which would be flexible, handle fairly large problems and be economical to use in terms of both user and computer time.

2.2 Extent of program coverage

CLS has restrictions on the number and dimensions of arrays for the linear systems that can be specified by the user. The restrictions introduced into CLS are not inherent in the mathematics but result from a desire to facilitate the operation of CLS under CP-CMS.

CLS restrictions are:

(1) The output vector, $q \leqslant 3000 \, \Delta$.
(2) The length of the sum of the input vector $\leqslant 18\,000 \, \Delta$.
(3) No more than 10 input vectors are permitted.
(4) No more than two precipitation inputs (prior to threshold splitting) are permitted. For a discussion of threshold splitting see Todini and Wallis (herein).
(5) No more than two thresholds per precipitation input are allowed.
(6) The number of parameters to be estimated (length of vector, $\mathbf{u}$) must not

exceed 120*NC*, where *NC* the number of constraints, equals the number of flow inputs plus an additional one if precipitation inputs are also included amongst the inputs. Note. The first value of each kernel function applies to the time zero transfer (i.e. instantaneous transfer of input to output).

A slightly larger CLS problem can be run by not invoking the CLS equality constraint option in which case the solution derived uses either an unconstrained ordinary least square solution or an inequality constrained one ($u \geqslant 0$). If the CLS constraint options are used then inputs are transferred via the parameter Φ.

Users who prefer other choices of constraints will have to reprogram the INPUT subroutine.

All data sets must be of equal length with the same time interval, and if more than one input is used then they should both be in the same units. If precipitation inputs are used, then it is best to have them expressed in the same units as the outflows.

2.3 Advantages of CLS

Natale and Todini (1973, 1974) have shown that the incorporation of single inequality and equality constraints for a linear channel routing problem leads to very stable and reasonable estimates of the parameter u. Natale and Todini used the inequality constraint $u \geqslant 0$, the equality constraint $\mathbf{Gu} = 1$. They were able to demonstrate for a channel network, with two inputs and negligible lateral inflow, that CLS gave reasonable impulse responses and accurate split sample predictions. With synthetic data and Monte Carlo simulations they were able to show that the variance of û was greatly lessened by the introduction of the aforementioned equality and inequality constraints. In addition, the $E\{\hat{u}\}$ for the constrained estimation had only a small bias from the true values and, unless lengths and number of sample were extraordinarily large, the constrained estimation was consistently clearly superior.

Subsequently Todini and Wallis (herein) investigated the idea of using CLS to model the essentially non-linear daily rainfall—runoff process. For accurate daily rainfall—runoff modelling they found it necessary to separate the precipitation input into different input vectors based upon different areas or, more usually, upon different antecedent moisture conditions.

When tested with split samples their results were found to be no more divergent than those generated by the use of the most complex of non-linear explicit soil moisture accounting models (ESMA models). ESMA models, of which the most famous is the Stanford Watershed Model (Crawford and Linsley, 1966), are difficult to use without special and rather prolonged training from an experienced user. As users will find, CLS does not have a particularly demanding training requirement.

Data requirements for CLS rainfall—runoff modelling are lower than ESMA modelling, a similar finding may also be said to apply to the use of CLS for channel routing compared to the direct solution of the St Venant equations.

For daily rainfall—runoff modelling, CLS has another advantage over ESMA models: the fitting procedure tends to be less demanding of computer resources and the resulting predicting algorithm is a great deal less demanding in terms of data as well as of computer needs. As far as it is known to the authors, there is no program similar to CLS and it is suggested that CLS could be useful in many hydrologic modelling situations, where data is sparse and budgetary or time constraints are too severe for alternative model choices to be realizable.

3.1 Formulae

$$q = Hu + \epsilon = \sum_{i=1}^{N} H_i u_i + \epsilon \qquad (3)$$

where:

$$q = \begin{bmatrix} Q(1) \\ Q(2) \\ \vdots \\ Q(m) \end{bmatrix} \quad \text{is the outflow vector}$$

$$\epsilon = \begin{bmatrix} \epsilon(1) \\ \epsilon(2) \\ \vdots \\ \epsilon(m) \end{bmatrix} \quad \begin{array}{l} \text{is a random error which takes into account modelling} \\ \text{and data errors} \\ N \text{ is the number of input vectors} \end{array}$$

$$u_i = \begin{bmatrix} u_i(1) \\ u_i(2) \\ \vdots \\ u_i(k_i) \end{bmatrix} \quad i\text{th impulse response}$$

$$H_i = \begin{bmatrix} P_i(1) & & & & 0 \\ P_i(2) & P_i(1) & & & \\ P_i(3) & P_i(2) & P_i(1) & & \\ \vdots & \vdots & \vdots & & \\ P_i(m-1) & P_i(m-2) & P_i(m-3) & \dots & P_i(m-k_i+2) \\ P_i(m) & P_i(m-1) & P_i(m-2) & \dots & P_i(m-k_i+1) \end{bmatrix}$$

where H_i is the ith input matrix

H_i matrix can be set up by using the ith input vector:

$$P_i = \begin{bmatrix} P_i(1) \\ P_i(2) \\ \vdots \\ P_i(m) \end{bmatrix}$$

The CLS minimizes the following functional:

$$J(\epsilon' \epsilon) = \tfrac{1}{2}u'H'Hu - u'H'q \qquad (4)$$

subject to the following optional choice of constraints:

(1) No constraints (unconstrained ordinary least squares)

(2) $u \geqslant 0$

(3) $\begin{cases} u \geqslant 0 \\ Gu = 1 \end{cases}$

where the G matrix is defined below.

If $r = 0$, G is a $(1, Nk)$ matrix for which the elements are:

$$g_{1,(i-1)k+j} = \frac{\sum\limits_{\tau=1}^{m-j+1} P_i(\tau)}{\sum\limits_{\tau=1}^{m} Q(\tau)} \qquad \begin{matrix} i = 1, \ldots, N \\ j = 1, \ldots, k \end{matrix} \tag{5}$$

to represent the following constraint

$$\sum_{i=1}^{N} \sum_{j=1}^{k} u_{(i-1)k+j} \sum_{\tau=1}^{m-j+1} P_i(\tau) = \sum_{\tau=1}^{m} Q(\tau) \tag{6}$$

which takes into account the water losses between the N precipitation inputs P_i and the output Q, if $P_i(\tau) = 0$ for $1 - k \leqslant \tau \leqslant 0$.

If $r > 0$, G is an $(r + 1, Nk)$ matrix for which the elements are all zeroes except:

$$g_{s,(s-1)k+j} = 1$$

$$g_{r+1,(i-1)k+j} = \frac{\sum\limits_{\tau=1}^{m-j+1} P_i(\tau)}{\sum\limits_{\tau=1}^{m} \left[Q(\tau) - \sum\limits_{s=1}^{r} P_s(\tau) \right]} \qquad \begin{matrix} s = 1, \ldots, r \\ i = r+1, \ldots, N \\ j = 1, \ldots, k \end{matrix} \tag{7}$$

to represent equation 3 and the following water balance equation

$$\sum_{i=r+1}^{N} \sum_{j=1}^{k} u_{(i-1)k+1} \sum_{\tau=1}^{m-j+1} P_i(\tau) = \sum_{\tau=1}^{m} \left[Q(\tau) - \sum_{s=1}^{r} P_s(\tau) \right] \tag{8}$$

relevant to the whole system or r input tributary flows, $N - r$ precipitation discharges and one outflow discharge vector, provided $m \gg k$.

Once the parameters u have been estimated, CLS provides an estimate of the *a priori* unknown runoff coefficient relevant to each P_i precipitation input by means of equation 2, i.e.

$$\hat{\Phi}_i = \sum_{j=1}^{k} \hat{u}_{(i-1)k+j} \qquad i = r+1, \ldots, N \tag{9}$$

All the above equations have been written for convenience with k equal for all N inputs, but the CLS program allows for variable k.

Note. The possibility exists of finding a certain combination of flow and precipitation inputs which produces a non-positive definite matrix $(H'H)$, as required for the existence of a solution of our quadratic programming problem. To avoid the above inconvenience each input vector and the output vector is divided by the square root of its sum of squares, such scaling seems to assure the existence of the solution.

Statistics of residuals

$\hat{\mathbf{q}}$ the predicted outflow vector

$\hat{\boldsymbol{\epsilon}} = \hat{\mathbf{q}} - \mathbf{q}$ the vector of residual errors

$$\sqrt{V} = \sqrt{\dfrac{\displaystyle\sum_{i=1}^{m} \hat{\epsilon}_i^2 - \dfrac{\left(\displaystyle\sum_{i=1}^{m} \hat{\epsilon}_i\right)^2}{m}}{m - 1}} \qquad \text{standard deviation of errors}$$

$$T_V = \sum_{i=1}^{m} q_i^2 - \dfrac{\left(\displaystyle\sum_{i=1}^{m} q_i\right)^2}{m} \qquad \text{total variance}$$

$$E_V = \left[\sum_{i=1}^{m} q_i^2 - \dfrac{\left(\displaystyle\sum_{i=1}^{m} q_i\right)^2}{m}\right] - \left[\sum_{i=1}^{m} \hat{\epsilon}_i^2 - \dfrac{\left(\displaystyle\sum_{i=1}^{m} \hat{\epsilon}_i\right)^2}{m}\right] \qquad \text{explained variance}$$

$\hat{\epsilon}_{\max}$ = maximum $\hat{\boldsymbol{\epsilon}}$

$\hat{\epsilon}_{\min}$ = minimum $\hat{\boldsymbol{\epsilon}}$

$q_{\max}$ = maximum $\mathbf{q}$

m_q = index of $q_{\max}$

L = integer $(\sqrt{m/2})$

LL = maximum $(1, m_q - L) + 1$ index of lower limit of search

LU = minimum $(m, m_q + L) - 1$ index of upper limit of search

$\hat{q}_{\max}$ = maximum $\hat{\mathbf{q}}$ between LL and L

$m_{\hat{q}}$ = index of $\hat{q}_{\max}$

If $LL \leqslant m_{\hat{q}} \leqslant UL$

then print $p = m_{\hat{q}} - m_q$ phasing error at peak

$\% = \left(\dfrac{\hat{q}_{\max} - q_{\max}}{q_{\max}}\right) \times 100$ percentage error between peaks

k = number of runs of $\hat{\boldsymbol{\epsilon}}$ above and below zero

n_i = vector of lengths of runs

$$K = \sum_{i=1}^{k} \left(\sum_{j=1}^{n_i} \hat{\epsilon}_j\right)^2 \bigg/ \sum_{j=1}^{m} \hat{\epsilon}_j^2 \qquad \text{measure of persistence (Todini and Wallis, herein)}$$

3.2 CLS flowchart

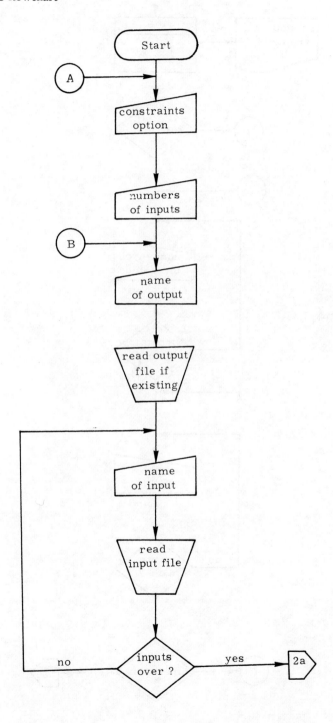

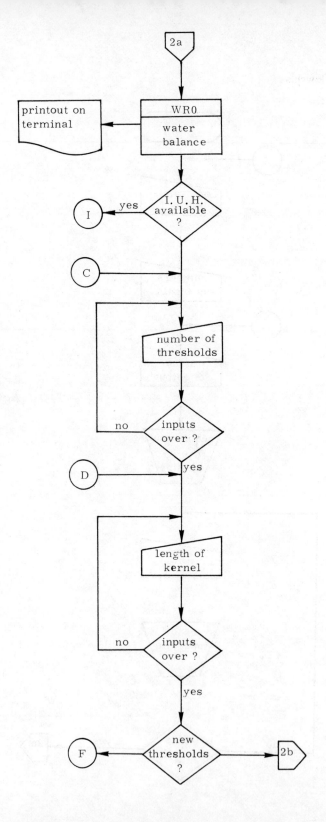

303

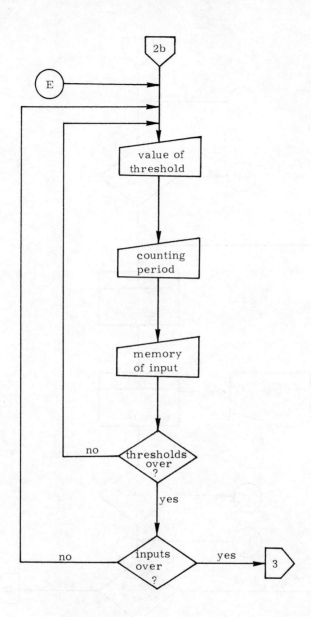

304

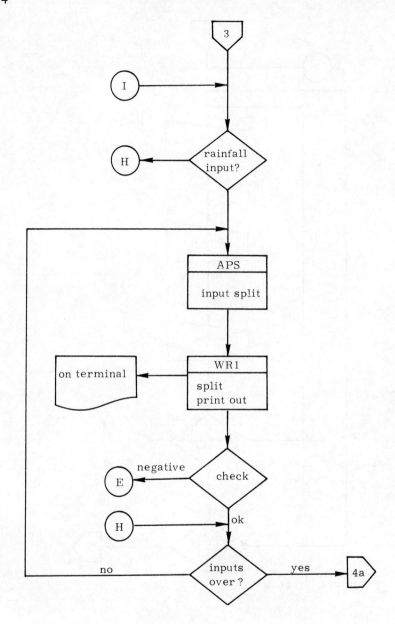

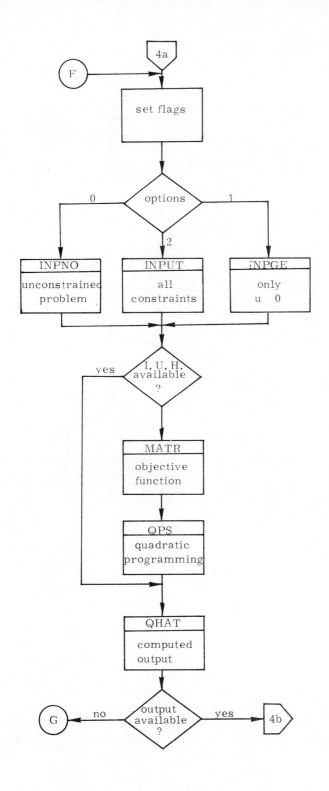

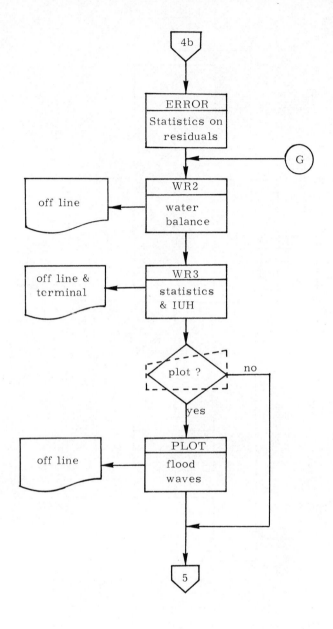

307

Parameter changes

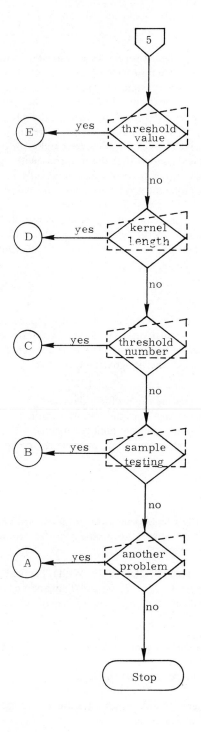

3.3 Timing

We have not yet devised an accurate algorithm for estimating the amount of CPU time that the user can expect to incur when processing a typical CLS problem. Most of the computation time used by CLS is taken by the subroutine that makes the correlation matrix and comparatively little by the other routines. For successive runs with the same data set we have attempted to arrange the program logic to prevent unnecessary recalculation of those portions of the correlation matrix that remain unchanged between successive steps of a typical trial and error optimization.

To economize on CPU time, it is suggested that the user start with kernel lengths that appear likely to be too short rather than too long, and only to increase the kernel length when it becomes apparent that the kernel recessions have been severely truncated.

Basically CLS is very fast; for example, a single problem run with one 1096 Δt input flow vector, one precipitation vector with a threshold, and two impulse response functions of lengths 35 and 35, took 30 seconds of CPU time on an IBM 360-67, operating under CP-CMS.

3.4 Input—output files for CLS

CLS is designed to operate under the CP-CMS. The input data sets must be pre-stored separately in the user's virtual machine under the designation INPUT NAME, where name is an 8-character BCD string. The output vector, q, from the linear system must be prestored under the designation OUT NAME, where name is an 8-character BCD string.

FT01F001   Used by CSL for reading the problem data sets.
FT05F001   Used by CLS for reading from the remote terminal.
FT06F001   Used by CLS for writing on the remote terminal.
FT08F001   Used by CLS for extensive offline printing the complete results if requested by the user.

3.5 Useful hints for the CLS user

Upon giving the command CLS, the user, sitting at his terminal will be expected to respond to a series of queries that define the problem to be attempted. These demands in order of their appearance are:

(a) WHICH CLS CONSTRAINT OPTION DO YOU WISH TO USE? (− − −):
Response is a single integer 0, 1 or 2, where 0 means no constraints, 1 means $u \geqslant 0$, and 2 means the full set of equality and inequality constraints.
(b) NAME OF OUTPUT (− − −):
Response is appropriate 8-character or less BCD name (left justified).
(c) HOW MANY INPUTS? (− − −):
Response is double digit integer $N \leqslant 10$ (right justified).
(d) NAME OF INPUT (− − −):
This question appears iteratively N times. Responses are the appropriate 8-character of less BCD names (left justified).

(e) NUMBER OF THRESHOLDS (− − −):

    Response is 0, 1 or 2. This query may appear twice if there are two precipitation inputs.

(f) LENGTH OF KERNEL FOR INPUT (− − −):

    Response is double digit integer (right justified).

(g) INPUT THRESHOLD VALUE (− − −):

    Response is a floating point number, picked in conjunction with the length and memory of antecedent moisture period, so as to yield a volume of water in the upper precipitation class somewhere between 5% and 45%. The user will find that similar solutions can be obtained with rather different sets of these three parameters.

INPUT LENGTH OF ANTECEDENT MOISTURE COUNTING PERIOD (− − −):

    Response is a two-digit integer (right justified)

INPUT MEMORY OF ANTECEDENT MOISTURE (− − −):

    Response is a two-digit integer (right justified).

Note. The (g) queries appear only for precipitation inputs, and in accordance with the number of thresholds previously established. CLS now processes the input data through the threshold separating subroutine APS, prints out the resulting statistics and queries the user as to whether or not he wishes to proceed.

The query is:

(h) O.K.? (− − −):

    Response is YES or NO, where NO causes an iteration back to query (g) and a YES allows CLS to print the statistics of the solution.

(i) DO YOU WANT A PLOT? (− − −):

    Response is YES or NO, where YES generates the complete statistics of the problem on the offline printer as well as some additional terminal output.

(j) DO YOU WANT TO VARY THE THRESHOLDS? (− − −):

    Response is YES or NO, with YES causing an iteration back to query (g).

(k) DO YOU WANT TO VARY THE LENGTH OF THE KERNELS? (− − −):

    Response is YES or NO, with YES causing an interation back to query (f).

(l) DO YOU WANT TO VARY THE NUMBER OF THRESHOLDS? (− − −):

    Response is YES or NO, with YES causing an iteration back to query (e).

(m) DO YOU WISH TO USE THESE KERNEL FUNCTIONS FOR SPLIT SAMPLE TESTING? (− − −):

    Response is YES or NO, with YES causing a reiteration of queries (c) and (d).

(n) DO YOU WANT ANOTHER PROBLEM? (− − −):

    Response is YES or NO, with YES causing an iteration back to query (a).

4. Glossary of Italian terms for the following program

METODO
method

NOME USCITA
name of output

NUMERO INGRESSI
how many inputs?

NOME INGRESSO
name of input

NOME, TIPO, VOLUME, C. DEF.
name, type, volume, runoff coefficeint

OUT. QQ
discharge output file

INP.PP
rainfall input file

NUMERO SOGLIE PER . . .
number of thresholds for . . .

TEMPO BASE 1 PER . . .
length of kernel 1 for . . .

TEMPO BASE 2 PER . . .
length of kernel 2 for . . .

VALORE SOGLIA PER . . .
threshold value for . . .

VALORE
value

STATISTICHE SUI RESIDUI
residual errors statistics

MEDIA, DEV. STAND
mean, standard deviation

COEFF. DI DET., COEFF. DI PERS.
determination coefficient, persistency coefficeint

ERRORE PERCENTUALE TRA I COLMI
percentage error between peaks

SFASAMENTO TRA I COLMI
phasing error at peak

RISPOSTA IMPULSIVA
impulsive response

PLOT?
do you want a plot?
CAMBIO SOLO VALORE SOGLIE?
do you want to vary the thresholds?

CAMBIO TEMPI BASE?
do you want to vary the length of the kernels?

CAMBIO NUMERO SOGLIE?
do you want to vary the number for thresholds?

UTILIZZO I.U.H. CALCOLATI?
do you wish to use these kernels functions for split sample testing?

NUOVO PROBLEMA?
do you want another problem?

COEEF. DEFL., VAL. SOGLIA, TEMPO ACCUM., MEMORIA
runoff coefficient, threshold value, accumulation time, memory

VOLUME MASSIMO RIMOSSO
maximum moved volume

MINIMIZZAZIONE CON VINCOLI DI UGUALE E DI MAGGIORE-UGUALE
minimization subject to equality and inequality constraints

STATISTICHE SUI RESIDUI
residual statistics

NEL CAMPO DI OSS. FRA ... E ... DELTA T
in the range between ... and ... delta T

PORTATA MAX. OSS. = ... A ... DELTA T
maximum observed discharge = ... at ... delta T

4.1 Sample problem input
INPUT KIZU file

```
(I2,2I4,A2)
(8F10.4)
0106621280PP   KIZU RIVER JULY.62 - DEC 65.  WMO DATA
```

444.872	633.860	108.709	322.783	725.844	117.072	5.017	46.829
81.950	0.0	20.069	0.0	18.397	232.471	3.345	65.226
25.087	41.811	76.933	0.0	8.362	0.0	1.672	0.0
0.0	382.992	2187.569	95.330	0.0	0.0	0.0	0.0
1.672	1.672	25.087	0.0	0.0	0.0	0.0	31.777
1.672	33.449	1.672	133.796	235.816	188.987	16.725	5.017
0.0	3.345	0.0	0.0	6.690	127.106	153.866	2607.354
56.863	0.0	122.089	0.0	0.0	0.0	0.0	0.0
11.707	80.278	3.345	1.672	130.451	122.089	11.707	0.0
0.0	0.0	0.0	88.640	188.987	30.104	40.139	28.432
0.0	0.0	3.345	0.0	36.794	18.397	0.0	3.345
0.0	0.0	23.414	0.0	0.0	0.0	103.692	709.120
0.0	0.0	0.0	0.0	13.380	252.540	232.471	8.362
58.536	20.069	16.725	3.345	0.0	8.362	26.759	1.672
0.0	0.0	0.0	0.0	1.672	13.380	162.228	105.365
1.672	0.0	0.0	0.0	50.174	262.575	145.503	21.742
3.345	0.0	0.0	13.380	18.397	8.362	0.0	1.672
3.345	312.749	321.111	18.397	3.345	3.345	10.035	3.345
0.0	0.0	0.0	1.672	190.660	11.707	6.690	0.0
3.345	0.0	1.672	0.0	100.347	282.644	83.623	0.0
3.345	0.0	0.0	11.707	6.690	5.017	118.744	53.518
0.0	3.345	11.707	26.759	3.345	0.0	10.035	26.759
25.087	15.052	0.0	0.0	26.759	282.644	182.297	20.069
10.035	45.156	30.104	11.707	70.243	105.365	60.208	13.380
11.707	23.414	16.725	21.742	3.345	15.052	56.863	31.777
0.0	20.069	0.0	28.432	25.087	11.707	25.087	6.690
1.672	3.345	0.0	11.707	16.725	3.345	8.362	3.345
1.672	8.362	13.380	13.380	0.0	11.707	178.952	13.380
0.0	80.278	20.069	8.362	1.672	20.069	0.0	0.0
5.017	3.345	0.0	0.0	0.0	1.672	1.672	0.0
60.208	40.139	5.017	0.0	0.0	3.345	1.672	0.0
1.672	0.0	0.0	110.382	130.451	51.846	429.820	46.829
11.707	95.330	63.553	1.672	0.0	0.0	0.0	0.0
3.345	46.829	81.950	13.380	0.0	0.0	209.057	68.571
5.017	0.0	80.278	25.087	0.0	0.0	0.0	8.362
117.072	307.731	76.933	0.0	0.0	0.0	0.0	21.742
307.731	6.690	0.0	259.230	28.432	53.518	16.725	197.349
130.451	25.087	3.345	0.0	0.0	1.672	1.672	100.347
185.642	6.690	0.0	25.087	53.518	58.536	3.345	230.799
521.805	112.054	687.378	25.087	0.0	349.542	195.677	630.515
474.977	46.829	16.725	43.484	145.503	337.835	0.0	3.345
21.742	147.176	774.345	337.835	292.679	25.087	15.052	1.672
490.029	694.068	260.903	53.518	403.061	3.345	3.345	26.759
5.017	110.382	102.020	332.818	26.759	3.345	30.104	0.0
1.672	145.503	23.414	43.484	80.278	46.829	3.345	40.139
8.362	145.503	247.523	0.0	45.156	60.208	254.213	21.742
58.536	336.163	3.345	25.087	91.985	23.414	60.208	222.436
11.707	0.0	8.362	43.484	0.0	25.087	0.0	0.0
0.0	25.087	237.488	244.178	0.0	0.0	3.345	76.933
197.349	0.0	1.672	13.380	0.0	8.362	337.835	232.471
28.432	0.0	25.087	538.530	361.250	199.022	257.558	36.794
3.345	56.863	18.397	393.026	125.434	147.176	30.104	1.672
0.0	6.690	6.690	31.777	344.525	36.794	214.074	449.890
274.282	369.612	36.794	6.690	3.345	5.017	0.0	0.0
105.365	0.0	65.226	270.937	23.414	102.020	20.069	41.811
3.345	5.017	71.915	0.0	0.0	0.0	204.039	118.744
5.017	0.0	23.414	259.230	18.397	0.0	0.0	0.0
135.469	56.863	5.017	0.0	0.0	0.0	0.0	0.0
0.0	742.569	1.672	0.0	0.0	16.725	55.191	5.017
83.623	0.0	5.017	0.0	0.0	0.0	0.0	0.0
0.0	347.870	130.451	0.0	0.0	0.0	0.0	23.414
0.0	1.672	0.0	0.0	0.0	0.0	0.0	1.672
0.0	0.0	15.052	0.0	0.0	46.829	108.709	11.707
0.0	41.811	51.846	1.672	0.0	0.0	11.707	56.863
212.402	56.863	3.345	11.707	1.672	6.690	3.345	75.260
122.089	58.536	8.362	0.0	18.397	13.380	21.742	75.260
13.380	0.0	0.0	8.362	1.672	3.345	3.345	10.035
3.345	0.0	23.414	0.0	35.122	118.744	6.690	25.087
0.0	0.0	18.397	0.0	0.0	0.0	0.0	0.0
1.672	0.0	0.0	0.0	35.122	6.690	6.690	0.0
63.553	297.696	97.002	5.017	98.675	207.384	85.295	86.968

8.362	0.0	262.575	30.104	8.362	0.0	0.0	21.742
115.399	55.191	90.312	58.536	1.672	3.345	1.672	1.672
15.052	177.280	132.124	416.441	316.094	91.985	98.675	18.397
1.672	3.345	40.139	90.312	40.139	43.484	1.672	10.035
0.0	18.397	23.414	172.263	0.0	18.397	8.362	15.052
3.345	36.794	8.362	157.211	46.829	0.0	13.380	262.575
70.243	8.362	3.345	18.397	11.707	188.987	18.397	31.777
0.0	1.672	16.725	48.501	252.540	6.690	10.035	0.0
140.486	48.501	83.623	3.345	3.345	0.0	0.0	0.0
98.675	48.501	97.002	88.640	0.0	1.672	107.037	220.764
180.625	374.629	21.742	0.0	0.0	0.0	1.672	0.0
0.0	0.0	0.0	0.0	0.0	118.744	0.0	0.0
33.449	235.816	36.794	98.675	0.0	16.725	152.193	11.707
8.362	61.881	118.744	5.017	0.0	0.0	0.0	505.081
1.672	0.0	13.380	0.0	0.0	0.0	0.0	0.0
0.0	0.0	0.0	5.017	36.794	235.816	0.0	0.0
0.0	40.139	25.087	0.0	0.0	0.0	80.278	1.672
0.0	35.122	5.017	0.0	0.0	309.404	0.0	0.0
0.0	15.052	40.139	25.087	0.0	0.0	0.0	382.992
224.109	16.725	3.345	3.345	51.846	262.575	73.588	861.313
95.330	0.0	0.0	0.0	0.0	0.0	0.0	0.0
0.0	45.156	546.892	571.979	183.970	0.0	50.174	113.727
0.0	301.042	190.660	108.709	304.386	244.178	120.417	81.950
194.005	10.035	0.0	0.0	3.345	76.933	143.831	43.484
0.0	75.260	28.432	142.159	10.035	0.0	28.432	41.811
98.675	5.017	0.0	0.0	0.0	21.742	0.0	8.362
0.0	0.0	0.0	1.672	10.035	10.035	61.881	102.020
103.692	269.265	65.226	0.0	1.672	56.863	418.113	78.605
0.0	0.0	100.347	70.243	30.104	20.069	3.345	1.672
0.0	28.432	13.380	5.017	3.345	21.742	43.484	58.536
15.052	0.0	13.380	0.0	68.571	247.523	61.881	128.779
600.410	469.959	33.449	274.282	225.781	11.707	0.0	0.0
0.0	0.0	0.0	11.707	81.950	137.141	117.072	58.536
20.069	0.0	95.330	401.389	175.608	0.0	0.0	75.260
50.174	0.0	11.707	55.191	137.141	28.432	0.0	0.0
0.0	20.069	20.069	0.0	0.0	0.0	70.243	81.950
0.0	3.345	10.035	11.707	0.0	3.345	138.814	188.987
0.0	8.362	11.707	40.139	11.707	10.035	0.0	0.0
0.0	0.0	5.017	1.672	0.0	0.0	0.0	0.0
0.0	0.0	13.380	35.122	1.672	5.017	0.0	0.0
0.0	13.380	13.380	0.0	0.0	10.035	10.035	8.362
0.0	0.0	0.0	1.672	45.156	60.208	0.0	0.0
0.0	8.362	71.915	97.002	0.0	10.035	80.278	75.260
28.432	6.690	15.052	35.122	6.690	0.0	1.672	0.0
0.0	40.139	100.347	85.295	43.484	26.759	28.432	5.017
3.345	11.707	18.397	6.690	15.052	23.414	0.0	0.0
0.0	1.672	10.035	13.380	23.414	31.777	8.362	145.503
262.575	56.863	78.605	0.0	0.0	0.0	56.863	41.811
1.672	40.139	91.985	33.449	0.0	0.0	6.690	10.035
0.0	10.035	1.672	13.380	0.0	20.069	45.156	11.707
6.690	0.0	8.362	25.087	0.0	3.345	0.0	1.672
0.0	20.069	15.052	0.0	0.0	3.345	18.397	11.707
5.017	160.555	38.466	18.397	75.260	1239.288	587.031	16.725
35.122	50.174	3.345	0.0	93.657	50.174	11.707	0.0
0.0	0.0	0.0	0.0	6.690	86.968	25.087	5.017
6.690	0.0	0.0	0.0	282.644	0.0	16.725	5.017
10.035	257.558	1.672	0.0	0.0	11.707	125.434	30.104
10.035	1.672	25.087	177.280	45.156	10.035	66.898	6.690
135.469	165.573	1.672	35.122	511.771	585.359	41.811	0.0
1.672	0.0	0.0	3.345	0.0	5.017	25.087	3.345
329.473	160.555	38.466	8.362	0.0	0.0	563.617	55.191
0.0	1.672	0.0	50.174	1080.405	199.022	102.020	147.176
28.432	6.690	0.0	33.449	394.699	168.918	15.052	0.0
0.0	0.0	0.0	0.0	0.0	45.156	548.564	162.228
25.087	0.0	31.777	291.007	479.994	640.549	252.540	65.226
8.362	0.0	1.672	521.805	172.263	25.087	35.122	40.139
120.417	317.766	26.759	679.016	163.900	386.336	160.555	147.176
90.312	6.690	3.345	91.985	18.397	5.017	0.0	0.0
63.553	28.432	60.208	48.501	705.775	297.696	102.020	8.362
0.0	0.0	65.226	0.0	0.0	0.0	0.0	0.0
0.0	21.742	0.0	16.725	60.208	1.672	8.362	0.0
0.0	0.0	1.672	38.466	3.345	1.672	33.449	48.501
0.0	0.0	0.0	108.709	93.657	6.690	0.0	0.0
0.0	0.0	0.0	0.0	0.0	0.0	230.799	70.243
0.0	0.0	40.139	78.605	6.690	423.130	712.465	486.684
31.777	0.0	837.899	1005.144	388.009	396.371	2749.513	280.972

1.672	0.0	0.0	26.759	11.707	1.672	3.345	0.0
83.623	10.035	0.0	0.0	0.0	0.0	0.0	0.0
76.933	23.414	0.0	0.0	0.0	0.0	0.0	1.672
25.087	321.111	38.466	0.0	0.0	65.226	6.690	0.0
0.0	0.0	0.0	0.0	0.0	0.0	0.0	0.0
0.0	132.124	123.762	0.0	10.035	1.672	18.397	1.672
0.0	280.972	272.610	75.260	3.345	0.0	0.0	142.159
40.139	5.017	95.330	0.0	0.0	23.414	125.434	0.0
0.0	0.0	344.525	347.870	5.017	0.0	0.0	46.829
56.863	0.0	0.0	66.898	40.139	26.759	1.672	5.017
45.156	0.0	1.672	194.005	18.397	0.0	43.484	3.345
0.0	15.052	0.0	229.126	50.174	0.0	86.968	55.191
5.017	1.672	0.0	13.380	163.900	53.518	23.414	0.0

R; T=0.10/0.47 13:47:42

OUT KIZU file

```
(12,2I4,A2)
(8F10.3)
0106621280QQ   KIZU RIVER JULY 62-DEC65. WMO DATA
```

33.800	60.600	226.200	155.500	166.600	231.800	162.400	105.600
95.700	75.500	51.400	41.700	26.200	29.700	74.100	41.600
34.000	27.100	26.300	35.200	19.800	14.700	6.300	5.700
3.300	4.200	85.800	714.800	208.400	128.600	89.200	60.400
50.700	45.800	39.200	37.000	30.300	26.500	28.000	25.400
26.800	28.000	25.000	25.000	59.700	48.600	50.200	31.600
26.100	24.600	23.200	19.900	20.200	18.300	25.700	37.500
615.200	261.300	149.600	115.400	75.400	59.300	48.200	43.300
38.400	42.400	48.200	41.500	36.100	44.800	56.000	43.900
34.400	31.100	31.900	26.800	37.000	47.800	33.500	33.600
33.100	33.700	24.300	22.700	30.800	32.800	28.400	25.400
23.600	23.600	24.600	25.400	26.100	25.400	23.600	36.100
106.700	44.400	33.100	28.800	25.700	24.600	31.800	51.300
37.500	32.100	31.200	25.900	23.900	23.600	22.000	22.500
23.100	21.000	19.200	18.600	19.300	19.900	19.300	22.700
34.000	22.700	21.100	19.600	18.900	27.300	59.700	37.900
30.900	27.700	22.000	22.200	22.200	20.700	19.700	19.600
17.200	18.700	56.300	77.100	44.100	33.500	29.100	27.500
25.400	23.400	21.100	19.400	21.400	40.400	39.100	26.700
24.300	20.600	21.200	20.900	20.200	22.200	53.200	45.700
35.000	29.800	26.700	23.900	23.200	22.100	20.800	32.500
27.600	23.700	21.900	21.600	21.300	20.700	19.100	18.100
18.700	18.600	17.400	17.400	17.400	16.800	36.400	58.600
39.200	29.300	28.500	26.900	25.800	26.200	26.600	31.300
28.100	27.400	28.900	26.900	24.300	22.500	22.100	22.100
21.400	20.800	25.800	22.900	23.200	21.800	20.100	17.300
16.900	20.200	16.800	18.000	18.100	18.600	18.000	16.700
16.500	16.200	16.200	17.000	17.100	16.900	17.700	26.200
28.100	24.100	23.300	23.800	22.900	20.200	20.900	22.100
20.100	18.500	18.700	18.500	16.700	18.600	18.500	18.600
18.000	19.600	20.900	19.000	19.300	19.700	24.100	25.200
20.300	18.700	17.500	16.100	22.800	32.200	28.700	35.700
43.300	53.800	80.000	81.500	56.900	45.500	39.800	35.600
33.400	30.400	29.000	36.200	28.400	24.700	22.000	40.700
44.700	33.200	29.200	29.700	27.300	23.300	22.800	20.800
19.500	28.200	65.400	47.400	35.500	30.300	28.000	25.100

24.700	50.000	44.000	34.600	45.900	44.800	36.400	36.300
48.500	55.300	48.200	41.300	36.100	31.800	28.800	26.100
39.700	43.300	31.000	25.500	23.700	25.800	26.500	23.300
45.100	138.200	154.700	290.500	177.800	109.900	146.700	129.200
265.600	302.300	161.800	127.200	105.200	140.800	143.000	93.100
76.100	72.000	67.000	310.100	229.600	207.100	128.800	98.900
80.200	209.500	309.500	213.500	185.400	222.600	149.000	108.000
92.300	81.000	83.400	95.100	125.800	93.400	70.100	64.900
56.200	47.400	69.800	45.300	45.400	49.100	42.000	39.400
36.800	29.700	47.100	60.000	38.100	39.800	53.800	61.900
45.700	44.100	90.800	57.000	40.700	36.600	39.200	38.400
68.400	45.800	35.900	28.000	26.100	25.700	22.400	20.000
17.700	15.100	24.200	56.900	58.600	29.000	20.300	15.900
20.100	38.800	21.700	16.500	15.500	14.900	16.600	60.200
41.500	26.700	20.900	17.400	138.000	127.500	77.000	102.600
63.300	41.100	42.500	33.500	91.000	75.900	59.100	42.500
29.800	28.500	30.100	25.900	26.200	83.400	40.100	53.200
130.400	98.000	114.500	74.100	51.400	39.300	30.800	30.800
29.200	37.800	31.200	31.300	84.100	56.300	49.700	45.100
44.200	36.400	34.600	39.800	31.800	29.500	26.100	40.000
50.700	34.200	30.300	35.000	52.100	36.000	31.300	29.400
28.100	37.700	42.000	31.300	27.100	25.100	24.000	23.700
22.600	22.800	136.000	64.600	44.400	33.900	33.000	32.400
31.200	30.700	29.800	26.000	24.500	22.500	21.700	21.300
20.800	19.900	63.700	53.100	35.500	30.300	27.300	24.800
22.100	21.400	20.400	20.200	19.900	19.000	20.800	20.500
19.000	17.500	17.900	18.100	18.200	17.900	18.000	24.800
21.600	18.500	18.500	20.200	18.500	18.900	18.000	17.300
21.100	32.800	24.100	20.300	18.900	17.900	17.900	17.600
18.000	22.500	24.000	20.100	18.900	18.000	18.200	18.000
19.900	18.500	17.500	16.600	16.600	16.400	16.400	16.200
16.000	15.900	15.300	15.800	15.300	15.400	17.100	17.100
16.600	14.000	12.400	13.000	13.000	12.800	11.900	12.200
11.800	10.800	10.800	10.800	10.800	10.800	11.400	11.400
11.400	12.200	36.800	36.400	22.700	32.200	65.800	41.600
35.300	29.300	26.700	65.000	47.800	36.700	31.500	27.600
26.000	31.300	32.400	34.600	36.800	29.400	26.900	25.400
24.700	23.900	32.000	39.700	128.900	152.500	101.300	87.800
65.700	54.800	48.600	41.900	36.600	34.200	32.600	30.500
28.100	25.800	24.900	24.700	25.000	26.000	24.000	25.200
24.300	23.800	21.500	24.800	27.800	34.300	30.600	30.400
51.300	39.000	33.800	28.600	26.300	26.600	37.700	30.200
25.500	23.300	20.000	18.200	23.200	54.300	33.800	29.700
27.000	32.400	38.900	33.300	31.800	29.200	27.000	24.700
24.000	30.100	27.000	33.200	37.800	27.500	26.800	35.600
51.600	86.200	155.500	96.100	67.900	52.800	44.500	38.800
35.500	32.400	29.300	26.100	24.700	23.200	25.200	27.200
21.800	25.900	40.600	28.000	30.500	26.500	21.400	37.600
31.500	25.700	23.800	30.500	25.000	19.300	15.000	12.700
53.700	48.600	28.500	22.800	19.800	16.400	13.500	12.500
12.700	11.600	11.100	13.400	11.600	11.500	16.800	17.300
13.200	11.600	11.600	11.800	11.000	9.800	9.000	8.500
10.500	9.600	8.100	8.300	7.800	10.500	23.900	17.200
14.000	12.200	11.000	8.100	8.700	8.400	7.000	6.200
21.800	47.100	20.400	11.400	9.200	10.100	32.300	99.000
217.800	75.600	34.000	21.800	16.500	13.800	11.800	10.800
9.500	9.000	10.400	113.200	181.000	83.200	42.800	28.500
37.900	30.400	66.600	71.700	44.000	105.900	126.000	83.700
89.800	91.300	53.500	30.900	21.200	22.500	33.600	67.800
38.600	27.600	19.800	20.000	47.200	27.000	19.600	26.300
33.000	32.900	19.300	16.300	14.300	12.700	12.300	10.800
9.800	8.800	8.800	10.100	8.200	8.000	8.000	7.500
12.800	16.400	61.800	33.900	20.600	14.700	12.600	55.300
58.300	27.500	21.900	29.000	27.600	23.500	20.500	16.700
15.000	12.500	12.800	12.500	12.000	11.200	12.900	14.200
20.600	14.400	12.700	16.200	11.900	16.000	25.600	27.600
46.200	223.500	111.200	54.500	106.000	84.400	50.800	39.200
31.000	25.800	28.300	20.300	27.800	37.500	31.500	35.700
27.200	23.500	19.900	36.800	117.000	60.400	38.600	32.600
41.000	30.600	27.800	26.100	31.700	36.600	27.600	23.900
21.800	20.700	18.600	19.600	18.300	16.500	16.100	21.500
22.800	17.600	16.700	16.500	15.400	14.700	15.400	35.700
25.000	19.400	17.500	17.300	17.400	16.500	15.300	14.200
13.600	13.200	12.900	13.900	12.500	12.100	11.600	11.400
11.900	11.900	12.500	12.500	12.500	12.200	12.500	12.400
12.300	12.000	12.200	11.800	10.800	10.800	10.500	9.700

9.200	9.700	9.700	9.700	10.000	13.300	12.600	11.400
10.800	9.400	9.000	14.600	15.700	12.800	11.300	15.400
18.700	14.700	12.300	15.200	16.700	14.500	14.300	14.000
13.400	13.700	15.600	21.400	18.300	16.100	15.000	13.400
12.700	11.700	12.100	13.000	12.700	14.600	15.900	15.400
14.600	14.300	13.700	13.400	13.100	12.900	13.500	16.000
44.600	40.600	37.400	30.600	23.500	18.300	18.400	19.400
18.900	17.400	21.200	25.800	22.400	18.900	18.200	17.000
17.600	16.400	15.000	15.000	13.700	12.800	15.300	14.400
13.200	12.800	12.300	12.000	12.400	11.900	12.000	11.900
11.300	11.700	11.800	11.400	11.400	11.600	10.300	10.400
10.600	10.300	10.200	10.000	10.200	28.000	667.100	173.900
87.100	62.500	41.500	22.400	18.600	27.800	25.100	18.800
15.200	13.400	12.600	11.800	10.600	12.000	12.000	11.800
10.600	9.600	9.000	8.800	8.300	15.400	16.500	11.200
10.200	9.400	16.800	16.900	17.800	10.200	9.000	10.200
11.800	11.400	9.600	9.200	16.000	15.200	9.600	11.800
11.200	15.500	33.000	0.0	0.0	30.100	282.000	109.400
65.400	48.800	38.300	32.000	27.600	25.800	24.000	20.700
19.900	54.200	38.800	33.500	25.400	21.100	20.400	136.200
47.700	29.100	25.400	22.400	21.100	391.200	199.600	118.200
109.900	77.800	55.100	42.200	36.000	116.600	84.300	51.800
35.100	28.500	23.900	20.900	19.500	18.300	28.200	141.600
77.000	38.800	30.500	30.500	94.800	139.100	264.800	193.800
113.000	58.800	42.200	37.200	191.300	99.600	63.800	57.200
152.800	56.400	86.000	63.000	258.100	160.400	211.400	147.200
129.900	122.600	75.800	54.100	57.200	44.900	31.800	25.400
23.700	31.600	32.100	30.000	42.400	265.900	132.400	67.700
47.900	35.500	28.200	30.000	22.700	18.500	15.900	14.800
12.600	12.600	15.100	12.700	13.500	13.900	12.400	9.800
8.700	8.000	8.000	7.500	9.000	8.700	9.200	8.600
7.800	6.800	6.000	5.800	8.700	16.100	10.700	7.400
6.600	5.300	5.000	4.800	4.600	4.300	5.800	7.600
15.400	10.000	7.600	8.300	12.200	9.200	49.900	373.200
132.000	41.800	25.000	398.200	651.900	224.400	868.800	1591.800
342.400	187.200	126.300	101.400	85.600	69.400	61.400	56.000
50.800	42.300	45.000	43.800	43.200	36.100	38.600	36.400
34.300	37.500	37.900	35.100	31.700	32.000	29.900	29.000
27.600	36.000	53.000	33.600	24.100	27.000	28.000	28.700
25.700	24.400	23.600	22.200	22.200	21.100	20.600	20.300
20.300	20.000	26.000	30.800	23.700	21.300	20.100	19.900
19.000	18.000	51.300	53.200	40.900	29.000	24.300	23.500
25.400	28.700	24.000	26.600	24.000	21.200	23.100	26.400
22.800	20.300	20.300	56.400	118.400	63.000	40.400	32.400
31.500	32.000	26.300	24.500	24.500	28.600	25.800	23.600
21.900	22.400	21.500	21.600	51.000	27.200	23.200	22.400
23.200	18.800	17.600	19.500	25.800	33.500	25.800	26.900
32.700	26.600	23.200	22.100	22.800	22.000	31.500	27.600

R; T=0.10/0.46 14:04:33

4.2 Sample problem terminal sheet

```
$ cls
EXECUTION BEGINS....


    CONSTRAINED LINEAR SYSTEMS   - COPYRIGHT OF IBM ITALIA 1975
    LICENSED MATERIAL            - PROGRAM PROPERTY OF IBM


    METODO - (0,1,2) - : (2)


    NOME USCITA - (A8) - : (kizu    )


    NUMERO INGRESSI - (I2) - : ( 1)


    NOME INGRESSO - (A8) - : (kizu    )



    NOME        TIPO       VOLUME      C. DEF.


    KIZU        OUT.OQ       54341.

    KIZU        INP.PP       88859.
    ------------------------------
    **TOTALE**  INP.PP       88859.      0.612


    NUMERO SOGLIE PER KIZU     - (0,1,2) - : (1)


    TEMPO BASE 1 PER KIZU      - (I3) - : ( 14)


    TEMPO BASE 2 PER KIZU      - (I3) - : ( 24)


    VALORE SOGLIA   PER KIZU     - (R) - : (14000.   )


    VALORE L - (I4) - : (    5)


    VALORE M - (I2) - : ( 2)



    NOME                    VOLUME

    KIZU     (1)             88859.
    KIZU     (2)                 0.

    0. K.   ? (SI-NO) : (no)


    VALORE SOGLIA   PER KIZU     - (R) - : (1400.   )


    VALORE L - (I4) - : (   5)


    VALORE M - (I2) - : ( 2)



    NOME                    VOLUME

    KIZU     (1)             69122.
    KIZU     (2)             19737.

    0. K.   ? (SI-NO) : (si )
```

STATISTICHE SUI RESIDUI

MEDIA = -0.00022   DEV.STAND. = 28.51329   MAX+ = 348.754   MAX- = -403.051

COEFF.DI DET. = 0.85603   COEFF.DI PERS. = 3.88090

ERRORE PERCENTUALE FRA I COLMI = -25.3 %

SFASAMENTO FRA I COLMI =   0 DELTA T

RISPOSTA IMPULSIVA - KIZU   (1)

0.0060   0.2024   0.0658   0.0332   0.0300   0.0262   0.0293   0.0223   0.0290   0.0520
0.0182   0.0030   0.0175   0.0158   0.0141

RISPOSTA IMPULSIVA - KIZU   (2)

0.0782   0.3596   0.0746   0.0558   0.0484   0.0290   0.0039   0.0148   0.0140   0.0102
0.0114   0.0088   0.0068   0.0081   0.0066   0.0098   0.0088   0.0094   0.0079   0.0017
0.0047   0.0045   0.0   0.0   0.0036

PLOT ? - (SI-NO) - : (sI)

CAMBIO SOLO PARAMETRI SOGLIE ? - (SI-NO) - : (no)

CAMBIO TEMPI BASE ? - (SI-NO) - : (no)

CAMBIO NUMERO SOGLIE ? - (SI-NO) - : (no)

UTILIZZO I.U.H. CALCOLATI ? - (SI-NO) - : (no)

   NUOVO PROBLEMA ? - (SI-NO) - : (no)
R; T=5.58/6.79 13:28:18

4.3 Sample problem ouput

CONSTRAINED LINEAR SYSTEMS - COPYRIGHT IBM ITALIA 1975
LICENSED MATERIAL - PROGRAM PROPERTY OF IBM
PROGRAM PROPERTY OF IBM ITALIA

CONSTRAINED LINEAR SYSTEMS - PROGETTO KIZU
****

NOME	TIPO	VOLUME	COEFF. DEFL.	VAL. SOGLIA	TEMPO ACCUM.	MEMORIA
KIZU	OUT.OO	54341.				
KIZU	(1) INP.PP	69122.	0.565	140C.	5	2
KIZU	(2) INP.PP	19737.	0.780			
TOTALE	INP.PP	8885 9.	0.612			

INGRESSO KIZU   VOLUME MASSIMC RIMOSSC =   5377.

MINIMIZZAZIONE CON VINCOLI DI UGUALE E DI MAGGICFF-UGUBIE
****

STATISTICHE SUI RESIDUI

MEDIA = -0.00022   DEV.STAND. = 28.51329   MAX+ = 348.754   MAX- = -403.051

COEFF.DI DET. = 0.85603   COEFF.DI EFFS. = 3.83090

ERRORE PERCENTUALE FRA I COLMI = -25.3 %

SFASAMENTO FRA I COLMI = 0 DELTA T

NEL CAMPO DI OSS. FRA 1160 ? 1192 DELTA T

PORTATA MAX. OSS. = 1591.80 A 1176 DELTA T

RISPOSTA IMPULSIVA - KIZU   (1)

```
 0.0060   0.2024   0.0658   0.0332   0.0200   0.0262   0.0293   0.0223   0.0290   0.0520
 0.0182   0.0030   0.0175   0.0158   0.0141

                                                                    RISPOSTA IMPULSIVA - KIZU    (1)

       0.020    0.040    0.061    0.081    0.101    0.121    0.142    0.162    0.182    0.202
 -0 -I-*----I--------I--------I--------I--------I--------I--------I--------I--------I--------I
  0-I========I--------I--------I--------I--------I--------I--------I--------I--------I--------I
  2-I=======*    I=======================================================================*
  4-I========*   I======================================================================-*
  6-I========*   I=======================================================================I
  8-I=========*
 10-======*
 12-I*
    I========*
 14-I====*
```

```
0.0782   0.3596   0.0746   0.0558   0.0484   C.0290   0.0039   0.0148   0.0140   0.0102
0.0114   0.0088   0.0068   0.0081   0.0066   0.0098   0.0088   0.0094   0.0079   0.0017
0.0047   0.0045   0.0      0.0      0.0036
```

RISPOSTA INPUSIVA - KIZU   (2)

```
          0.036    0.072    0.108    0.144    0.180    0.216    0.252    0.288    0.324    0.360
 -0------------------------------------------------------------------------------------------
  0-I-------I--------I--------I--------I--------I--------I--------I--------I--------I--------I
    I=====================================================================================*
  2-I=================================================================================-----I
    I============================================================================---I-----I
  4-I==============*
    I=========*
  6-I=*
    I==*
  8-I==*
    I==*
 10--==*
    I=*
 12-I=*
    I=*
 14-I*
    I=*
 16-I=*
    I=*
 18-I=*
    I*
 20--*
    I*
 22-I*
    *
 24-I*
```

```
                                                        PORTATA (MC/SEC) - KIZU

    C        160       320       480       640       800       960      1120      1280      1440      160
 1-0-+-------I---------I---------I---------I---------I---------I---------I---------I---------I---------I
    I==+=O
 3-I=======O====+
    I=====O==+
 5-I=========+==O
    I============+====O
 7-I========O+
    I=====*
 9-I====*
    I===+O
11--==*
    I=*
13-I+O
    I+O
15-I===+O
    I=*
17-I=*
    I*
19-I*
    I=*
21--*
    +O
23-+O
    *
25-*
    +O
27-I====+==========O
    I=========================================+======O
29-I============*
    I=======*
31--====+=O
    I===+=O
33-IO=+
    I=*
35-I=+O
    I=*
37-I*
    I*
39-I*
    I*
41--*
    I*
43-I*
    I*
45-I==*
    I==+O
47-I==+O
    I+O
49-I*
    I*
51--*
    I*
53-I*
    I*
55-I+O
    I=+============O
57-I=========================================+====================O
    I============O=+
59-I=======+O
    I======+===O
61--===+O
    IO=+
63-I==*
    I=+O
65-IO+
    I=*
67-I=O+
    IO+
69-IO+
    I=+O
71--==*
    I=*
73-I=*
    I+O
75-I*
    I*
77-I=*
    I=+O
79-I=*
    I=*
81--O+
    O=+
83-O+
    O+
```

```
 85-0+                173-C+               261--=C+
    I0+                  0+                   I0+
 87-0+                175-0+               263-I0+
    0+                   0+                   I0+
 89-C+                177-C+               265-I0+
    0+                   0+                   0+
 91-0+                179-0+               267-I*
    0+                   0+                   I=*
 93-0+                181-C+               269-I*
    0+                   0+                   0+
 95-0+                183-I=+0             271-C+
    I0+                  I==*                 I=+0
 97-I=====+==0        185-I0+              273-I=*
    I=+0                 I*                   I0+
 99-I0+               187-I*               275-0+
    I*                   I*                   I*
101--*                189-I*               277-I*
    I*                   I+0                  0+
103-I+==0             191--+=0             279-C+
    I==+=0               I+0                  I*
105-I=+=0             193-I*               281-C+
    I=*                  I*                   I*
107-I*                195-I*               283-I===*
    I+0                  I*                   I=+0
109-I*                197-I*               285-I0+
    I*                   C+                   I*
111--*                199-0+               287-0+
    I*                   I*                   C+
113-0+                201--*               289-I*
    C+                   0+                   I==+=0
115-C+                203-C+               291--=*
    C+                   0+                   I0+
117-0+                205-C+               293-I+=0
    C+                   0+                   I=*
119-C+                207-C+               295-I=*
    I+0                  0+                   I0+
121--=*               209-C+               297-I==*
    0+                   0+                   I=+0
123-C+                211-C+               299-I=0+
    0+                   0+                   I0+
125-C+                213-C+               301--0+
    I*                   C+                   I*
127-I==+0             215-0+               303-I*
    I=+0                 0+                   I*
129-I+0               217-C+               305-I=*
    I*                   0+                   I=+0
131--*                219-C+               307-I*
    I*                   0+                   0+
133-I*                221-0+               309-I*
    I*                   0+                   I*
135-I*                223-C+               311--*
    0+                   I+0                  I*
137-C+                225-I*               313-I+=0
    C+                   0+                   I=======*
139-I==+0             227-I*               315-I======0=+
    I===+0               I*                   I===============0+
141--=*               229-0+               317-I====0=====+
    I0+                  0+                   I===0=+
143-I*                231-C+               319-I=======0+
    I*                   C+                   I=====0=+
145-I*                233-C+               321--==============0==+
    I*                   C+                   I================0+
147-I*                235-C+               323-I======0==+
    I*                   0+                   I====0=+
149-0+                237-C+               325-I====0+
    I=*                  C+                   I=====0=+
151--0+               239-C+               327-I=======*
    I*                   0+                   I===0+
153-0+                241-C+               329-I===*
    0+                   C+                   I==0+
155-0+                243-C+               331--====*
    0+                   0+                   I============0=====+
157-0+                245-0+               333-I=========0==+
    I+0                  C+                   I===========*
159-I==+0             247-C+               335-I=====0=+
    I=*                  0+                   I===0=+
161--0+               249-C+               337-I===0+
    I*                   C+                   I========0==+
163-I*                251-C+               339-I=============0===+
    0+                   C+                   I==========*
165-0+                253-I*               341--=======0=+
    I*                   I=*                  I============*
167-I*                255-I*               343-I=====0==+
    I=*                  I=+===0              I====0+
169-I*                257-I=*               345-I===0+
    C+                   I0=+                 I===0+
171-C+                259-I=C==+            347-I===0+
    0+                   I=0==+               I==0=+
```

```
349-I=====0+          437-I===0+           525-0+
     I===0+                I=0+                 I*
351--=C=+             439-I=0+             527-0+
     I=0=+                 I0+                  C+
353-I0=+              441--C+              529-I*
     I0+              443-I0+                   I*
355-I==0+                 I0+              531-0+
     I=*              445-I*                    C+
357-I=*                   C+              533-0+
     I=0+             447-0+                    C+
359-I0+                   I=+0            535-0+
     I0+              449-I==*                  C+
361--0+                   I0+             537-0+
     I*               451-0+                    *
363-I=*                   I0+             539-*
     I==+0            453-I===+0
365-I0+                   I0+             541-*
     I=*              455-I*
367-I=0+                  I*              543-I*
     I==+0            457-I*                   0+
369-I=*                   I=*             545-0+
     I=*              459-I0+                   *
371--====+0               I*              547-*
     I===*            461--*
373-I=*                   0+              549-*
     I=*              463-C+                    *
375-I=*                   0+              551-*
     I=+0             465-0+                    *
377-I===*                 I*              553-*
     .  I=*          467-I=======+0       555-*
379-I=*                   I==0+                 *
     I*               469-I0+             557-*
381--*                    I0+             559-*
     I*               471--0+                   *
383-I*                    I=*             561-*
     I*               473-T*                   +C
385-I*                    I+0             563-I=+=0
     *                475-I+0                   I=*
387-0+                    I*              565-I*
     I==*             477-0+                   I=*
389-I==+0                 I*              567-I==0+
     I*               479-I*                   I=+C
391--*                    0+              569-I=*
     +0               481-0+                   I+C
393-I*                    0+              571--+0
     I=+0             483-I===+0               I===*
395-I*                    I===*           573-I=*
     I*               485-I0+                   I=*
397-+0                    I*              575-I+0
     *                487-0+                   I*
399-I*                    0+              577-I*
     I==+=0           489-I*                    I+0
401--=+==C                0+              579-I=*
     I+=0             491--*                   I=*
403-I*                    0+              581--=*
     I*               493-0+                    C+
405-I=======*             0+              583-0+
     I=======+0       495-I*                   C+
407-I===+=0               0+              585-0+
     I=====+0         497-C+                    I*
409-I==+0                 0+              587-I=*
     I=+0             499-0+                    I=+0
411--=+0                  0+              589-I=====0=+
     I=+0             501-C+                   I=====0==+
413-I====+===0            0+              591--===0=+
     I===+=0         503-0+                   I==0=+
415-I===+=0               I*              593-I=0=+
     I=+0             505-C+                   I=0+
417-I+0                   0+              595-I=0+
     I+0             507-0+                   I=*
419-I+0                   I*              597-I=+0
     I*               509-0+                   I=+0
421--+0                   0+              599-I=*
     I====*           511-0+                    I*
423-I=*                   0+              601--*
     I==+0            513-I*                    I*
425-I=======*             I=+0            603-I*
     I=====+0         515-I+0                   I*
427-I======+C             I*              605-I+0
     I===*            517-0+                    I*
429-I==*                  0+              607-0+
     I=+0             519-0+                   C+
431--+C                   0+              609-0+
     I+0             521--*                    0+
433-I+=0                  I+0             611-0+
     I=+0             523-I*                    0+
435-I+0                   C+
     I+0
```

```
613-I+O          701-*            789-I*
     IO+              *                +O
615-O+           703-*            791-+O
     I*               +O               I==+==O
617-I==+O        705-*            793-I==*
     I=*              *                I+O
619-IO+          707-+O           795-I+O
     I*               *                I+O
621--*           709-*            797-I+O
     I*               *                I+O
623-I=+O         711--+==O        799-I+O
     I*               I*               +O
625-I+O          713-*            801-+O
     I*               *                *
627-O+           715-*            803-+C
     I*               +O               +O
629-I*           717-+O           805-+O
     I==+O            *                *
631--=*          719-+O           807-*
     I*               *                *
633-O+           721--+===O       809-I*
     I=*              I=+=O            *
635-I=*          723-I+O          811-*
     I=*              +O               O+
637-I*           725-+O           813-*
     I*               +O               I*
639-O+           727-I=+=O        815-I+=O
     C+               I==O==+          I+O
641-O+           729-I===========* 817-I=+O
     I+O              I===+=O          I==========O=+
643-I*           731--=+O         819-I======+=======O
     I=*              I+O              I==+==O
645-I=*          733-I+O          821--=====+====O
     I*               +==O             I====+===O
647-O+           735-+=O          823-I=+=O
     I=*              +=O              I=+O
649-I==*         737-+==O         825-I+=O
     I===O+           +O               I+=O
651--=====O==+   739-+O           827-I*
     I==O==+          I======+O         I*
653-I=O=+        741--=========O+ 829-I*
     IO=+            I====+O           I=*
655-IO+          743-I+O          831--+=O
     IO+              I+=O             I=*
657-IO+          745-I+O          833-I+O
     IO+              I+O              I*
659-I*           747-I===+=O       835-I*
     O+               I===+==O          I=*
661-I*           749-I+===O       837-I=====O+
     O+               I=====+O          I==+=O
663-I+O          751--=====O+     839-I=*
     O+               I====*           I=*
665-O+           753-I====*       841--=*
     C+               I====*           I+O
667-I=+O         755-I==*         843-I*
     I*               I+O              I+O
669-I+O          757-I+O          845-I+O
     I*               I+O              I=+O
671--*           759-I=+O         847-I*
     I=*              I==O+            I*
673-I*           761--=*          849-I*
     I*               I+O              I*
675-I+O          763-I+O          851-O+
     I+O              I*               O+
677-I*           765-I=*          853-C+
     I*               I*               C+
679-+O           767-I*           855-O+
     +O               I*               *
681--==+===O     769-IO+          857-I*
     I=C+            I=*               O+
683-I*           771--*           859-C+
     I*               I*               C+
685-I*           773-+O           861-*
     I*               *                *
687-*            775-*            863-*
     +O               *                I=*
689-+O           777-*            865-I+=O
     *                *                I*
691-*            779-*            867-O+
     *                *                I*
693-*            781-*            869-I*
     +O               *                O+
695-I+=O         783-*            871-*
     I*,              *                *
697-*            785-+O           873-*
     *                I+O              *
699-*            787-I==+O        875-*
     *                I=*              *
```

```
877-*                    965-*
    *                        *
879-*                    967-*
    *                        *
881-*                    969-*
    *                        *
883-*                    971-*
    *                        *
885-*                    973-*
    *                        *
887-*                    975-*
    *                        *
889-*                    977-*
    *                        *
891-*                    979-*
    *                        *
893-*                    981-*
    *                        *
895-*                    983-*
    *                        *
897-*                    985-*
    *                        *
899-*                    987-+=0
    *                        +0
901-*                    989-*
    *                        I+=====0
903-+0                   991--=======================0==========+
905-*                        I=========+========0
    *                    993-I====+==0
907-*                        I==+===0
    +0                   995-I+====0
909-+0                       I+0
    *                    997-I*
911-*                        I+=0
    +0                   999-I+0
913-I*                       I+0
    +0                  1001-+0
915-*                        +0
    +0                  1003-+0
917-I*                       +0
    *                   1005-+0
919-*                        +0
    *                   1007-+=0
921-*                        +0
    *                   1009-*
923-*                        *
    I*                  1011-*
925-I*                       *
    I*                  1013-*
927-+0                       +===0
    +0                  1015-I*
929-*                        +0
    *                   1017-*
931-*                        *
    *                   1019-I+=0
933-*                        I*
    *                   1021--*
935-*                        +0
    *                   1023-+0
937-*                        +=0
    *                   1025-+0
939-*                        +0
    *                   1027-+0
941-*                        +0
    *                   1029-I+0
943-*                        +0
    0+                  1031-+0
945-I=*                      +=0
    I=+=0               1033-+0
947-I=*                      +=0
    I+0                 1035-I=+0
949-I*                       +0
    I*                  1037-+=0
951--*                       I+=====0
    I*                  1039-I=========0======+
953-I*                       I====0+
    I*                  1041--==0+
955-I*                       I==*
    I+0                 1043-I=*
957-I*                       I=*
    I*                  1045-I+0
959-0+                       I+=0
    0+                  1047-I+0
961-0+                       I*
    0+                  1049-I*
963-*                        I==+=0
    *                   1051--=+=0
                             I=*
```

```
1053-I*
     I*
1055-I*
     I=======*
1057-I=+0
     I+0
1059-I+0
     I*
1061--+0
     I==============0========+
1063-I========0==+
     I======+0
1065-I=====+0
     I===*
1067-I==+0
     I=+0
1069-I=+0
     I======+=0
1071--=====*
     I=0+
1073-I=*
     I+0
1075-I+0
     I*
1077-I*
     I*
1079-I*
     I======0+
1081--===+0
     I=*
1083-I+0
     I+0
1085-I====*
     I=======+==0
1087-I================+==0
     I========-=*
1089-I======r
     I==+=0
1091--=+=0
     I=+0
1093-I=======0=+
     I=====+0
1095-I*=*
     I==*
1097-I==0=====+
     I==+0
1099-I====+0
     I==*
1101--==========0===+
     I=======0+
1103-I============*
     I=======*
1105-I=======+0
     I======*
1107-I===+0
     I==*
1109-I==+0
     I=+0
1111--*
     I*
1113-I*
     I+0
1115-I0+
     I*
1117-I=*
     I========0=====+
1119-I======0+
     I===*
1121--=+0
     I=*
1123-I+0
     I+0
1125-I+0
     I+=0
1127-+=0
     +0
1129-+0
     +0
1131-+0
     *
1133-*
     *
1135-*
     *
1137-*
     *
1139-*
     *
```

```
1141-*
      *
1143-*
      *
1145-*
      *
1147-*
      *
1149-+C
      I*
1151-*
      *
1153-*
      *
1155-*
      *
1157-*
      *
1159-*
      +==0
1161-+=C
      *
1163-*
      +0
1165-+C
      +0
1167-I==+==0
      I============0=========+
1169-I=======+======C
      I=+==0
1171--+======0
      I==================+==C
1173-I=============================C========+
      I=============+-----0
1175-I=====================================0===================+
      I================================================================
1177-I=================+===C
      I=========+==0
1179-I======+=====0
      I=====+==0
1181--===0+
      I===*
1183-I==+0
      I==*
1185-I==*
      I=+=0
1187-I=+0
      I=+0
1189-I=+0
      I=+0
1191--=*
      I=*
1193-I=*
      I0+
1195-IC+
      I0+
1197-0+
      0=+
1199-0+
      0+
1201-0+
      0=+
1203-I==+0
      I0+
1205-0+
      C+
1207-I*
      I*
1209-0+
      0+
1211--*
      0+
1213-0+
      C+
1215-0+
      0+
1217-0+
      0+
1219-I*
      I+0
1221-0+
      0+
1223-0+
      0+
1225-0+
      0+
1227-I==+0
      I==+=0
```

```
1229-I=*
      I*
1231--*
      I*
1233-I+0
      I+0
1235-I+0
      I+0
1237-I*
      0+
1239-I*
      I+0
1241--*
      0+
1243-C+
      I==+=0
1245-I=====0+
      I=0+
1247-I0+
      I0+
1249-I+0
      I=*
1251--*
      I+0
1253-I+C
      I*
1255-I*
      I*
1257-I*
      I*
1259-0+
      0+
1261--+0
      I*
1263-0+
      I*
1265-0+
      0+
1267-C+
      0+
1269-I+=0
      I=*
1271-0+
      I+0
1273-I0+
      I*
1275-0+
      0+
1277-I*
      I+0
1279-I*
      I*
```

FRUSA: Flood Routing using Simplified Algorithms

CRISTINA MUGNAI
Computer Science Institute, University of Pisa, Italy

LORENZO PANATTONI
IBM Scientific Center, Pisa, Italy

1 Introduction

FRUSA is a FORTRAN IV package which runs under CP-67/CMS operating system on an IBM 360/67 computer. The program has been designed for the computation of flood wave propagation in rivers by means of three different approximate methods: Muskingum, Linear Diffusion and Variable Parameter Diffusion. The method and the parameters to be used accordingly can be chosen using the interactive facilities of the CP-67/CMS system. The computed waves in the downstream section of the reach are then compared with the measured ones as an aid in the evaluation of the various methods.

2.1 General description

FRUSA allows the computation of flood wave propagation in natural or artificial channels by means of any one of three simplified computation methods, the Muskingum, the Linear Diffusion and the Variable Parameter Diffusion method.

The Muskingum method (McCarthy, 1940) consists in the numerical solution of the continuity equation coupled with a second equation deduced from the hypothesis that water storage is directly proportional to the discharges at the end sections of the reach.

In this method the discharges at the downstream section are directly computed from the corresponding values at the upstream section using the discharge input data and only two additional parameters, K and x (see Section 2.3). No other information on the river bed characteristics is required.

The Linear Diffusion method (Hayami, 1951; Dooge, 1969) is based on a linear convective diffusion equation (see Section 2.3). This equation is derived from the St Venant equations, by disregarding the terms that contain velocity derivatives in the momentum equation and then assuming the derivative coefficients to be constant. The downstream discharges are computed from the upstream ones by the solution of a convolution integral, for which the analytical expression of the impulse response is known. As in the Muskingum method only the knowledge of two parameters, D1 and D2, is required. The Variable Parameter Diffusion method (Price, 1973a) is also based on a convective diffusion equation, but with no constant coefficients. This equation must be solved by a finite difference scheme. The computation of the downstream discharges requires, in addition to the upstream and initial values, knowledge of the speed of the flood peak (a function of the peak discharges), of the river bottom slope, and of the average channel width.

The program FRUSA exploits the interactive facilities of the CP-67/CMS operating system. After reading the input data, the program generates queries which allow the user to choose the river reach, the algorithm to be used and the corresponding parameters. At the end of the computation the computed downstream discharges are printed together with the observed ones.

A detailed description of the FRUSA features is contained in Section 3.2.

2.2 Purposes and objectives

The program FRUSA has been designed in order to get a flexible tool for the solution of flood routing problems in rivers by means of approximate methods. In particular, repetitive computation of the same flood can be easily repeated, varying the choice of algorithm and the parameters' values. From a summary of the results, typed online at the communications terminal and, particularly, from all the results printed by the offline printer, it is then possible to draw conclusions about the adequacy of each method and about the influence of input parameters upon the computed results.

2.3 Formulae

Muskingum method

The algorithm is based on the two following equations:

$$\frac{dS}{dt} = I - O \tag{1}$$

$$S = K[xI + (1 - x)O] \tag{2}$$

where S is the total water storage in the considered reach, I is the incoming discharge at the upstream section, O is the outgoing discharge at the downstream section, K is a proportionality parameter and x is a weighting parameter. Substituting for S in equation 1 the expression (2) and expressing the resulting equation with finite differences, leads to

$$O(t + \Delta t) = c_1 O(t) + c_2 I(t + \Delta t) + c_3 I(t) \tag{3}$$

where the coefficient c_1, c_2 and c_3 are expressed in terms of K, x and the time step Δt.

Linear Diffusion method

Disregarding the inertial terms in the St Venant equations, combining them in a second order equation and taking the derivative coefficients as constants, the following linear equation, similar to the convective-diffusion equation, is obtained:

$$\frac{\partial Q}{\partial t} = D_1 \frac{\partial^2 Q}{\partial x^2} - D_2 \frac{\partial Q}{\partial x} \tag{4}$$

where Q is the discharge and D_1 and D_2 are two constants. For a given upstream condition $Q_u(t)$ the corresponding discharge at the downstream section can be obtained from the convolution integral:

$$Q_d(t) = \int_0^t u(\tau)Q_u(t-\tau)d\tau \tag{5}$$

where $u(t)$ has the form

$$u(t) = \frac{L}{\sqrt{4\pi D_1 t^3}} \, e^{-\frac{(D_2 t - L)^2}{4D_1 t}} \tag{6}$$

and L is the length of the river reach.

Variable Parameter Diffusion method

This method is based on an equation similar to (4), but with coefficients that are no longer constant, leading to

$$\frac{\partial Q}{\partial t} = \frac{\alpha}{L} Q \frac{\partial^2 Q}{\partial x^2} - c(Q) \frac{\partial Q}{\partial x} \tag{7}$$

where Q is the discharge, L is the total length of the reach, α is a coefficient depending on the average channel width and on the bottom slope (function of the abscissa) and c is the speed of the flood peak which depends on the peak discharge. It should be noted that α can also depend on the discharge when the channel width varies considerably with discharge. With the available data that we have for the Arno river we have not yet found the need to make α on explicit function of Q. Equation 7 must be integrated by a finite difference scheme following the procedure described in the work of Price (1973a). It is noteworthy, however, that effective use of the method largely depends on how accurately the function $c(Q)$ can be defined; and this function is strictly connected with the amount and reliability of the flood records on the river reach considered.

3.1 Input—output files

The main input file for the program FR USA contains the discharge values at some (at least two) locations along the river. This file has to be previously created by the user in his virtual machine, with the name PORTATE but can be any word of at most eight characters, and must be specified when initializing the program (see next section). Another input file is used when the Variable Parameter Diffusion method is chosen. This file,* contains data defining the two quantities α and c of equation 7, as functions of the river bed shape and discharge respectively.

*Identified by the name ALFAC and by the type ARNO.

The input data can be filed in free format provided that this format is contained in the first two lines of the data file.

Two different types of output are allowed. The first one appears at the communications terminal and contains a summary of the results allowing the user to draw conclusions about the adequacy of the method used or about parameter sensitivity. In particular the values of the mean, the maximum positive and negative differences between computed and input discharges are printed. The second output type contains a display of all results and, being larger in size, is printed offline on the fast printer.

The following input-output files are used:

FT01 F001   for the input file with the discharge data
FT02 F001   for the input file with supplementary data for the Variable Parameter Diffusion method
FT05 F001   for terminal input data
FT06 F001   for terminal output data
FT08 F001   for offline output data on the fast printer.

3.2 Useful hints for the user

Initialization

The program FRUSA is initialized by the user at the communications terminal by typing the word FRUSA followed by the file type of the input data file. This various parameters needed for computation are then specified by the user responding to FRUSA generated queries. All numerical quantities must be expressed in the metric system of units. These queries in order of their appearance are:

(a) ABSCISSAE OF THE UPSTREAM AND DOWNSTREAM SECTIONS OF THE REACH (2F.8)

The response must contain the abscissae of the upstream and downstream sections of the considered reach. An empty carriage return causes run termination.

(b) ALGORITHM (I1)

         1 = MUSKINGUM
         2 = LINEAR DIFFUSION
         3 = VARIABLE PARAMETER DIFFUSION

The response must be a digit by means of which the desired algorithm is selected: 1 for Muskingum, 2 for Linear Diffusion and 3 for Variable Parameter Diffusion. An empty carriage return causes transfer to point (a).

(c) TIME AND SPACE STEPS (F6.0, F8.0)

The response must contain the time and space steps to be used in the computation. In particular the time step is used to determine the succession of times at which the computation has to be performed. The typed value is altered by the program to the closest multiple or submultiple of the input data characteristic time step. On the other hand the specification of the space step value allows the determination of the downstream discharges by successive application of the algorithm in several intermediate subreaches, each of whose lengths are approximately equal to the specified step. Thus use of the space step value is optional for the Muskingum and Linear Diffusion methods, but is not applicable to the Variable Parameter Diffusion method. An empty carriage return causes the transfer to point (b).

(d) VALUES OF K AND X (F10.0, F6.0)

This demand is generated only for the Muskingum ('K' and 'X') and Linear Diffusion ('D1' and 'D2') methods. The response must contain the values of the two constants appearing in the equation. An empty carriage return causes transfer to point (c).

Checks on the user's responses are made by the program. An error causes the message: 'DATA ERROR' and the repetition of the program enquiry.

The typing of the string '0000' (four zeros) in response to any of the previously observed demands causes program termination.

3.3 Flow chart

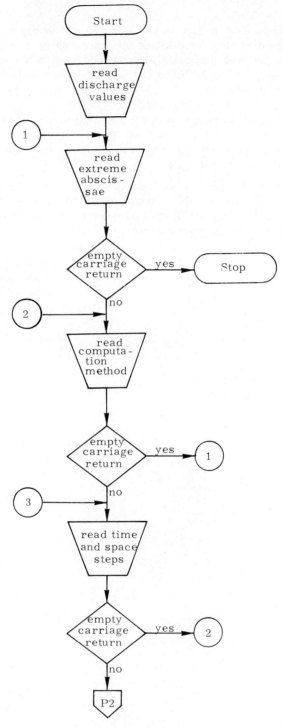

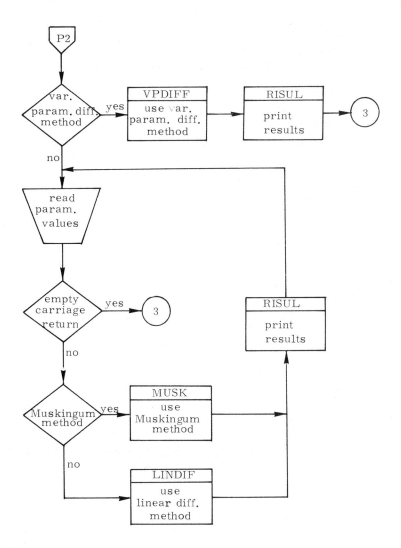

4.1 Sample problem description

The calculation of the discharge of the Arno river flood of the 27 January, 1948, at the Politeama gauging station (12.170 km from the sea), starting from the known discharges at Leoncini (40.600 km from the sea), has been chosen as a sample problem.

In the following three Sections the input file, the terminal sheet and the offline print relevant to this example are shown. The example shows results obtainable by the program using the Muskingum and Linear Diffusion algorithm with different choices for the parameter values.

338

Glossary of Italian terms for the following program

ASCISSE ESTREME DEL TRATTO
abscissae of the upstream and downstream sections of the reach

ALGORITMO
algorithm

DIFFUSIONE LINEARE
linear diffusion

DIFFUSIONE A PARAM. VARIABILI
variable parameter diffusion

PASSO TEMPORALE E SPAZIALE
time and space steps

VALORI DI K E X
value of K and X constants

RISULTATI A . . .
results at . . .

. . . METRI DALLA FOCE
. . . metres from the mouth

SCARTO MEDIO
mean deviation

MASSIMA PORTATA LETTA
maximum measured discharge

MASSIMA PORTATA CALCOLATA
maximum computed discharge

MASSIMO CALCOLATO OTTENUTO . . . MINUTI PRIMA DI QUELLO LETTO
maximum discharge computed . . . minutes before the measured one

PIENA DEL
flood of (day, month, year)

VALORI LETTI A
measured values at

LETTI, CALCOLATI
measured, computed

4.2 Sample problem input

The input files, listed below, contain the discharge values recorded at each hydrometric station for the flood event of 27 January, 1948, and the data for the computation of the quantities α and $c(Q)$ of equation 7. The first two records of the file with discharge data (name = PORTATE, type = 270148) describe the format of the relevant data. The third record contains the number of data at each gauging station, the number of stations for which discharge data are available and, finally, the value of the time interval.

The other records contain the discharge values and in particular for each station, the first record contains the name of the station, its distance from the mouth and the identification of the event, while the other records contain the discharge values.

The second input file (name = ALFAC, type = ARNO) contains the following quantities:

(a) first record: the number of subreaches with different morphological characteristics and the upstream abscissa of the whole considered reach;
(b) the following two records (one for each of the above specified subreaches): the downstream abscissa, the slope and the mean width of the subreach;
(c) next record: the number of coupled data, discharge and celerity, for the computation of $c(Q)$ of equation 7;
(d) other record: discharge values and corresponding value of c.

```
FILE: PORTATE  270148   A


(1X,I5,2X,I5,2X,F5.C)
(1X,3A4,2X,F10.0,2X,3A4/(10F8.2))
   57      8  3600.
CALLCNE              54030.   27  01  1948
 683.90  700.11  732.63  780.69  844.85   947.12 1086.71 1291.32 1438.08 1543.21
1608.14 1662.84 1702.14 1694.90 1704.01 1689.03 1663.13 1623.37 1579.95 1517.45
1489.02 1455.52 1474.34 1454.18 1437.05 1472.62 1602.45 1650.34 1716.50 1793.50
1860.19 1923.17 1952.08 1954.15 1969.40 1971.69 1929.12 1928.22 1885.51 1856.24
1798.03 1767.12 1728.66 1665.88 1615.94 1555.24 1494.62 1424.63 1358.06 1293.77
1205.99 1151.28 1047.14  989.16  996.22  948.81  884.74
LECNCINI             40600.   27  01  1948
 663.37  676.30  695.06  724.37  767.06  831.77  926.05 1067.18 1219.45 1355.60
1462.34 1546.52 1608.26 1642.57 1664.75 1673.05 1675.30 1654.79 1623.59 1579.04
1535.78 1504.33 1490.59 1476.65 1460.91 1464.70 1515.16 1575.62 1632.14 1691.30
1745.53 1800.73 1845.74 1875.63 1899.21 1917.02 1921.46 1921.72 1913.13 1897.86
1869.04 1836.14 1802.00 1758.48 1705.49 1645.37 1583.73 1517.77 1451.30 1367.16
1315.12 1249.89 1172.52 1100.57 1057.06 1016.99  967.86
S. GICVANNI          35810.   27  01  1948
 643.42  662.46  681.81  708.03  745.42  800.82  883.28 1005.40 1148.60 1286.66
1400.78 1493.46 1563.70 1608.49 1640.24 1656.50 1664.95 1654.55 1631.24 1594.34
1557.76 1522.80 1503.07 1487.09 1471.10 1468.81 1505.40 1553.36 1605.47 1660.58
1713.80 1767.09 1813.70 1848.73 1876.49 1897.76 1906.64 1913.32 1910.06 1899.76
1878.09 1850.17 1818.33 1780.64 1732.89 1677.65 1617.67 1553.85 1489.69 1422.98
1354.61 1287.04 1213.72 1141.07 1089.25 1044.27  996.86
PETTORI              22100.   27  01  1948
 552.72  593.61  626.21  654.98  685.49  723.72  776.74  894.33  958.96 1082.11
1206.02 1316.05 1404.40 1474.03 1524.64 1563.90 1592.55 1610.13 1617.44 1611.89
1596.07 1573.53 1550.86 1530.15 1511.69 1497.96 1498.30 1513.74 1540.12 1573.40
1611.38 1651.35 1694.44 1734.71 1772.40 1806.31 1834.54 1856.06 1870.99 1870.12
1879.49 1872.17 1859.37 1838.04 1810.87 1776.22 1733.72 1694.54 1629.49 1566.45
1498.63 1427.85 1350.03 1271.46 1203.80 1143.85 1089.00
POLITEAMA            12170.   27  01  1948
 490.52  532.26  570.74  606.19  639.64  675.16  717.67  775.66  853.93  955.57
1070.15 1184.73 1285.90 1369.45 1435.50 1485.25 1524.61 1555.24 1575.65 1591.23
1593.69 1587.08 1573.75 1557.18 1539.04 1522.88 1512.91 1512.61 1522.44 1540.54
1566.19 1596.18 1629.13 1664.12 1698.90 1731.52 1761.36 1787.63 1814.38 1835.30
1849.88 1857.65 1858.66 1853.13 1840.63 1821.89 1795.79 1761.13 1715.52 1670.66
1609.21 1534.11 1456.75 1377.47 1299.12 1227.40 1163.00
SOSTEGNO             10290.   27  01  1948
 483.08  523.99  562.94  599.01  633.01  668.50  710.26  766.11  841.14  933.74
1052.62 1167.39 1270.40 1356.59 1425.21 1477.41 1515.03 1550.44 1575.20 1586.11
1592.62 1587.36 1574.94 1558.93 1541.12 1524.99 1514.37 1513.04 1521.71 1538.71
1563.41 1592.78 1625.33 1660.07 1694.87 1727.66 1757.49 1784.57 1811.26 1832.71
1847.94 1856.43 1858.10 1853.40 1841.95 1823.68 1799.36 1764.66 1723.94 1671.36
1616.08 1542.63 1466.26 1398.96 1310.34 1238.04 1173.74
CASCINE N.            6072.   27  01  1948
 467.61  505.43  544.01  581.05  616.19  651.81  691.57  762.24  811.49  901.70
1008.83 1121.57 1228.09 1319.56 1392.90 1450.73 1493.68 1530.25 1555.17 1574.99
1586.20 1586.13 1578.24 1565.33 1549.40 1533.48 1520.89 1516.09 1520.36 1532.95
1553.13 1578.76 1608.33 1641.86 1675.85 1708.58 1738.46 1766.73 1794.12 1817.69
1835.94 1848.04 1853.67 1852.62 1845.40 1831.26 1810.23 1781.35 1745.21 1701.09
1646.20 1579.12 1502.90 1423.94 1341.54 1267.60 1203.08
MARE                    30.   27  01  1948
 453.99  488.03  525.13  562.11  597.94  633.56  671.95  735.26  778.66  859.10
 955.42 1063.32 1168.94 1258.41 1336.49 1402.79 1455.79 1499.38 1534.54 1559.74
```

```
1575.46 1592.12 1580.41 1572.06 1559.16 1544.17 1530.40 1521.64 1520.47 1527.34
1542.05 1562.99 1589.33 1619.00 1651.36 1693.81 1714.79 1784.24 1772.51 1796.06
1819.59 1835.88 1846.33 1850.31 1847.95 1838.98 1823.25 1800.16 1769.67 1731.36
1683.76 1624.73 1553.70 1477.63 1398.86 1319.64 1247.33
```

```
FILE: ALFAC     ARNO     A

     2     54030.
 15873.    0.C00304    120.
    30.    0.C00026    120.
     4
  1400.       1.60
  1600.       1.20
  1800.       0.90
  2000.       0.70
```

4.3 Sample problem terminal sheet

The program is initialized by typing 'FRUSA 270148'. Then, after the specification of the various parameters, the computation is carried out and the mean, the maximum positive and the maximum negative deviation of the computed values from the recorded ones at the downstream section are typed. Several iterations are shown with different algorithms or parameter values before the typing of the string '0000' terminates the run.

```
frusa 270148

EXECUTION BEGINS...
ASCISSE ESTREME DEL TRATTO (2F8.0)
40600.  12170.
ALGORITMO (I1): 1=MUSKINGUM
                2=DIFFUSIONE LINEARE
                3=DIFFUSIONE A PARAM. VARIABILI
1
PASSO TEMPORALE E SPAZIALE (F6.0,F10.0)
900.
VALORI DI K E X (F10.0,F6.0)
20000.    0.1

    RISULTATI A POLITEAMA    -   12170. METRI DALLA FOCE

 SCARTO MEDIO=   71.1801(MC/SEC)
 MAX +      =   117.7527
 MAX -      =  -177.8406


 MASSIMA PORTATA LETTA     = 1858.6599(MC/SEC)
 MASSIMA PORTATA CALCOLATA = 1853.4851(MC/SEC)

 MASSIMO CALCOLATO OTTENUTO   22. MINUTI *PRIMA* DI  QUELLO LETTO


VALORI DI K E X (F10.0,F6.0)
15000.    0.1

    RISULTATI A POLITEAMA    -   12170. METRI DALLA FOCE

 SCARTO MEDIO=   32.3209(MC/SEC)
 MAX +      =    47.0186
 MAX -      =   -77.1934


 MASSIMA PORTATA LETTA     = 1858.6599(MC/SEC)
 MASSIMA PORTATA CALCOLATA = 1876.3843(MC/SEC)

 MASSIMO CALCOLATO OTTENUTO   75. MINUTI *PRIMA* DI  QUELLO LETTO


VALORI DI K E X (F10.0,F6.0)

PASSO TEMPORALE E SPAZIALE (F6.0,F10.0)

ALGORITMO (I1): 1=MUSKINGUM
                2=DIFFUSIONE LINEARE
                3=DIFFUSIONE A PARAM. VARIABILI
2
PASSO TEMPORALE E SPAZIALE (F6.0,F10.0)
900.
VALORI DI D1 E D2 (F10.0,F6.0)
20000.    2.5

    RISULTATI A POLITEAMA    -   12170. METRI DALLA FOCE

 SCARTO MEDIO=   42.0975(MC/SEC)
 MAX +      =    84.5627
 MAX -      =   -76.3882


 MASSIMA PORTATA LETTA     = 1858.6599(MC/SEC)
 MASSIMA PORTATA CALCOLATA = 1900.5308(MC/SEC)

 MASSIMO CALCOLATO OTTENUTO  113. MINUTI *PRIMA* DI  QUELLO LETTO


VALORI DI D1 E D2 (F10.0,F6.0)
20000.    2.

    RISULTATI A POLITEAMA    -   12170. METRI DALLA FOCE

 SCARTO MEDIO=   28.9050(MC/SEC)
 MAX +      =    58.0249
 MAX -      =   -59.5239


 MASSIMA PORTATA LETTA     = 1858.6599(MC/SEC)
 MASSIMA PORTATA CALCOLATA = 1885.9944(MC/SEC)

 MASSIMO CALCOLATO OTTENUTO   80. MINUTI *PRIMA* DI  QUELLO LETTO


VALORI DI D1 E D2 (F10.0,F6.0)
0000
R; T=1.64/2.69 15:47:35
```

4.4 Sample problem offline print

The recorded upstream discharges and the recorded and computed downstream discharges are printed out. The values of the deviations of the computed values as well as the measured ones are printed with the values of the parameters used in the calculation.

```
                METODO MUSKINGUM

          PIENA DEL 27  01  1948
```

VALORI LETTI A LEONCINI	VALORI A POLITEAMA	
	LETTI	CALCOLATI
663.37	490.52	490.52
676.30	533.26	514.29
695.06	576.74	542.84
724.37	606.19	569.20
767.06	635.64	595.47
831.77	675.16	623.80
926.95	717.87	657.37
1067.13	775.66	700.16
1219.45	653.03	755.04
1355.60	955.57	834.90
1462.34	1070.15	922.85
1546.52	1184.73	1015.59
1603.26	1285.80	1107.96
1642.57	1365.45	1196.08
1664.75	1435.50	1275.51
1673.05	1485.25	1345.25
1675.30	1524.61	1404.39
1654.79	1555.28	1453.93
1623.59	1576.65	1491.68
1579.04	1591.23	1517.55
1533.78	1593.65	1530.91
1504.33	1587.08	1534.49
1490.59	1593.75	1530.36
1476.65	1567.19	1523.88
1460.91	1536.04	1516.09
1464.79	1522.88	1506.44
1519.16	1513.91	1497.47
1575.82	1512.61	1498.49
1632.14	1522.48	1509.53
1691.30	1540.54	1528.73
1745.53	1566.19	1555.21
1800.73	1596.18	1586.84
1845.74	1623.19	1622.96
1875.63	1664.12	1661.34
1899.21	1668.96	1698.77
1917.02	1733.52	1734.01
1921.46	1761.36	1766.57
1921.72	1787.83	1794.52
1913.13	1814.36	1817.78
1897.86	1825.30	1835.67
1869.04	1846.88	1848.07
1836.14	1857.65	1853.49
1802.00	1855.66	1852.10
1758.48	1863.13	1845.03
1705.43	1846.93	1831.85
1645.37	1621.99	1811.90
1583.72	1705.79	1784.90
1517.77	1761.12	1751.77
1451.30	1719.52	1712.82
1387.16	1670.66	1668.84
1315.12	1605.21	1621.33
1249.89	1534.11	1569.43
1172.52	1456.75	1515.22
1100.57	1373.47	1457.02
1057.60	1305.12	1395.48
1016.99	1227.40	1336.42
967.86	1163.09	1280.84

```
SCARTO MEDIO=    71.1801 (MC/SEC)
MAX +       =   117.7527
MAX -       = -177.9406
```

PCFTATA (MC/SEC) - PCLITAMA

430   770   910   1050   1190   1330   1470   1610   1750   1890

DT =   900.
K =   20000.00   Y = 0.1000
DX =   28431.00

METODO MUSKINGUM

PIENA DEL 27 01 1948

VALORI LETTI A LEONCINI	VALORI A ECIITEAMA LETTI	CALCOLATI
663.37	490.52	490.52
676.30	532.26	521.79
695.06	570.74	557.49
724.37	606.19	589.00
767.06	630.64	619.62
831.77	675.16	652.56
926.55	717.87	692.14
1067.18	775.66	743.62
1219.45	852.93	814.52
1355.60	955.57	904.22
1462.34	1070.15	1005.42
1546.52	1184.73	1108.89
1608.26	1285.80	1208.61
1642.57	1360.45	1300.23
1664.75	1435.50	1379.28
1673.05	1485.25	1445.44
1675.30	1524.61	1498.48
1654.79	1555.28	1539.93
1623.59	1578.65	1567.58
1579.04	1591.23	1581.83
1539.78	1593.69	1582.67
1504.33	1587.08	1573.95
1490.59	1573.75	1558.73
1476.65	1557.18	1543.25
1460.51	1539.04	1528.14
1464.79	1522.88	1512.82
1519.16	1512.91	1501.16
1575.82	1517.61	1503.51
1632.14	1522.48	1518.50
1691.30	1540.54	1543.17
1745.53	1566.19	1575.86
1800.73	1566.18	1613.73
1845.74	1620.19	1655.68
1875.63	1664.12	1698.73
1899.21	1698.96	1739.16
1917.02	1731.52	1775.86
1921.46	1761.36	1808.38
1921.72	1787.83	1834.73
1913.13	1814.38	1855.13
1897.86	1835.30	1869.04
1869.04	1849.88	1876.38
1836.14	1857.65	1875.67
1802.00	1858.66	1867.54
1759.48	1853.13	1853.41
1705.49	1840.93	1832.72
1645.37	1821.89	1804.78
1583.72	1795.79	1769.51
1517.77	1761.12	1728.14
1451.30	1719.52	1681.13
1387.16	1670.66	1629.57
1315.12	1609.21	1575.05
1249.89	1534.11	1516.61
1172.52	1456.75	1456.45
1100.57	1377.47	1392.58
1057.60	1299.12	1326.50
1016.99	1227.40	1264.99
967.86	1163.09	1208.35

SCARTO MEDIO=   32.3200 (MC/SEC)
MAX +   =   47.0186
MAX -   =   -77.1934

PORTATA (MC/SEC) - POLITEAMA

630   770   910   1050   1190   1330   1470   1610   1750   1890

DT =   900.
K =   15000.00   Y = 0.1000
DX =   28431.00

METODO DIFFUSIONE LINEARE

PIENA DEL 27 01 1948

VALORI LETTI A LEONCINI	VALORI A COLLITEAMA LETTI	CALCOLATI
663.37	490.52	663.37
676.30	532.26	663.42
695.06	570.74	665.50
724.37	606.19	672.16
767.06	639.64	684.81
831.77	675.16	705.45
926.55	717.87	737.35
1067.18	775.66	785.58
1219.45	853.93	857.21
1355.60	955.57	954.49
1462.34	1070.15	1068.83
1546.52	1184.73	1186.67
1608.26	1285.80	1297.30
1642.57	1366.45	1394.89
1664.75	1435.50	1475.36
1673.05	1485.25	1537.57
1675.30	1524.61	1583.23
1654.79	1555.28	1614.63
1623.59	1578.65	1632.07
1579.04	1591.23	1634.70
1539.79	1593.69	1623.36
1504.33	1587.08	1601.25
1490.59	1573.75	1573.62
1476.65	1557.18	1546.64
1460.91	1539.04	1524.08
1464.79	1527.88	1504.66
1519.16	1512.91	1489.98
1575.82	1512.61	1489.47
1632.14	1522.48	1508.05
1691.30	1540.54	1540.46
1745.53	1566.19	1581.96
1800.73	1596.18	1628.88
1845.74	1629.19	1678.52
1875.63	1664.12	1728.31
1899.21	1698.96	1774.08
1917.02	1731.52	1813.30
1921.46	1761.36	1845.92
1921.72	1787.83	1871.13
1913.13	1814.38	1888.43
1897.86	1835.30	1898.24
1869.04	1849.88	1900.53
1836.14	1857.65	1894.53
1802.00	1858.66	1879.99
1758.48	1853.13	1858.71
1705.49	1840.93	1831.37
1645.37	1821.89	1796.96
1583.72	1795.79	1754.98
1517.77	1761.12	1706.38
1451.30	1719.52	1652.46
1387.16	1670.66	1594.27
1315.12	1609.21	1533.50
1249.89	1534.11	1470.31
1172.52	1456.75	1405.19
1100.57	1377.47	1338.04
1057.60	1299.12	1268.49
1016.99	1227.40	1202.50
967.86	1163.09	1144.55

SCARTO MEDIO=   42.0975 (MC/SEC)
MAX +   =   84.5627
MAX -   = -76.3882

PORTATA (MC/SEC) - POLITEAMA

640   790   940   1090   1240   1390   1540   1690   1840   1990

DT =   900.
D1 =   20000.00   D2 =   2.50

348

METODO DIFFUSIONE LINEARE

PIENA DEL 27 01 1948

VALORI LETTI A LEONCINI	VALORI A ECLITEAMA LETTI	CALCOLATI
663.37	460.52	663.37
676.30	532.26	663.41
695.06	570.74	665.02
724.37	606.19	670.41
767.06	630.64	680.93
831.77	675.16	698.41
926.95	717.87	725.72
1067.18	725.56	767.26
1219.45	853.53	829.25
1355.60	955.57	914.43
1462.34	1070.15	1016.72
1546.52	1184.73	1125.21
1608.26	1255.80	1230.40
1642.57	1360.45	1326.44
1664.75	1435.50	1408.99
1673.05	1495.25	1476.12
1675.30	1524.61	1528.44
1654.79	1555.28	1567.39
1623.59	1576.65	1593.11
1579.04	1591.23	1604.73
1539.78	1593.69	1602.78
1504.33	1587.08	1589.67
1490.59	1573.75	1569.75
1476.65	1557.18	1548.31
1460.91	1539.04	1529.11
1464.79	1522.88	1511.74
1519.16	1513.91	1497.75
1575.82	1512.61	1494.91
1632.14	1522.48	1508.17
1691.30	1540.54	1534.19
1745.53	1566.19	1569.36
1800.73	1596.18	1610.65
1845.74	1629.19	1655.60
1875.63	1664.12	1701.88
1899.21	1698.96	1745.81
1917.02	1731.52	1784.86
1921.46	1761.36	1818.52
1921.72	1787.83	1845.85
1913.13	1814.38	1866.17
1897.86	1835.30	1879.60
1869.04	1849.88	1885.99
1836.14	1857.65	1884.65
1802.00	1855.66	1875.21
1758.48	1853.13	1858.99
1705.49	1840.93	1836.61
1645.37	1821.89	1807.33
1583.72	1795.79	1770.71
1517.77	1761.12	1727.41
1451.30	1719.52	1678.50
1387.16	1670.66	1624.91
1315.12	1605.21	1568.10
1249.80	1534.11	1508.41
1172.52	1456.75	1446.31
1100.57	1377.47	1381.88
1057.60	1299.12	1314.85
1016.99	1222.40	1249.91
967.80	1163.09	1191.19

SCARTO MEDIO= 28.9050(MC/SEC)
MAX +   = 58.0240
MAX -   = -59.5230

PORTATA (MC/SEC) - POLITEAMA

```
     630    770    910   1050   1190   1330   1470   1610   1750   1890
```

DT =   900.
D1 =   20000.00   D2 =   2.00

FROGS: Flood Routing Generalized System

FRANCESCO GRECO
IBM Scientific Center, Pisa, Italy

CRISTINA MUGNAI
Computer Science Institute, University of Pisa, Italy

LORENZO PANATTONI
IBM Scientific Center, Pisa, Italy

1. Introduction

The Flood Routing Generalized System (FROGS) is designed to simulate flood wave propagation along natural or artificial watercourses. The system is based on the solution of the St Venant equations in their complete form using an implicit finit difference scheme and allowing for different boundary conditions. Knowledge of the geometrical characteristics and of the roughness of the river bed is required. The geometrical desciption of the river bed is given by means of cross-sections: to express the passive resistance either the Manning, Bazin or Keulegan formulas can be chosen. The system is built up in an interactive mode and various results can be displayed on an IBM 2250 video unit, in order to facilitate the calibration of the model for flood routing on a specific reach and the simulation of the phenomenon under different conditions. The system is written in FORTRAN IV Language and all the programs run under CP-67/CMS.

Subroutines of the Graphic Subroutine Package (GSP) are used for displaying results on the IBM 2250 video unit (C27-6932).

2. General description

Starting from the known values of water levels and discharges (initial conditions) and from the boundary conditions, FROGS is designed to determine the values of the same quantities, levels and discharges in any cross-section at any time, provided that geometry and roughness of the river be given.

The roughness of the river can be described by one of the three possible formulae: Manning, Bazin and Keulegan.

The geometry of the river, for the sake of generality, must be given by means of cross-sections in sufficient number to give an adequate description of the geometry

352

of the river bed. Each section is located by its abscissa from a given point of the watercourse and is defined by a profile referred to a common datum.

Initial conditions are supplied by backwater calculation starting from a downstream depth and assuming a constant value of discharge. For boundary conditions, water levels or discharges at the upstream section, and rating curve or water levels at the downstream section can be chosen; but, for calibrating, additional data are needed. When a rating curve is given as the downstream boundary condition, the Jones formula can be used to obtain a better simulation of the phenomenon.

2.1 Purpose and objectives

The main functions involved in using the system are

(a) calibration of the model for flood routing on a specific reach of natural or artificial watercourse, and then
(b) simulating the flood wave propagation under different conditions.

Using the system it is possible to compute from the known state of the river, that is, from the level and discharge values in any section, at a given moment, the same quantities at the next time step. Starting from the knowledge of the river at the initial time, the levels and discharges can be determined in any section at any time. In those sections, for which recorded data are available, the measured and computed hydrographs can be compared and some idea of the model's efficiency can be obtained.

With the help of these comparisons the model can be set up varying the parameters in order to obtain the best fit betwen the two hydrographs. And it is specifically in this connection that the use of an interactive computing system and a video unit are very helpful. In fact the contemporaneous influence of the various parameters and their interdependence are not known *a priori*, and by means of an interactive system the values of the parameters can be varied in an extremely simple way, and by the use of a video unit complete results can be immediately displayed, making the evaluation of the influence of the various parameters very easy.

2.2 Formulae

The St Venant equations are adopted in the following form:

$$\frac{\partial Q}{\partial x} + B \frac{\partial z}{\partial t} - q = 0$$

$$\frac{\partial z}{\partial x} + S_f + \frac{1}{g} \left[\frac{\partial Q/A}{\partial t} + \frac{Q}{A} \frac{\partial Q/A}{\partial x} \right] = 0$$

in which x = current abscissa (positive in the direction of flow); t = time; Q = discharge across a section; B = width of water surface; z = water level as referred to a horizontal datum; g = acceleration of gravity; A = cross-sectional area; S_f = friction head losses; q = lateral in or outflow (positive for inflow, negative for ouflow).

Wetted area, wetted perimeter and superficial width are determined, for each cross-section, as functions of depth.

To express the passive resistance the choice of one of the following three formulae is allowed:

$$S_f = n^2 \, \frac{Q^2}{A^2 R^{4/3}}$$ Manning–Strickers formula

$$S_f = \frac{Q^2 (\sqrt{R} + v)^2}{A^2 \cdot R^2 \cdot 7569}$$ Bazin formula

$$S_f = \frac{Q^2}{A^2 \, 324 \cdot R \cdot (\log_{10}\epsilon/(12.2R))^2}$$ Prandtl–Keulegan formula

In order to solve the St Venant equations the finite difference implicit scheme explained in Greco and Panattoni (herein) has been adopted.

To carry out the computation when critical flow occurs along the river, mainly in correspondence with drops in the bed, the St Venant equations are substituted, in the relevant grid elements, by two other equations: the first expressing the conservation of mass and the second defining the critical flow.

When a steady flow rating curve is given as a boundary condition, a closer description of the phenomenon can be obtained by applying the Jones correction formula:

$$Q = Q_0 \sqrt{1 + \frac{1}{S_0 C} \cdot \frac{\Delta z}{\Delta t}}$$

where Q_0 is the steady flow discharge, $C = (1/B)(\partial Q/\partial y)$ the velocity of wave propagation and S_0 is the bottom slope.

3. Input–output files

FROGS leaves total freedom in naming input files and in formatting data. In fact filename and filetype can be chosen in any way by the user, following the CMS requirements. Hence the data can be filed in the format most suitable to the user, provided that the format description is stored in the first two lines of the file.

The contents of the input files are the following:

(a) *cross-section data file* contains for each section the coordinates of several points of its boundary;
(b) *geometrical data file* contains for each section the values of wetted area, wetted perimeter and surface width as a function of the water level;
(c) *rating curve data file* contains the values of water levels and corresponding discharges at a given gauging station;
(d) *flood event data file* contains water levels or discharges measured at the various gauging stations during a given flood event;
(e) *tributary data file* contains inflow data for the various tributaries during a given event.

354

Another input file, the *default data file* containing the default values of all the parameters, is used by FROGS. The generation and the maintenance of this file is made easy by the interactive facilities of the system FROGS.

According to FORTRAN programming under CP-67/CMS, the following input-output files are used:

FT01 F001   for input and output of the default data file; this file is read and, at the end of the run, is restored with the last updated values;

FT02 F001   for input of data from geometrical data file, rating curve file, flood event file and tributary file;

FT05 F001   for terminal input data;

FT06 F001   for terminal output data;

FT07 F001   for output to be punched; computed hydrographs at the various gauging stations;

FT08 F001   for output to the offline printer of all additional material needed to specify the problem and its solution, see command STAMPA in Section 4.2.

4. Interactive facilities and commands

4.1 Initialization

The system is initialized by the user at a communications terminal by typing , under the CMS operating system, the word FROGS.* As a consequence of this command the programs are loaded and the execution begins. First the program reads the default values of the various parameters from the default data file, after which it types the message 'TYPE THE COMMANDS' and then it is ready for reading, interpreting and executing the next command. The request for a new command is made via a question mark.

4.2 Terminal commands

The allowed commands are divided into three main groups and are listed below. Except for the operating commands, the commands can be given in any desired order.

Operating commands. There are two operating commands:

GO which causes the start of a computation with the last defined values of the parameters. At the end of the execution the program asks again for a new command.

STOP which causes the end of the run and the storage, in the default data file, of the last defined default values.

Definition commands. These commands are used for changing the contents, numerical or alphabetic, or the parameters. They have the form CODE = ..nnn.nnn..

---

*From this point onwards the underlined part of a word of a command is the part necessary for the recognition of the word by the program.

or CODE = aaaa respectively. CODE is the conventional name, recognized by the program for the parameter, ..nnn.nnn.. is a free format numerical field and aaaa is an alphabitic field, containing the new value for the parameter identified by CODE. Numerical quantities must be expressed in the metric system. Typing the word DEFAULT before a command, the default value of that command is changed with the new typed value. At the end of the run the new default value is stored in the default data file.

XMONTE = ...nnn.nnn... Must be used for changing the value of the upstream section absicissa of the considered reach. No restriction is set on the numerical field. If the point is omitted, it is assumed after the last digit.

XVALLE = ...nnn.nnn... Analogous to the previous. It refers to the downstream section abscissa.

XSCALA = ...nnn.nnn... Analogous to the previous. It refers to the abscissa of the hydrometer with a rating curve.

APPQ = ...nnn.nnn... This parameter refers to the desired accuracy for the discharge values in the Newton iterative process for the solution of the non-linear system arising from the finite difference scheme.

APPZ = ...nnn.nnn... The same as APPQ but referred to the water level values.

DZ = ...nnn.nnn... By this command the value of the increment for the numerical computation of the derivatives with respect to the water level can be varied.

XATTRITO (I) = ...nnn.nnn... This command may be used for dividing the considered river reach into several subreaches with different roughness coefficients. More precisely it defines the downstream end abscissa of the Ith subreach. The value of I must not exceed 9. If (I) is omitted, it is assumed equal to 1.

COEFFICIENTE (I) = ...nnn.nnn... By this command the value of the roughness coefficient for the Ith subreach is defined. The value of I must not exceed 10, and, if omitted, it is assumed equal to 1.

SCABREZZA = aaaa. It allows the choice between three different roughness formulae. More precisely aaaa can be:
MANNING for the Manning–Strickler formula,
KEULEGAN for the Prandtl–Keulegan formula and
BAZIN for the Bazin formula.

STAMPA = aaaa. This command allows the choice between the various possibilities for the output on the offline fast printer. aaaa can be:
NO for not printing,
ONDE for printing the computed and measured waves at each gauging station,
PROFILI for printing, in addition, the water profiles at each time step and
ITERAZIONI for printing, in addition, the values at each iteration of the unknowns of the non-linear system.

PERFORAZIONE = aa. This command refers to the possibility of punching the computed and measured waves at each gauging station. aa can be:
SI for punching and
NO for not punching

VIDEO = aa. It refers to the possibility of using the IBM 2250 video unit for the display of the results. aa can be:

SI for using the video unit and

NO for not using it.

The features of the display on the video unit are explained in some detail at the end of this paragraph.

JONES = aa. It refers to the possibility of applying the Jones correction formula to the steady flow rating curve in order to transform it to a loop rating curve. aa can be:

SI for using the Jones formula and

NO for not using it.

FILE aaaa. This command allows the choice of the input files different from the default ones, by giving their filename and filetype. The alphabetic field can be:

GEOMETRIA for changing the filename and filetype of the file with the geometrical data,

SCALA for the file with the rating curve,

ONDA for the file with the hydrometrical data and

AFFLUENTI for the file with the tributary inflow data.

As a consequence of this command the program asks the name and, successively, the type of the specified file; the user then has to enter the required alphanumeric strings (up to 8 characters)

CONDIZIONE MONTE = a. The command is to be used for changing the upstream boundary condition where a can be:

Z for the water levels and

Q for the discharges.

CONDIZIONE VALLE = a. Analogous to the previous but referring to the downstream condition, where a can be:

Z for the water levels and

R for the rating curve.

Display commands. This group contains those commands which are to be used for writing at the communications terminal the values of the parameters. The commands are:

DISPLAY PARAMETRI for writing the values of all the parameters mentioned in the definition commands.

DISPLAY DEFAULT for writing all default values.

DISPLAY FILES for writing the filename and filetype of the files containing geometrical data, rating curve data, the flood event data and the tributary data.

DISPLAY CONDIZIONI for writing the upstream and downstream boundary conditions.

DISPLAY list, where list is a sequence of codes defined in the definition commands, divided by commas. It can be used for writing the value of one or more parameters.

A formal error in a command causes the typing at the user terminal of the message

'COMANDO ERRATO' (command error) and the request for a new command. Several controls are also made on the contents of the command: the relevant messages, as they are self-explanatory, are not described here. These errors cause a return to the request for a new command.

4.3 Video unit display

As it has been pointed out previously the choice VIDEO = SI causes the use of the video unit as output unit. The relevant programs exploit the facilities of the GSP (Graphic Subroutine Package). In particular the choice among the various types of display is made using eight of the thirty-five attention sources available to the GSP user, namely the first seven programmed function keys and the light pen. According to the source used, the following displays can be obtained and the following actions can be taken:

KEY 1 The water profile as computed at that time and the river bed bottom in the considered reach are displayed (Figure 1).

KEY 2 As a function of the time, the measured water levels in the upstream section and the computed and measured ones at one gauging station displayed (Figure 2). The choice of the hydrometer is made at the communications terminal following a request of the program.

KEY 3 Displays the drawing of any chosen section with the current water level (Figure 3). The choice of a section can be made from the communications terminal as a response to a program query or via light pen (see below).

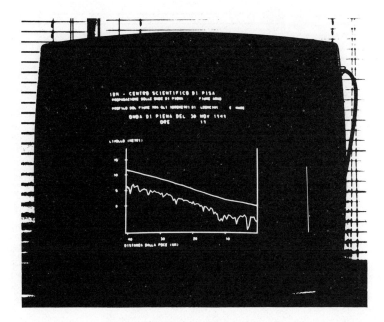

Figure 1. Display obtained using key 1

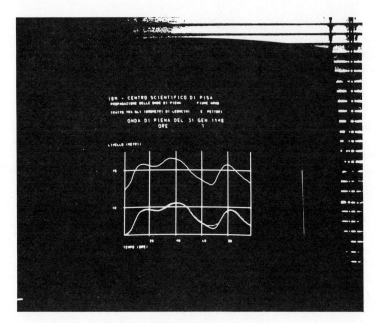

Figure 2. Display obtained using key 2

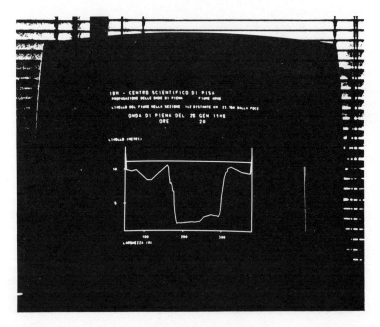

Figure 3. Display obtained using key 3

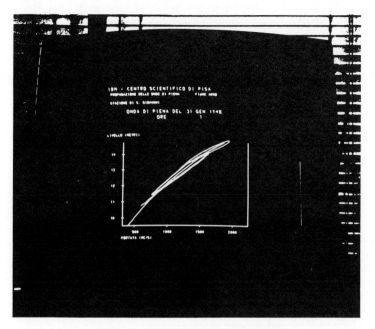

Figure 4. Display obtained using key 4

KEY 4 The measured steady flow rating curve and the computed loop rating curve at the gauging station, whose abscissa is defined by the parameter XSCALA, is displayed (Figure 4).

KEY 5 Any previous choice is reset.

KEY 6 Instigates a pause in execution while maintaining the image on the screen. For the restart, key 6 must be hit again.

KEY 7 After processing the last time step the program fixes the display and awaits the depression of this key before continuing to print the final statistics.

LIGHT PEN It has the same effect as key 3 with the only difference being that the choice of the section abscissa is by means of the light pen on the display of the water profile.

During the processing, displays are updated. By appropriate key selection it is possible to pass from one display to another at any time during the computation or at the end before hitting key 7.

5. FROGS flowchart

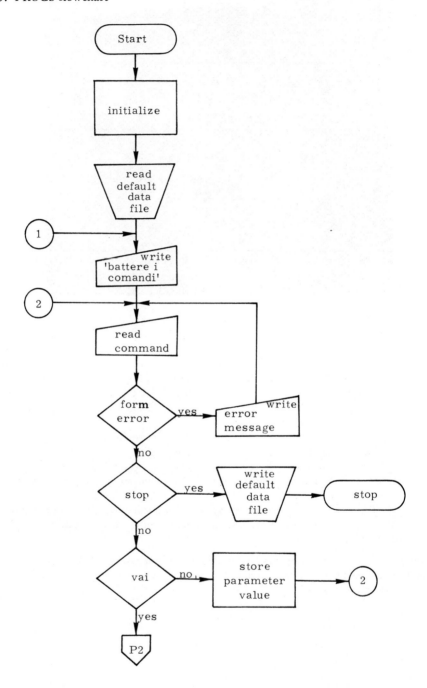

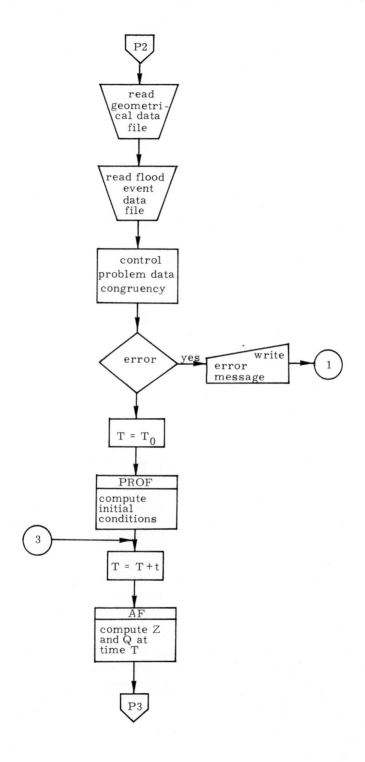

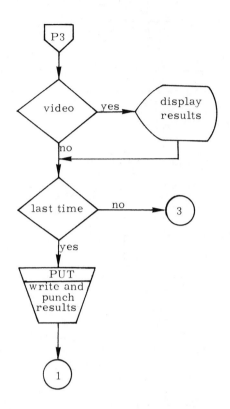

6. Timing

The processing time can be roughly expressed by the following formula:

$$T = k \cdot nt \cdot nx$$

where nt is the number of time steps, nx is the number of cross-sections and k is a proportionality factor. k mainly depends on the number of iterations and on the basis of our computational experience has a value ranging from 0.010 to 0.030 seconds, depending mainly on the choice of the starting values for the Newton iterative process.

The input–output operation time is not included in the previous formula; it depends obviously on the amount of input–output data.

7. Sample problem

The simulation of the 3 January, 1951, flood event in the reach of the Arno river between the gauging station of Leoncini (40.6 km from the river mouth) and the sea is chosen as sample problem. In this reach other gauging stations, at S. Giovanni alla Vena (35.810 km from the sea) and at Politeama in Pisa (12.170 km from the sea) are here considered. A steady flow rating curve is also available at S. Giovanni alla Vena.

The Manning formula is adopted to express friction losses. Three subreaches with a different value of the roughness coefficient are considered:

Leoncini to Pisa (12.50 km from the sea) $n = 0.035$
subreach in Pisa up to 9.50 km to the sea $n = 0.040$
Pisa to the sea $n = 0.030$

As boundary conditions water levels at the extreme sections of the reach are chosen.

Glossary of Italian terms for the following program

BATTERE I COMANDI
type the commands

XMONTE
upstream section abscissa

XVALLE
downstream section abscissa

DISPLAY SCABREZZA, COEFFICIENTI
display roughness formula and coefficients

COEFF. DI SCABREZZA
roughness coefficient

COEFF (i)
roughness coefficient of ith subreach

XATTRITO
downstream end abscissa of ith subreach

DISP XATT, COEF
display downstream end abscissa

DISP CONDIZIONI
display conditions

CONDIZIONE DI MONTE, CONDIZIONE DI VALLE
upstream condition, downstream condition

FILE ONDA
flood wave file

NOME?
name?

TIPO?
type?

VAI
go

DURATA DEL CALCOLO: . . . MINUTI . . . SECONDI . . . CENTESIMI
computation time: . . . minutes . . . seconds . . . hundredths

. . . CENTESIMI IN MEDIA PER OGNI PASSO TEMPORALE
. . . hundredths on the average for every step

. . . PER OGNI MAGLIA
. . . for each loop

RISULTATI A...
results at...

. . . METRI DALLA FOCE
. . . metres from the mouth

SCARTI (METRI)
deviations (metres)

SCARTO MEDIO
mean deviation

SCARTI DALLA SCALA DI DEFLUSSO (MC/S)
deviations from the rating curve (cubic metres per second)

IN TOTALE . . . ITERAZIONI (. . . IN MEDIA)
total number of interations . . . (. . . on the average)

SCEGLIERE NUOVI VALORI DEI PARAMETRI, ALTRIMENTI: STOP
try new parameters values otherwise: stop

PIENA INIZIATA ALLE ORE . . . DEL . . .
flood started at . . . of (day, month, year)

ONDA MISURATA A
measured flood wave at

CALCOLATA, MISURATA
computed, measured

7.1 Sample problem input

In the following input listing part of the geometrical data file, the rating curve data file and the flood event data file are reported. The first two records of each file describe the format of the relevant data. The geometrical data file (name = GEOM, type = MARECALL) contains, in addition:

third record — the number of cross-sections and the abscissae of the first and of the last section in the file,
other records — cross-section data, which contain for each cross-section:
first record — the code number of the section, the abscissa and the number of the following sets of data,
other records — two sets of wetted area, wetted perimeter, surface width and water level data.

The rating curve data file (name = SCALASG, type = SCDFSG) contains, in addition:

third record — the number of coupled data, level and discharge, the bottom slope, the reference level and the values of A, B, C, relevant to the formula

$$Q = A(z - B)^c$$

to be used for obtaining Q from values of z greater than the last value in the file,

other records — water levels and corresponding discharges.

The flood event data file (name = ONDA, type = 030151) contains for each station, in addition:

third record — the name and the abscissa of the station, the reference level, the start of recording date and hour, the time step, the number of data, the data code (1 = level, 2 = discharge),

other records — flood data, levels or discharges according to the data code.

FILE: GEOM   MARECALL A

```
(I5,2F8.0)
(I5,F8.0,I5,I2/(8F10.4))
 1000    30.   54033.
    9    30.    22
  708.7952   242.6098   138.5026    1.6000   695.2341   235.5189   138.5026    1.5000
  695.2341   196.6098   138.5026    1.5000   636.9836   196.3246   137.9866    1.0700
  634.2766   192.6913   137.9626    1.0500   628.8650   191.7248   137.9146    1.0100
  628.8650   135.2850   137.9146    1.0100   546.7927   129.4638   131.7252    0.3900
  437.7107   127.2000   128.8046   -0.4600    84.9274   116.1000   116.2785   -3.3600
   67.8162   112.0500   112.1901   -3.5100    62.4037   104.4500   104.5760   -3.5600
   47.0400   100.4000   100.4876   -3.7100    32.8462    88.8500    88.9012   -3.8600
   28.5874    81.5000    81.5373   -3.9100    25.0000    62.0000    62.0343   -3.9600
   16.1500    56.0000    56.0268   -4.1100    13.5875    46.5000    46.5235   -4.1600
    5.6875    32.5000    32.5165   -4.3600     2.0500    16.0000    16.0138   -4.5100
    0.8333     8.3333     8.3433   -4.6100     0.0        0.0        0.0       -4.8100
   13   435.    39
  848.2422   233.5798   165.8642    1.9100   825.2859   229.5798   165.8642    1.7700
  815.4463   229.0020   165.8642    1.7100   781.0127   225.8269   165.8642    1.5000
  731.8188   224.0131   165.8642    1.2000   720.3394   209.3744   165.8642    1.1300
  702.3013   202.5300   165.8642    1.0200   702.3013   195.9133   165.8642    1.0200
  700.6604   195.9078   165.8541    1.0100   692.4614   188.9801   165.8042    0.9600
  687.5432   184.5716   165.7741    0.9300   684.2627   180.7660   165.7542    0.9100
  684.2627   163.9800   165.7542    0.9100   627.5696   159.9800   161.3889    0.5600
  611.5969   159.4800   160.7790    0.4600   579.9810   156.6800   157.9481    0.2600
  564.3972   155.0000   156.2540    0.1600   503.6543   148.7174   149.8605   -0.2400
  272.2124   140.5869   141.0952   -1.8400   237.3878   138.0145   138.4476   -2.0900
  230.5282   136.3690   136.7824   -2.1400   191.1655   126.0488   126.3732   -2.4400
  166.1914   123.6925   123.9765   -2.6400   160.1777   116.8534   117.1261   -2.6900
  142.9698   112.5862   112.8345   -2.8400   142.9698   107.5862   107.8346   -2.8400
  132.3950   103.9080   104.1407   -2.9400   127.3914    96.2356    96.4587   -2.9900
  103.9611    91.2069    91.3869   -3.2400    74.8750    75.0000    75.1263   -3.5900
   43.9705    62.3529    62.4311   -4.0400    40.9853    57.0588    57.1325   -4.0900
   22.2500    50.0000    50.0319   -4.4400     7.1562    36.2500    36.2627   -4.7900
    2.3750    27.5000    27.5075   -4.9400     0.3333    13.3333    13.3348   -5.0400
    0.3333     8.3333     8.3348   -5.0400     0.0        5.0000     5.0000   -5.0900
    0.0        0.0        0.0       -5.0900
   14   850.    33
  929.3606   228.3700   200.3486    2.3600   929.3606   228.3700   200.3486    2.3600
  864.1418   227.7029   199.6043    2.0300   830.6282   223.0592   199.2209    1.8500
  779.4863   220.4337   198.6346    1.6000   744.1624   220.0698   198.2286
  703.1240   218.7717   196.9136    1.2100   673.1587   179.7826   181.91
  641.3462   173.7044   175.8149    0.8700   639.6348   168.5284   179
  622.9199   165.7698   167.7782    0.7600   571.8176   163.9198
  546.2261   155.9698   157.4808    0.2900   494.9749   154.60
  240.0298   141.8000   142.4859   -1.7600   176.8359   130
  112.5651   118.0208   118.4289   -2.7100   101.2733
   90.6274   105.1041   105.4642   -2.9100    81.1020
     5415     82.0833    82.3753   -3.1600    64.
      08     70.1041    70.3557   -3.3100
             54.0625    54.1843   -3.810
             45.4167    45.5026
```

FILE: SCALASG   SCDFSG   A

```
(I5,5F10.5)
(8F10.2)
   64    0.0003    6.79    117.82    8.48    1.5
  0.30     25.70    0.40     40.90    0.50     56.00    0.60     71.00
  0.70     86.00    0.80    101.00    0.90    116.00    1.00    131.00
  1.10    146.00    1.20    161.00    1.30    176.00    1.40    192.00
  1.50    207.00    1.60    222.00    1.70    238.00    1.80    254.00
  1.90    270.00    2.00    286.00    2.10    303.0     2.20    319.00
  2.30    336.00    2.40    353.00    2.50    369.00    2.60    386.00
  2.70    403.00    2.80    422.00    2.90    440.00    3.00    458.00
  3.10    476.00    3.20    496.00    3.30    515.00    3.40    535.00
  3.50    555.00    3.60    576.00    3.70    597.00    3.80    618.00
  3.90    641.00    4.00    663.00    4.10    686.00    4.20    709.00
  4.30    732.00    4.40    756.00    4.50    779.00    4.60    804.00
  4.70    829.00    4.80    854.00    4.90    878.00    5.00    904.00
  5.10    930.00    5.20    957.00    5.30    983.00    5.40   1010.00
  5.50   1037.00    5.60   1065.00    5.70   1093.00    5.80   1121.00
  5.90   1150.00    6.00   1179.00    6.10   1208.00    6.20   1239.00
  6.30   1269.00    6.40   1300.00    7.00   1480.00    7.50   1646.00
```

FILE: ONDA   030151   A

```
(3A4,8X,F10.0,F10.2,2A2,A4,I41,2I2,I4,I2,F2.0,I5,I2,F10.0)
(10FP.C)
CALLONE              54030.      12.73        03011951 2 1   28 1
     4.2C    4.70     5.00     5.30     5.7C     6.1C     6.4C     6.7C     6.85     7.0C
     7.C5    7.07     7.00     7.00     6.90     6.85     6.70     6.55     6.40     6.20
     6.CC    5.80     5.50     5.30     5.10     4.90     4.70     4.5C
LFONCINI             40600.       9.22        03011951 1 1   37 1
     2.5C    2.75     3.00     3.25     3.81     4.50     5.07     5.58     6.CC     6.30
     6.45    6.58     6.65     6.73     6.75     6.75     6.73     6.70     6.62     6.54
     6.43    6.27     6.10     5.90     5.68     5.45     5.25     5.C5     4.88     4.7C
     4.55    4.43     4.33     4.15     4.02     3.98     3.90
S. GICVANNI          35810.       7.48        03011951 1 1   40 1
     2.9C    3.00     3.20     3.40     3.65     4.70     4.85     5.30     5.85     6.10
     6.3C    6.45     6.55     6.60     6.70     6.70     6.70     6.70     6.65     6.60
     6.5C    6.40     6.25     6.05     5.85     5.65     5.45     5.25     5.C5     4.85
     4.7C    4.55     4.40     4.30     4.20     4.10     4.00     3.90     3.80     3.70
FETTORI              22100.       3.08        03011951 5 1   36 1
     3.25    3.70     4.15     4.70     5.15     5.65     5.90     6.15     6.35     6.40
     6.45    6.55     6.60     6.63     6.65     6.65     6.6C     6.55     6.47     6.35
     6.2C    6.05     5.85     5.60     5.40     5.15     4.90     4.85     4.80     4.60
     4.5C    4.40     4.30     4.20     4.10     4.05
FOLITEAMA            12170.       0.02        03011951111 1   28 1
     5.25    5.50     5.65     5.80     5.95     6.1C     6.1C     6.15     6.2C     6.20
     6.20    6.20     6.15     6.05     5.95     5.80     5.65     5.50     5.25     5.05
     4.85    4.65     4.50     4.35     4.25     4.15     4.C5     3.95
SOSTEGNO             10280.      -0.06        03011951 1 1   40 1
     1.5C    1.70     1.90     2.10     2.30     2.60     2.8C     3.CC     3.25     3.60
     3.9C    4.10     4.25     4.40     4.50     4.60     4.65     4.70     4.75     4.75
     4.75    4.75     4.70     4.65     4.55     4.45     4.35     4.25     4.15     3.95
     3.8C    3.75     3.60     3.50     3.40     3.30     3.20     3.10     3.00     2.95
MARE                    30.       0.0         03011951 1 1   40 1
     0.      0.       0.       0.       0.       0.       0.       0.       0.       0.
     C.      0.       0.       0.       0.       C.       C.       C.       C.       0.
     0.      0.       0.       0.       0.       0.       0.       0.       0.       0.
     0.      0.       0.       0.       0.       C.       C.       C.       C.       C.
```

7.2 Sample problem terminal sheet

The problem is defined assigning, via the communications terminal, the desired values to the various parameters. Then, after the operating command VAI, the program is executed and, at the end, the deviations between the measured values and the computed ones at the various gauging stations are printed. Finally the command STOP terminates the run.

```
frogs

EXECUTION BEGINS...
BATTERE I COMANDI
xmonte = 40600.
?
xvalle = 30.
?
display scabrezza,coefficienti
FORMULA DI SCABREZZA = MANN
COEFF. DI SCABREZZA =  0.0350
?
coef(2) = 0.040
?
coefficiente(3) = 0.030
?
xattrito = 12500.
?
xatt(2) = 9500.
?
disp xatt,coef
ASCISSE SCABREZZA =  12500.   9500.
COEFF. DI SCABREZZA =  0.0350 0.0400 0.0300
?
disp condizioni
CONDIZIONE DI MONTE = Z  CONDIZIONE DI VALLE = Z
?
file onda
NOME ? (A8)
onda
TIPO ? (A8)
030151
?
vai


      RISULTATI A S. GIOVANNI   -   35810. METRI DALLA FOCE
            SCARTI (METRI)

   SCARTO MEDIO =     0.1552
   MAX +        =     0.5832
   MAX -        =    -0.3872

         SCARTI DALLA SCALA DI DEFLUSSO (MC/S)
   MEDIO =    -10.14
   MAX + =    104.37
   MAX - =   -129.14


      RISULTATI A PETTORI      -   22100. METRI DALLA FOCE
            SCARTI (METRI)

   SCARTO MEDIO =     0.0746
   MAX +        =     0.1780
   MAX -        =    -0.0934


      RISULTATI A POLITEAMA    -   12170. METRI DALLA FOCE
            SCARTI (METRI)

   SCARTO MEDIO =     0.1099
   MAX +        =     0.0014
   MAX -        =    -0.2492


      RISULTATI A SOSTEGNO     -   10280. METRI DALLA FOCE
            SCARTI (METRI)

   SCARTO MEDIO =     0.1895
   MAX +        =     0.5453
   MAX -        =    -0.2649

   IN TOTALE  159 ITERAZIONI  ( 4.42 IN MEDIA)


   SCEGLIERE NUOVI VALORI DEI PARAMETRI,ALTRIMENTI : STOP
   BATTERE I COMANDI
   stop
   R; T=15.05/17.25 15:10:48
```

7.3 Sample problem offline print-out

For each gauging station, recorded levels and computed discharges at the upstream sections and computed levels, computed discharges and recorded levels at the downstream station are printed. The values of the deviations between measured and computed values are also printed.

```
PIENA INIZIATA ALLE ORE   1 DEL 03  01  1951

    ONDA MISURATA A                      ONDA A S. GIOVANNI
    LEONCINI                             CALCOLATA            MISURATA

       11.72        576.00      10.96      576.CC       1C.38
       11.97        496.07      10.66      553.89       10.48
       12.22        603.60      10.68      587.9C       1C.68
       12.47        674.84      10.83      645.13       10.88
       13.03        844.77      11.22      774.79       11.13
       13.72       1058.70      11.79      962.75       12.18
       14.29       1231.55      12.36     1142.0C       12.33
       14.80       1391.13      12.88     1307.69       12.78
       15.22       1520.24      13.33     1445.9C       13.33
       15.52       1610.69      13.66     1549.11       13.58
       15.67       1640.65      13.88     1600.31       13.78
       15.80       1677.67      14.04     1644.51       13.93
       15.87       1689.24      14.14     1667.33       14.C3
       15.95       1716.11      14.23     1695.11       14.08
       15.97       1710.49      14.28     1700.97       14.18
       15.97       1700.03      14.31     1696.53       14.18
       15.95       1682.93      14.31     1684.71       14.18
       15.92       1664.31      14.30     1669.35       14.18
       15.84       1620.81      14.25     1635.8C       14.13
       15.76       1586.01      14.19     1602.24       14.08
       15.65       1538.92      14.10     1560.73       13.98
       15.49       1473.04      13.97     1501.98       13.88
       15.32       1411.79      13.82     1442.69       13.73
       15.12       1341.73      13.63     1376.44       13.53
       14.90       1269.42      13.43     1305.51       13.33
       14.67       1199.88      13.21     1237.13       13.13
       14.47       1146.20      13.00     1178.94       12.93
       14.27       1089.81      12.80     1121.69       12.73
       14.10       1045.59      12.63     1073.19       12.53
       13.92        995.07      12.45     1023.00       12.33
       13.77        957.36      12.29      981.52       12.18
       13.65        929.28      12.16      949.08       12.03
       13.55        906.09      12.05      922.6C       11.88
       13.37        851.41      11.90      876.53       11.78
       13.24        821.42      11.76      841.75       11.68
       13.20        821.02      11.69      830.20       11.58
       13.12        799.82      11.61      811.58       11.48
    SCARTI (METRI)

SCARIO MEDIO =    0.1552
MAX +       =     0.5832
MAX -       =    -0.3872

    SCARTI DALLA SCALA DI DEFLUSSC (MC/S)
MEDIC =      -10.14
MAX + =      104.37
MAX - =     -129.14
```

PIENA INIZIATA ALLE ORE 1 DEL 03 01 1951

ONDA MISURATA A LEONCINI		ONDA A FETTORI CALCCIATA		MISURATA
11.72	576.00	6.54	576.CC	
11.97	496.07	6.46	630.02	
12.22	603.60	6.39	613.65	
12.47	674.84	6.39	616.40	
13.03	844.77	6.51	658.27	6.33
13.72	1058.70	6.80	753.07	6.78
14.29	1231.55	7.24	889.85	7.23
14.80	1391.13	7.73	1048.48	7.78
15.22	1520.24	8.21	1205.36	8.23
15.52	1610.69	8.64	1338.47	8.73
15.67	1640.65	8.96	1433.1C	8.98
15.80	1677.67	9.21	1503.47	9.23
15.87	1689.24	9.39	1554.94	9.43
15.95	1716.11	9.54	1595.49	9.48
15.97	1710.49	9.65	1626.27	9.53
15.97	1700.03	9.74	1646.07	9.63
15.95	1682.93	9.80	1657.94	9.68
15.92	1664.31	9.83	1661.42	9.71
15.84	1620.81	9.84	1656.C3	9.73
15.76	1586.01	9.82	1642.19	9.73
15.65	1538.92	9.78	1618.58	9.68
15.49	1473.04	9.71	1584.23	9.63
15.32	1411.79	9.59	1541.17	9.55
15.12	1341.73	9.44	1486.32	9.43
14.90	1269.42	9.26	1422.55	9.28
14.67	1199.88	9.05	1352.22	9.13
14.47	1146.20	8.84	1284.95	8.93
14.27	1089.81	8.64	1222.14	8.68
14.10	1045.59	8.45	1164.95	8.48
13.92	995.07	8.27	1111.19	8.23
13.77	957.36	8.10	1062.16	7.98
13.65	929.28	7.95	1019.07	7.93
13.55	906.09	7.82	982.4C	7.88
13.37	851.41	7.69	944.17	7.68
13.24	821.42	7.55	906.61	7.58
13.20	821.02	7.44	877.10	7.48
13.12	799.82	7.35	852.86	7.38

SCARTI (METRI)

SCARTO MEDIO =	0.0746	
MAX + =	0.1780	
MAX - =	-0.0934	

```
PIENA INIZIATA AILF CRE  1 DEL 03  01  1951

    ONDA MISURATA A                    CNDA A FCIITEAMA
    LEONCINI                           CAICCIATA          MISUPATA


    11.72    576.00          2.83    576.CC
    11.97    496.07          2.99    625.39
    12.22    603.60          3.01    624.19
    12.47    674.84          3.00    620.37
    13.03    844.77          3.C5    633.56
    13.72   1C5P.70          3.20    680.21
    14.29   1231.55          3.50    768.63
    14.80   1391.13          3.91    894.24
    15.22   1520.24          4.37   1C38.9C
    15.52   1610.69          4.81   1183.85
    15.67   1640.65          5.17   1306.72    5.27
    15.80   1677.67          5.45   1401.57    5.52
    15.87   1689.24          5.66   1473.27    5.67
    15.95   1716.11          5.82   1528.23    5.82
    15.97   1710.49          5.94   1568.81    5.97
    15.97   1700.03          6.03   1598.45    6.12
    15.95   1682.93          6.C9   1622.11    6.12
    15.92   1664.31          6.14   1637.71    6.17
    15.84   1620.81          6.17   1645.Cf    6.22
    15.76   1586.01          6.17   1644.77    6.22
    15.65   1538.92          6.15   1635.33    6.22
    15.49   1473.04          6.11   1616.18    6.22
    15.32   1411.79          6.04   1586.C9    6.17
    15.12   1341.73          5.94   1544.28    6.07
    14.90   1269.42          5.80   1489.19    5.97
    14.67   1199.88          5.64   1424.49    5.82
    14.47   1146.20          5.46   1357.62    5.67
    14.27   1C89.81          5.27   1291.60    5.52
    14.10   1045.59          5.09   1230.26    5.27
    13.92    995.07          4.93   1173.05    5.07
    13.77    957.36          4.77   1119.86    4.87
    13.65    929.28          4.62   1071.68    4.67
    13.55    906.09          4.48   1029.28    4.52
    13.37    851.41          4.36    989.37    4.37
    13.24    821.42          4.23    950.85    4.27
    13.20    821.02          4.12    916.24    4.17
    13.12    799.82          4.C2    886.63    4.07
    SCARTI (METRI)

SCARTC MEDIO =    0.1099
MAX +        =    0.0014
MAX -        =   -C.2492
```

PIENA INIZIATA AILE CRE 1 DEL 03 01 1951

ONDA MISURATA A LEONCINI		ONDA A SOSTEGNC CALCOLATA		MISURATA
11.72	576.00	1.99	576.CC	1.44
11.97	496.07	2.10	618.87	1.64
12.22	6C3.60	2.13	623.C9	1.84
12.47	674.84	2.13	620.51	2.04
13.03	844.77	2.16	631.74	2.24
13.72	1058.70	2.28	673.66	2.54
14.29	1231.55	2.50	755.96	2.74
14.80	1391.13	2.83	876.36	2.94
15.22	1520.24	3.21	1017.99	3.19
15.52	1610.69	3.60	1163.44	3.54
15.67	1640.65	3.93	1289.44	3.84
15.80	1677.67	4.18	1388.16	4.04
15.87	1689.24	4.38	1463.11	4.19
15.95	1716.11	4.53	1520.42	4.34
15.97	1710.49	4.65	1562.94	4.44
15.97	1700.03	4.74	1594.19	4.54
15.95	1682.93	4.80	1618.85	4.59
15.92	1664.31	4.84	1635.41	4.64
15.84	1620.91	4.87	1643.75	4.69
15.76	1586.01	4.88	1644.44	4.69
15.65	1538.92	4.87	1636.11	4.69
15.49	1473.04	4.83	1618.14	4.69
15.32	1411.79	4.78	1589.27	4.64
15.12	1341.73	4.69	1548.85	4.59
14.90	1269.42	4.58	1495.4C	4.49
14.67	1199.88	4.44	1432.28	4.39
14.47	1146.20	4.28	1366.11	4.29
14.27	1089.81	4.11	1300.32	4.19
14.10	1045.59	3.96	1238.61	4.C9
13.92	995.07	3.81	1180.97	3.89
13.77	957.36	3.67	1127.35	3.74
13.65	929.28	3.54	1078.63	3.69
13.55	906.09	3.42	1035.59	3.54
13.37	851.41	3.30	995.34	3.44
13.24	821.42	3.19	956.64	3.34
13.20	821.02	3.09	921.61	3.24
13.12	799.82	3.0C	891.37	3.14

SCARTI (METRI)

SCARTO MEDIO =   0.1895
MAX +   =   0.5453
MAX -   =   -0.2649

FIENA INIZIATA AILE CRE 1 DEL 03 01 1951

ONDA MISURATA A LEONCINI			ONDA A MARE CALCOLATA	MISURATA
11.72	576.00	0.0	576.00	0.0
11.97	496.07	0.C	599.23	C.C
12.22	603.60	0.0	612.86	0.0
12.47	674.84	0.0	617.96	C.C
13.03	844.77	0.0	624.93	0.0
13.72	1058.70	0.C	648.50	C.C
14.29	1231.55	0.0	703.08	0.0
14.80	1391.13	0.C	792.97	C.C
15.22	1520.24	0.0	911.84	0.0
15.52	1610.69	0.0	1C47.68	C.C
15.67	1640.65	0.0	1180.31	0.0
15.80	1677.67	0.C	1295.47	C.0
15.87	1689.24	0.0	1387.07	0.0
15.95	1716.11	C.C	1454.80	C.C
15.97	1710.49	0.0	1510.54	0.0
15.97	1700.03	C.C	1553.76	C.C
15.95	1682.93	0.0	1587.04	0.0
15.92	1664.31	C.C	1612.04	C.C
15.84	1620.81	0.0	1628.92	0.0
15.76	1586.C1	0.C	1637.67	C.C
15.65	1538.92	0.0	1637.85	0.0
15.49	1473.04	0.C	1628.93	C.C
15.32	1411.79	0.0	1610.14	0.0
15.12	1341.73	0.0	1580.36	C.C
14.90	1269.42	0.0	1537.93	0.0
14.67	1199.88	C.0	1484.80	C.C
14.47	1146.20	0.0	1424.17	0.0
14.27	1089.81	C.C	1358.99	C.C
14.10	1045.59	0.0	1292.99	0.0
13.92	995.07	C.C	1230.89	C.C
13.77	957.36	0.0	1173.72	0.0
13.65	929.28	C.C	1121.30	C.C
13.55	906.09	0.0	1073.79	0.0
13.37	851.41	C.0	1030.50	C.C
13.24	821.42	0.0	989.84	0.0
13.20	821.02	C.0	952.4C	C.C
13.12	799.82	0.0	919.02	0.0

IN TOTALE 159 ITERAZIONI (4.42 IN MEDIA)

8. FROGS command sheet

To recognize a command, all the words appearing in it, or the first four characters of each word if longer, are required by the program. Free format is allowed for all the fields. Quantities are expressed in the metric system

Code	COMMAND Value	FUNCTION
Operating commands:		
VAI	not applicable	Computation is started.
STOP	not applicable	End of the run.
Definition commands	(name and value of the definition commands are separated by equal sign, except for the FILE command):	
Typing DEFAULT before a command, also the default value of the relevant parameter is changed.		
XMONTE	..nnn.nnn..	Upstream section abscissa.
XVALLE	..nnn.nnn..	Downstream section abscissa.
XSCALA	..nnn.nnn..	Rating curve section abscissa.
APPQ	..nnn.nnn..	Discharge accuracy.
APPZ	..nnn.nnn..	Water level accuracy.
DZ	..nnn.nnn..	Increment for computation of derivatives with respect to level.
XATTRITO(I)	..nnn.nnn..	Downstream end abscissa of Ith subreach.
COEFFICIENTE(I)	..nnn.nnn..	Roughness coefficient of Ith subreach.
SCABREZZA	aaaa	Roughness formula: aaaa = MANNING, KEULEGAN or BAZIN.
STAMPA	aaaa	Output: aaaa = NO, ONDE, PROFILI or ITERAZIONI.
PERFORAZIONE	aa	Punched output: aa = SI or NO.
VIDEO	aa	Display of results on IBM 2250: aa = SI or NO.
JONES	aa	Jones correction: aa = SI or NO.
CONDIZIONE MONTE	a	Upstream boundary condition: a = Z or Q.
CONDIZIONE VALLE	a	Downstream boundary condition: a = Z or R.
FILE	aaaa	Change of name and type of one of the files: aaaa = GEOMETRIA for geometrical data file, or SCALA for rating curve data file, or ONDA for flood event data file, or AFFLUENTI for tributaries data file; after the command FILE, user is required to type new filename and filetype successively.
Display commands	(no equal sign is required between the code and the value of the commands):	
DISPLAY	aaaa	Display of: aaaa = PARAMETRI all parameters, or DEFAULT all default values, or FILES name and type of all files or CONDIZIONI boundary conditions.
DISPLAY	list	List is a sequence of codes, separated by commas, of the parameters to be displayed.

Numerical Simulation of Direct Surface Runoff from a Small Watershed using Program KINGEN

DAVID A. WOOLHISER
US Department of Agriculture, Agricultural Research Service, CSU Foothills Campus, Fort Collins, Colorado, USA

1. Introduction

Program KINGEN is designed to simulate the direct surface runoff from small watersheds. The surface topography of the watershed is approximated as a cascade of planes and channels (Kibler and Woolhiser, 1970; Woolhiser, Hanson and Kuhlman 1970). Overland and open channel flow are modeled by the kinematic wave equations. A laminar-turbulent (Chézy) resistance law is used for overland flow. The Chézy resistance law is used for channel flow. Program input includes: (a) plane and channel geometry, which may be obtained from a topographic map, (b) empirical flow resistance parameters and (c) rainfall excess rates as a step function of time.

Two other options are also included: (a) the impulse response and (b) the resistance parameter optimization option. To obtain the impulse response a constant initial depth is set on all planes. To find the optimum resistance parameter K in the relationship $f = K/R_e$, where f is the friction factor and R_e is the Reynolds number, one must have an observed hydrograph as well as the topographic information. A trial value of K is input to the program. K is then modified and new hydrographs computed until the following objective function is minimized.

$$F = \sum_{i=1}^{m} [Q_o(i\Delta t) - Q_c(i\Delta t)]^2$$

where Q_o and Q_c are the observed and computed discharges at the time increment Δt.

2. Workshop problem

The sample problem is to simulate the outflow hydrograph for watershed $W - I$ at Edwardsville, Illinois, for the storm of June 26, 1942. A map of watershed $W - I$ is shown in Figure 1 and rainfall rates are tabulated in Table 1. At the time of this runoff event the cover on the watershed was alfalfa.

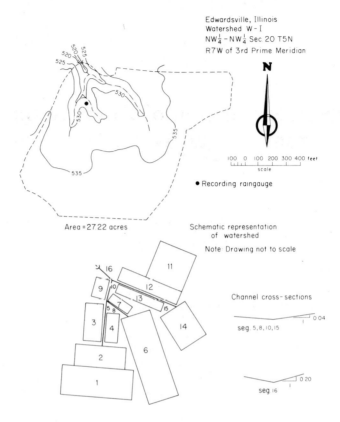

Figure 1.

The antecedent moisture conditions were high at the beginning of the storm. The infiltration rate can be estimated by an exponential decay function relation of the form

$$f = f_\infty + A(t - t_0)^{-a}$$

where f is the infiltration rate, f_∞ is the steady state infiltration rate (minimum), t is elapsed time, t_0 is the time to which the exponential function is asymptotic, and A and a are parameters unique to a given soil, initial saturation and rainfall rate (Smith, 1972).

For the particular soil, initial conditions, and rainfall rates, this equation becomes:

$$f \ (in/hr) = 0.12 in/hr + 1.85(t - 0.179)^{-0.58}$$

for $t > 0.46$ minutes and $f = R$, the rainfall rate, for $t \leqslant 0.46$ minutes.

The rainfall rates, infiltration rate calculated by the above expression and the observed outflow hydrograph are shown in Figure 2.

Table 1. 0.05 in accumulated precipitation fell during the hour preceding the event. Antecedent moisture conditions were high.

Time (min)	Precipitation rate (in/hr)	Accumulated precipitation (in)
0	4.00	0
3	5.70	0.25
7	4.60	0.58
10	2.80	0.81
13	1.50	0.95
17	0.60	1.05
21	0.24	1.09
26	0.42	1.11
36	0.17	1.18
43	0.08	1.20
78	0.16	1.25
93	0.27	1.29
111	0.14	1.37
133	0.02	1.42
158	0.19	1.43
184	0.0	1.51

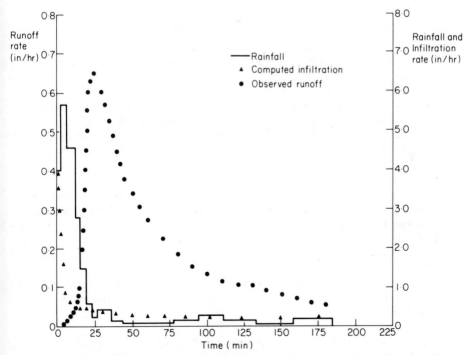

Figure 2. Rainfall, runoff and computed infiltration rates; Edwardsville, Illinois, W–I, June 26, 1942

378

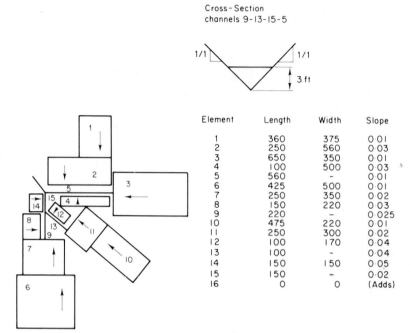

Figure 3. Watershed geometry

To approximate a rather complicated topography such as watershed W − I, it is convenient to first sketch in ridge lines on the map and then to draw in several flow lines at right angles to the contours. The channel network is then sketched in and cascades of planes are drawn on the map. The dimensions of the planes and channels are scaled from the map and the average slope of each plane and channel is estimated from the contour lines. A channel and plane geometry obtained in this manner is shown in Figure 3. Note that there are differences between this geometry and that shown in Figure 1 which was developed by another researcher. Obviously the selection of the geometry is a subjective procedure.

The next step is to·select an appropriate resistance parameter, K_0. Table 1 in my paper 'Unsteady, Free-Surface Flow Problems' (herein) may be used as a guide. Although there is no entry for alfalfa, a value of 3000 is chosen. This corresponds to the lower bound for short grass prairie. The transition Reynolds number is taken as 500 and the Chézy C for the channels is 25 corresponding to a Mannings's n of 0.06 at a depth of one foot.

The rainfall excess data, watershed geometry and resistance parameters have been entered into the data file WOOL 2 in accordance with the following input specifications.

Suggested modifications: It is suggested that the program be run with the existing data file. In subsequent runs K_0 could be changed for all planes to observe the sensitivity of the hydrograph to this parameter.

3. Input data for KINGEN

Card no.	Description

1   Col. 1—79 alphanumeric descriptive information, i.e. watershed, name, date, etc.

2   KOP, JOP, MICRO   format 3I5
KOP = 2 no optimization, KOP = 1 optimize
JOP — number of last plane or channel
MICRO — not used, leave blank.

3   NQ, TFIN, DELT, NSEC   format I5, 2F10.2, I5
NQ   = number of items in rainfall excess table
TFIN = time to end computations
DELT = equal time increments for output of computations (seconds)
NSEC = 1   input time in seconds
           2   input time in minutes
           Note: TFIN be in the same units as NSEC (i.e. NSEC = 1, TFIN in
           seconds; NSEC = 2, TFIN in minutes).

4a   TI(I), QI(I); NQ pairs   format 8F10.4
TI(I)   time of ith input
QI(I)   rainfall excess in in/hr

TI(NQ), QI(NQ) *must* be defined past TFIN.

4b   Continue time—rainfall pairs as needed.

5   RCRIT, AC   format 2F10.4
RCRIT = critical (transitional) Reynolds number
AC   = intensity coefficient (for additional roughness).

6   JCODE, RIN   format I5, F10.2
JCODE = 1   initial depth = 0
         = 2   initial depth calculated from RIN depth
         = 3   impulse input of magnitude HIMPLS (feet).

7a   J, XL(J), W(J), S(J), C(J), XK(J), NL(J), NR(J), NU(J), NC1(J), NC2(J), NX(J),
NPRINT(J)   format I5, 2F10.3, F7.5, F8.5, F6.2, I4, I5

J	=	number plane or channel	col. 1—5
XL (J)	=	length of the jth plane or channel	col. 6—15
W(J)	=	width of the jth plane or channel	col. 16—25
S(J)	=	slope of jth plane or channel	col. 26—32
C(J)	=	Chézy roughness coefficient	col. 33—40

$$C = \sqrt{\frac{8g}{f}}, \text{ but must be input for channels but}$$

can be left blank for planes and will be computed
by KINGEN

XK (J)	=	k in friction relationship $f = K/R$	col. 41—46
NL(J)	=	for channel, plane number contributing flow from left (for plane, leave blank)	col. 47—50
NR(J)	=	for channel, plane number contributing flow from right (for plane, leave blank)	col. 51—55
NU(J)	=	plane number contributing to upstream boundary $NU(J) = 0$ means no U/S input	col. 56—60

NC1(J)	=	channel number contributing to U/S boundary	col. 61−65
NC2(J)	=	channel number contributing to U/S boundary	col. 66−70
NX(J)	=	number of ΔX increments on plane or channel. Minimum 2	col. 71−75
NPRINT(J)	=	1 no print-out of hydrograph (use on intermediate segments)	col. 76−80
	=	2 print-out of hydrograph (use at least on last segment).	

7b   Continue plane and channel sequence

8   NCASE (if *previous card* was a channel)   format I3
        NCASE = 1   general trapezoidal channel
            = 2   tabular channel properties

9   A(J), ZL(J), ZR(J)   format 3F10.5

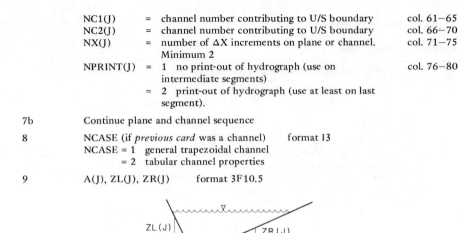

Note 1. For triangular channel, let A(J) be very small but not zero.
Note 2. If XL(J) = 0, NC1(J) + NC2(J) will be added for total output.

4. Sample problem offline print

EDWARDSVILLE, ILL. W1 EVENT OF 6/26/42   PREDICTION

TIME (MIN)	RAINFALL(IPH)	(CM/MIN)
0.0	0.500	0.02117
3.00	3.500	0.14817
7.00	3.800	0.16087
10.00	2.300	0.09737
13.00	1.000	0.04233
17.00	0.200	0.00847
21.00	-0.200	-0.00847
26.00	0.100	0.00423
36.00	0.0	0.0
110.00	0.0	0.0

RCRIT=   500.0   INTENSITY COEFF, AC=   0.0
PLANE NO.   6   L= 425.0   W= 500.0   S= 0.0100   C=   6.55   K= 3000.00

UPSTREAM BOUNDARY INPUT FROM   0
   INFLOW =   22.78   OUTFLOW =   16.71   ERROR =   0.63

TIME (/ IN)	DISCHARGE (CFS)	(IPH)	(CPM)
0.0	0.0	0.0	0.0
0.2500	0.0000	0.0000	0.0000
3.0000	0.0000	0.0001	0.0000
7.0000	0.0007	0.0726	0.0031
7.0000	0.0007	0.0726	0.0031
10.0000	0.0037	0.3793	0.0161
13.0000	0.0074	0.7525	0.0319
17.0000	0.0079	0.7987	0.0338
17.0000	0.0079	0.7987	0.0338
21.0000	0.0080	0.8128	0.0344
21.0000	0.0080	0.8128	0.0344
25.0000	0.0074	0.7508	0.0318
26.0000	0.0071	0.7263	0.0307
30.0000	0.0064	0.6552	0.0277
34.0000	0.0055	0.5603	0.0237
36.0000	0.0044	0.4477	0.0190
40.0000	0.0033	0.3333	0.0141
44.0000	0.0026	0.2653	0.0112
48.0000	0.0022	0.2194	0.0093
52.0000	0.0018	0.1861	0.0079
56.0000	0.0016	0.1609	0.0068
60.0000	0.0014	0.1411	0.0060
64.0000	0.0012	0.1251	0.0053
68.0000	0.0011	0.1121	0.0047
72.0000	0.0010	0.1012	0.0043
76.0000	0.0009	0.0920	0.0039
80.0000	0.0008	0.0841	0.0036
84.0000	0.0008	0.0773	0.0033
88.0000	0.0007	0.0714	0.0030
92.0000	0.0007	0.0662	0.0028
96.0000	0.0006	0.0616	0.0026
100.0000	0.0006	0.0575	0.0024
100.0000	0.0006	0.0575	0.0024

```
PLANE NO.     7   L=   250.0    W=   350.0    S= 0.0200    C=   6.55    K=  3000.00

UPSTREAM BOUNDARY INPUT FROM         6
   INFLOW =        38.08    OUTFLOW =       32.60     ERROR =        0.67
PLANE NO.     8   L=   150.0    W=   220.0    S= 0.0300    C=   6.55    K=  3000.00

UPSTREAM BOUNDARY INPUT FROM         0
   INFLOW =         8.04    OUTFLOW =        7.93     ERROR =       -0.59
CHANNEL NO.   9   L=   220.0    S= 0.0250    C=  25.00    N=1.5    RCRIT =     500.000

UPSTREAM BOUNDARY INPUT FROM         7     0     0
LATERAL INFLOW FROM         8     0
  34        34      260.2176E-02
   1        33      260.9040E-02
     A =   3.000000          ZL =   1.000000          ZR =   1.000000
PLANE NO.    10   L=   475.0    W=   220.0    S= 0.0100    C=   6.55    K=  3000.00

UPSTREAM BOUNDARY INPUT FROM         0
   INFLOW =        25.47    OUTFLOW =       18.28     ERROR =        0.79
PLANE NO.    11   L=   250.0    W=   300.0    S= 0.0200    C=   6.55    K=  3000.00

UPSTREAM BOUNDARY INPUT FROM        10
   INFLOW =        26.80    OUTFLOW =       22.77     ERROR =       -0.16
PLANE NO.    12   L=   100.0    W=   170.0    S= 0.0400    C=   6.55    K=  3000.00

UPSTREAM BOUNDARY INPUT FROM         0
   INFLOW =         5.36    OUTFLOW =        5.51     ERROR =       -0.48
CHANNEL NO.  13   L=   100.0    S= 0.0400    C=  25.00    N=1.5    RCRIT =     500.000

UPSTREAM BOUNDARY INPUT FROM        11     0     0
LATERAL INFLOW FROM         0    12
 195        35      260.1535E-02
 159        36      260.6306E-02
     A =   3.000000          ZL =   1.000000          ZR =   1.000000
PLANE NO.    14   L=   150.0    W=   150.0    S= 0.0500    C=   6.55    K=  3000.00

UPSTREAM BOUNDARY INPUT FROM         0
   INFLOW =         8.04    OUTFLOW =        8.27     ERROR =       -0.77
CHANNEL NO.  15   L=   150.0    S= 0.0200    C=  25.00    N=1.5    RCRIT =     500.000

UPSTREAM BOUNDARY INPUT FROM         0     9    13
LATERAL INFLOW FROM        14     0
 504        35      260.2277E-02
 504       500      260.5768E 01
     A =   3.000000          ZL =   1.000000          ZR =   1.000000
PLANE NO.     1   L=   360.0    W=   375.0    S= 0.0100    C=   6.55    K=  3000.00

UPSTREAM BOUNDARY INPUT FROM         0
   INFLOW =        19.30    OUTFLOW =       14.58     ERROR =        0.45
PLANE NO.     2   L=   250.0    W=   560.0    S= 0.0300    C=   6.55    K=  3000.00

UPSTREAM BOUNDARY INPUT FROM         1
   INFLOW =        23.16    OUTFLOW =       20.38     ERROR =       -0.38
```

```
PLANE NO.     3   L=   650.0   W=   350.0   S= 0.0100   C=   6.55   K=  3000.00

UPSTREAM BOUNDARY INPUT FROM        0
    INFLOW =       34.85    OUTFLOW =        23.62     ERROR =       1.11
PLANE NO.     4   L=   100.0   W=   500.0   S= 0.0300   C=   6.55   K=  3000.00

UPSTREAM BOUNDARY INPUT FROM        0
    INFLOW =        5.36    OUTFLOW =         5.46     ERROR =      -0.48
CHANNEL NO.    5   L=   560.0   S= 0.0150   C=  25.00   N=1.5   RCRIT =      500.000

UPSTREAM BOUNDARY INPUT FROM        3      0      0
LATERAL INFLOW FROM        4      2
350      39       260.6954E-02
282      33       260.6561E-02
    A =  3.000000          ZL =  1.000000          ZR =  1.000000
CHANNEL NO.   16   L=     0.0   S= 0.0300   C=  25.00   N=1.5   RCRIT =      500.000

UPSTREAM BOUNDARY INPUT FROM        0     15      5
LATERAL INFLOW FROM        0      0
372     334       260.1219E 02

        TIME (MIN)     DISCHARGE (CFS)     (IPH)      (CPM)
           0.0            0.0             0.0        0.0
           4.0000         0.1036          0.0041     0.0002
           8.0000         5.7811          0.2261     0.0096
          12.0000        16.9935          0.6647     0.0281
          16.0000        20.7329          0.8109     0.0343
          20.0000        18.6615          0.7299     0.0309
          24.0000        15.8390          0.6195     0.0262
          28.0000        13.6479          0.5338     0.0226
          32.0000        12.2532          0.4793     0.0203
          36.0000        11.4399          0.4474     0.0189
          40.0000        10.5415          0.4123     0.0175
          44.0000         9.3185          0.3645     0.0154
          48.0000         8.0026          0.3130     0.0133
          52.0000         6.7266          0.2631     0.0111
          56.0000         5.2928          0.2070     0.0088
          60.0000         4.2673          0.1669     0.0071
          64.0000         3.6566          0.1430     0.0061
          68.0000         3.2321          0.1264     0.0054
          72.0000         2.8937          0.1132     0.0048
          76.0000         2.6135          0.1022     0.0043
          80.0000         2.3767          0.0930     0.0039
          84.0000         2.1738          0.0850     0.0036
          88.0000         1.9981          0.0782     0.0033
          92.0000         1.8447          0.0722     0.0031
          96.0000         1.7102          0.0669     0.0028
         100.0000         1.5607          0.0610     0.0026
```

References

Abadie, J. (1970). *Integer and Non-linear Programming*. North-Holland, Amsterdam, 544 pp.

Amein, M. (1966). Streamflow routing on computer. *Water Resour. Res.*, 2, 1,123–130.

Ayres Jr., F. (1962). *Matrices*. McGraw-Hill, New York, 219 pp.

Beard, L. R. (1967). *Monthly streamflow simulation, computer program 23-C-L 267*. Hydrologic Engineers Center, US Corps of Engineers, Davis, California, 48 pp.

Benson, M. A., and Matalas, N. C. (1967). Synthetic hydrology based on regional statistical parameters. *Water Resour. Res.*, 6, 4,931–945.

Box, G. E. P., and Müller, M. E. (1958). A note on the generation of random normal deviates. *Ann. Math. Statist.*, 29, 610–611.

Box, G. E. P., and Jenkins, G. M. (1970). *Time Series Analysis: Forecasting and Control*. San Francisco, Holden-Day Inc., 553 pp.

Bravo, C. A., Harley, B. M., Perkins, F. E., and Eagleson, P. S. (1970). A Linear Distributed Model of Catchment Runoff. *Hydrodynamics Laboratory, Rep. 123*

Burnash, R. J. C., Ferral, R. L., and McGuire, R. A. (1973). A Generalized Streamflow Simulation System. *Conceptual Modeling for Digital Computers*, Sacramento River Flood Forecast Center.

Carlson, R. R., MacCormick, A. J. A., and Watts, D. G. (1970). Applications of linear random models to four annual streamflow series. *Water Resour. Res.*, 6, 4, 1070–1078.

Carter, R. W., and Godfrey, R. G. (1960). Storage and flood routing. *US Geological Survey Water Supply Paper 1543–B*.

Chow, V. T. (1959). *Open Channel Hydraulics*. McGraw-Hill, New York.

Clark, C. O. (1945). Storage and the unit hydrograph. *Amer. Soc. Civ. Engin.*, 110, 1416–1446.

Clarke, R. T. (1973). Mathematical models in hydrology. *Irrigation and Drainage Paper No. 19*. FAO, Rome.

Cole, J. A. and Sherriff, J. D. F. (1972). Some single and multi-site models of rainfall within discrete time increments. *J. Hydrol.*, 17, 97–113.

Commons, C. G. (1942). Flood hydrographs. *Civ. Engin.*, 12, 571–572.

Crawford, N. H. and Linsley, R. K. (1966). Stanford Watershed Model IV, Dept. Civil Engineering, *Tech. Rep. 39*, Stanford University.

Crosby, D. S. and Maddock, T. (1970). III. Estimating coefficients of a flow generator for monotone samples of data. *Water Resour. Res.*, 6, 4, 1079–1086.

Cunge, J. A. (1969). On the subject of flood propagation computation method (Muskingum method). *Journal of Hydraulic Research*, 7, 2.

Cunge, J. A. and Wegner, M. (1964). Intégration numérique des equations d'écoulement de Barré de Saint Venant par un schéma implicite de differences finies. *La Houille Blanche*, 1, 33–39.

De Marchi, G. (1945). Sul onda di piena che seguirrebbe al crollo della diga di Cancano. *L'Energia Elettrica*, 22, 157–169.

De Saint-Venant, Barré (1871). Théorie du mouvement non-permanent des eaux avec application aux crues des rivières et à introduction des marées dans leur lit. *Comptes rendus*, 73, 148–154 et 237–240, Acad. Sci., Paris.

Ditlevser, O. (1971). *Extremes and first passage times with applications in civil engineering*. Doctoral thesis, Technical University of Denmark, Copenhagen, Denmark, 414 pp.

Dooge, J. C. I. (1959). A general theory of the unit hydrograph. *Journal of Geophysical Research*, 64, 2, 241–256.

Dooge, J. C. I. (1969). Conceptual models of surface runoff. *Proc. 'Piene: Loro Previsione e Difesa del Suolo'.* Accademia Nazionale dei Lincei, Roma.

Dooge, J. C. I. (1972a). Problemi attuali di scienza e di cultura. *Quaderno* **169**, 179–207. Accademia Nazionale dei Lincei, Roma.

Dooge, J. C. I. (1972b). Mathematical models of hydrologic systems. *International Symposium on Modelling Techniques in Water Resources Systems. Proc.,* Vol. 1, 171–189. Department of the Environment, Ottawa.

Dooge, J. C. I. (1973). The linear theory of hydrologic systems. *US Dept. of Agriculture Tech. Bulletin No. 1468.* US Govt. Printing Office.

Dorn, W. S. (1963). Non-linear programming – A survey. *Management Science,* **9**, 2.

Dronkers, J. J. (1964). *Tidal Computations in Rivers and Coastal Waters,* North-Holland, Amsterdam.

Eagleson, P. S., Mejia, R., and March, F. (1965). The computation of optimum realizable unit hydrographs from rainfall and runoff data. *Hydrodynamics Laboratory, Rep. N. 84.* MIT.

Edson, C. G. (1951). Parameters for relating unit hydrographs to watershed characteristics. *Amer. Geophys. Union Trans.,* **32**, 4, 591–596.

Erikson, E. (1970). Groundwater time series: an exercise in stochastic hydrology. *Nordic Hydrology,* **3**, 181–205.

Evangelisti, G. (1966). *Analysis of Unsteady Flow in Open Channels by Characteristics.* NATO Advances Institute, Bressanone.

Fantoli, G. (1925). Sul passagio dell'onda di piena nella supposta rotta di un serbatoio. *Annali di Utilizzazione delle Acque,* fasc. 1.

FAO Report AE18 (1970). Methodes de génération des séries longues de pluie, de température et de débit. Rome.

Fawkes, P. E. (1972). *Roughness in a Model of Overland Flow.* M.S. thesis. Colorado State University, Fort Collins, 109 pp.

Feller, W. (1951). The asymptotic distribution of the range of sums of independent random variables. *Ann. Math. Stat.,* **22**, 427–432.

Feyerherm, A. M. and Bark, L. D. (1965). Statistical methods for persistent precipitation patterns., *J. Applied Met.,* **4**, 320–328.

Fiering, M. B. (1967). *Streamflow Synthesis.* London, Macmillan, 139 pp.

Fiering, M. B. (1968). Schemes for handling inconsistent matrices. *Water Resour. Res.,* **4**, 2, 291–297.

Freeze, R. A. (1972). Role of subsurface flow in generating surface runoff 1. Base flow contributions to channel flow. *Water Resour. Res.,* **8**, 3, 601–623.

Gabriel, K. R., and Neumann, J. (1957). On a distribution of weather cycles by length. *Quart. J. R. met. Soc.,* **83**, 375–380.

Garcia, L. E., Dawdy, D. R. and Mejia, J. M. (1972). Long memory monthly streamflow simulation by a Broken Line model. *Water Resour. Res.,* **8**, 4, 1100–1105.

Grace, R. A. and Eagleson, P. S. (1966). The synthesis of short-time-increment rainfall sequences. *Hydrodynamics Lab. Rep. 91,* Department of Civil Engineering, Massachusetts Institute of Technology.

Graeff (1875). Mémoire sur le mouvement des eaux dans les réservoirs à alimentation variable. *Mém.,* **21**, 393–538, Acad. Sci. Paris.

Greco, F. and Panattoni, L. (1975). An implicit method to solve Saint Venant equations, *J. Hydrol.,* **24**, 171–185.

Hammersley, J. M. and Handscomb, D. C. (1964). *Monte Carlo Methods.* Methuen, London.

Harley, B. M., Perkins, F. E. and Eagleson, P. S. (1970). A modular distributed model of catchment dynamics, *Ralph M. Parsons Laboratory Rep. 133,* Dept. of Civil Engineering, M.I.T., 537 pp.

Harris, R. A. (1964). A computer program for a pumped storage scheme, *Water and Water Engng.,* **68**, 450–451.

Hawken, W. H., and Ross, C. N. (1921). The calculation of flood discharges by use of a time–contour plain. *Inst. Engin. Austral. J.,* **2**, 85–92.

Hayami, S. (1951). *On the Propagation of Flood Waves,* Disaster Prevention Research Institute, Kyoto University.

Henderson, F. M. (1963). Flood waves in prismatic channels. *Journal of Hydraulics Division, Proc. ASCE.,* **89**, H-Y4.

Henderson, F. M. (1969). *Open Channel Flow*, Macmillan, New York.

Hopkins, J. W. and Robillard, P. (1964). Some statistics of daily rainfall occurrence for the Canadian Prairie provinces. *J. Applied Met.*, 3, 600—602.

Horton, R. E. (1938). The interpretation and application of runoff plot experiments with reference to soil erosion problems. *Proc. SSSA*, 3, 240.

Hurst, H. E. (1951). Long-term storage capacity of reservoirs. *Trans. Amer. Soc. Civil Engr.*, 116, 770—799.

Hurst, H. E. (1956). Methods of using long-term storage in reservoirs, *Proc. Instn. Civ. Engrs.*, 1, 519—543.

Hurst, H. E. (1957). A suggested statistical model of some time series which occur in nature. *Nature*, 180, 494.

IBM Corporation. *Graphic Subroutine Package (GSP) for FORTRAN IV, COBOL and PLI*, Form C27—6932.

Isaacson, E., Stoker, J. J. and Troesch, A. (1954). *Numerical Solution of Flood Prediction and River Regulation Problems.* Report 2 and 3, New York University, Institute of Mathematical Sciences.

Iwagaki, Y. (1955). Fundamental studies on the Runoff Analysis by Characteristics. *Disaster Prevention Research Institute Bulletin No. 10*, Kyoto University, Kyoto, Japan, 25 pp.

Izzard, C. F. (1944). The surface profile of overland flow. *Trans. A.G.U.*, pp. 959—968.

Izzard, C. F. (1946). Hydraulics of runoff from developed surfaces. *Proc. 26th Annual Meeting, Highway Res. Board*, 26, 129.

Jenkins, G. M. and Watts, D. G. (1968). *Spectral analysis and its applications*, Holden-Day, San Francisco, Calif. 525 pp.

Johnstone, D. and Cross, W. P. (1949). *Elements of Applied Hydrology.* Ronald Press, New York.

Judge, G. G. and Yancey, T. A. (1969). The use of prior information in estimating the parameters of economic relationships. *Metroeconomica*, XXI.

Kaplan, W. (1962). *Operational Methods for Linear Systems.* Addison-Wesley, Reading, Mass.

Kaufmann, A. (1968). *Points and arrows — the theory of graphs.* Translated from the French *Des Points et des Flèches — la théorie des graphes*, Dunod.

Kendall, M. G. and Stuart, A. (1958). *The Advanced Theory of Statistics* Vol. 1 Chapter III. Moments and Cumulants.

Kibler, D. F. and Woolhiser, D. A. (1970). The kinematic cascade as a hydrologic model. *Colorado State University, Hydrology Paper 39*, 25 pp.

Kleitz, Ch. (1877). Sur la théorie du mouvement non-permanent des liquides et sur son application à la propagation des crues des rivières. *Ponts et des Chaussées, Annales*, Sem 2, 48, 133—196.

Klemes, V. (1974). The Hurst phenomenon — a puzzle? *Water Resour. Res.*, 10, 675—689.

Kraijenhoff van de Leur, D. A., Schulze, F. E. and O'Donnell, T. (1966). Recent Trends in Hydrograph Synthesis. *Proc. Technical Meeting 21*, TNQ Committee for Hydrological Research, The Hague.

Langbein, W. B. (1956). Discussion of 'Methods of using long-term storage in reservoirs' by H. E. Hurst. *Proc. Instn. Civ. Engrs.*, 1, 565—658.

Laurenson. E. M. and O'Donnell, T. (1969). Data error effects in unit hydrograph derivation. *Proc. ASCE (Hydraulics Division)*, 95, HY-6.

Lewis, P. A. W., Goodman, A. S. and Miller, J. M. (1969). A pseudo-random number generator for the System 360. *IBM Systems Journal*, 8(2), 136—146.

Li, Ruh-Ming (1972). *Sheet Flow Under Simulated Rainfall.* M.S. thesis Colorado State University, Fort Collins, 111 pp.

Lighthill, M. J. and Whitham, G. B. (1955). On kinematic waves I, Flood movements in long rivers. *Royal Soc. London Proc. A.*, 229, 281—316.

Linsley, R. K. Jr., Kohler, M. A. and Paulhus, J. L. H. (1949). *Applied Hydrology*. McGraw-Hill. New York.

Linsley, R. and Crawford, N. (1974). Continuous simulation models in urban hydrology. *Geophysical Research Letters*, 1, 1, 59—62.

Lipschutz, S. (1968). *Linear Algebra (Theory and Problems).* McGraw-Hill, New York.

Lloyd, E. H. (1967). Stochastic reservoir theory. *Advances in Hydroscience*, ed. V. T. Chow, Vol. 4, 281—339, Academic Press.

388

Maclaren, M. D. and Marsaglia, G. (1965). Uniform random number generators. *J. Assoc. Comp. Mach.*, 12, 83–89.

McCarthy, G. I. (1940). *The Unit Hydrograph and Flood Routing.* US Engineer School, Fort Belvoir.

Maass, A., Hufschmidt, M. M., Dorfman, R., Thomas Jr., H. A., Marglin, S. A. and Fair, G. M. (1962). *Design of Water Resource Systems*, Harvard University Press, Cambridge, Mass.

Mandelbrot, B. B. (1965). Une classe de processus homothétiques à soi; application à la loi climatologique de H. E. Hurst. *Compt. Rend. Acad. Sci. Paris*, 260, 3274–3277.

Mandelbrot, B. B. (1971). A fast fractional Gaussian noise generator. *Water Resour. Res.*, 7, 3, 543–553.

Mandelbrot, B. B. (1972). Broken line process derived as an approximation to fractional noise. *Water Resour. Res.*, 8, 5, 1354–1356.

Mandelbrot, B. B. and Wallis, J. R. (1968). Noah Joseph, and operational hydrology. *Water Resour. Res.*, 4, 5, 909–918.

Mandelbrot, B. B. and Wallis, J. R. (1969a). Computer experiments with fractional Gaussian noises. Part 1 — Averages and variances. *Water Resour. Res.*, 5, 1, 228–241.

Mandelbrot, B. B. and Wallis, J. R. (1969b). Computer experiments with fractional Gaussian noises. Part 2 — Rescaled ranges and spectra. *Water Resour. Res.*, 5, 1, 242–259.

Mandelbrot, B. B. and Wallis, J. R. (1969c). Computer experiments with fractional Gaussian noises. Part 3 — Mathematical appendix. *Water Resour. Res.*, 5, 1, 260–267.

Mandelbrot, B. B. and Wallis, J. R. (1969d). Some long-run properties of geophysical records. *Water Resour. Res.*, 5, 2 321–340.

Mandelbrot, B. B. and Wallis, J. R. (1969e). Robustness of the rescaled range R/S in the measurement of non-cyclic long-run statistical dependence. *Water Resour. Res.*, 5, 5, 967–988.

Massau, J. (1889). L'intégration graphique. *Assoc. Ingénieurs Sortis des Ecoles Spéciales de Gand, Annales*, 435 pp.

Matalas, N. C. (1967). Mathematical assessment of synthetic hydrology. *Water Resour. Res.*, 3, 4, 937–945.

Matalas, N. C. (1974). Generation of synthetic flow sequences. In: *Systems Approach to Water Management*, New York.

Matalas, N. C. and Huzzen, C. S. (1967). A property of the range of partial sums. *Proc. International Hydrology Symposium, Fort Collins*, Colorado State University, Vol. 1, pp. 252–257.

Matalas, N. C. and Wallis, J. R. (1971). Statistical properties of multivariate fractional noise processes. *Water Resour. Res.*, 7, 6, 1460–1468.

Matalas, N. C., and Wallis, J. R. (1976). Generation of synthetic flow sequences. *Systems Approach to Water Management*, American Elsevier, New York.

Mejia, J. M. (1971). On the generation of multivariate sequences exhibiting the Hurst phenomenon and some flood frequency analysis. Doctoral thesis, Colorado State University, Ft. Collins, Colo, 135 pp.

Mejia, J. M., Rodriguez-Iturbe, I. and Dawdy, D. R. (1972). Streamflow simulation 2: The broken line process as a potential model for hydrologic simulation. *Water Resour. Res.*, 8, 4, 931–941.

Mielke, P. W. (1973). Another family of distributions for describing and analysing precipitation data. *J. Applied Met.*, 12, 2, 275–280.

Minshall, N. E. (1960). Predicting storm runoff from small experimental watersheds. *J. Hydr. Div., ASCE*, 86, HY-8.

Moran, P. A. P. (1959). *The Theory of Storage.* Methuen, London.

Morgali, J. R. (1970). Laminar and turbulent overland flow. *Proc. ASCE*, 96, HY-2, 441–460.

Moss, M. E. (1972). Reduction in uncertainties in autocorrelation by the use of physical models. *Proc. International Symposium on Uncertainties in Hydrologic and Water Resource Systems*, University of Arizona, Tucson, Vol. 1, pp. 203–229.

Mulvany, T. J. (1850). On the use of self-registering rain and flood gauges. *Proc. Institution of Civil Engineers of Ireland*, 4, 2, 1–8.

Nash, J. E. (1958). The form of the instantaneous unit hydrograph. *IUGG General Assembly of Toronto*, Vol. III, Publ. No. 45, IASH, Gentbugge, pp.114–121.

Nash, J. E. (1960). A unit hydrograph study, with particular reference to British catchments. *Proc. the Institution of Civil Engineers*, **17**, November.

Nayfeh, A. H. (1973). *Pertubation Methods*. Wiley, New York.

Natale, L. and Todini, E. (1972). Modelli Lineari in Idrologia. *XIII Convegno di Idraulica e Costr. Idr., Milano.*

Natale, L. and Todini, E. (1973). Black-box identification of a flood wave propagation linear model. *XV Congress IAHR, Istanbul.*

Natale, L. and Todini, E. (1974). A constrained parameter estimation technique for linear models in hydrology, *Publ. No. 13*, Institute of Hydraulics, University of Pavia,

Neave, H. R. (1973). On using the Box-Müller transformation with multiplicative congruential pseudo-random number generator. *Jour. Roy. Statist. Soc* (Series C), **22**(1), 92–97.

O'Connell, P. E. (1971). A simple stochastic modelling of Hurst's law. *Proc. International Symposium on Mathematical Models in Hydrology: Warsaw.* I.A.H.S.

O'Connell, P. E. (1973). Multivariate synthetic hydrology: A correction. *Journal of the Hydraulics Division, ASCE, Proc. Paper 10192*, pp.2391–2396.

O'Connell, P. E. (1974). *Stochastic modelling of long-term persistence in streamflow sequences.* Ph.D. thesis, Imperial College, University of London, 284 pp.

O'Kelly, J. J. (1955). The employment of the unit-hydrographs to determine the flows of Irish arterial drainage channels. *Inst. Civ. Engin. (Ireland), Proc.*, **4**, 3, 365–412.

Osborn, H. B., Mills, W. C. and Lane, L. J. (1972). Uncertainties in estimating runoff-producing rainfall for thunderstorm rainfall–runoff models. *International Symposium on Uncertainties in Hydrologic and Water Resources Systems, Tucson*, University of Arizona, Tucson, Vol. 1, pp. 189–202.

Panattoni, L. (1974). Metodi di soluzione numerica per la propagazione delle piene nei fiumi, *Proc. Symposium on Discrete Methods in Engineering*, C.I.S.E., pp. 464–474.

Parzen, E. (1962). *Stochastic Processes*. Holden-Day, San Francisco.

Pipes, L. A. and Harvill, L. R. (1970). *Applied Mathematics for Engineers and Physicists* (3rd ed.). McGraw-Hill, New York.

Price, R. K. (1973a). Flood Routing Methods for British Rivers. *Report III, Hydraulics Research Station Wallingford.*

Price, R. K. (1973b). Variable parameter diffusion method for flood routing, *Rep. INT 115*, Hydraulics Research Station, Wallingford.

Quimpo, R. G. (1968). Stochastic analysis of daily river flows. *Proc. Am. Soc. Civ. Engrs., J. Hydrol. Div.*, **94**, HY-1, 43–58.

Rao, R. A., Delleur, J. W., and Sarma, B. P. (1972). Conceptual models for urbanizing basins. *Proc. ASCE*, **98**, HY-7, 1205–1220.

Raudkivi, A. J. and Lawgun, N. (1970). A Markov chain model for rainfall generation. *IASH-Unesco Symposium on the results of research on representative and experimental basins: Wellington (N.Z.)*, pp. 269–278.

Richtmyer, R. D. and Morton, K. W. (1967). *Difference Methods for Initial Value Problems*, Wiley–Interscience, New York, 405 p.

Rodriguez-Iturbe, I., Mejia, J. M. and Dawdy, D. R. (1972). Streamflow simulation 1: A new look at Markovian models, fractional Gaussian noise and crossing theory. *Water Resour. Res.*, **8**, 4, 921–930.

Sage, A. P. and Melsa, J. L. (1971a). *System Identification*, Academic, New York.

Sage, A. P. and Melsa, J. L. (1971b). *Estimation Theory with Applications to Communication and Control*. McGraw-Hill, New York.

Sariahmed, A. and Kisiel, C. C. (1968). Synthesis of sequences of summer thunderstorm volumes for the Atterbury watershed in the Tucson area. *IAHS Publ. No. 81*. The use of analog and digital computers in hydrology: Vol. II. Tucson Symposium, pp. 439–448.

Schaake, J. C. (1965). Synthesis of the inlet hydrograph. Johns Hopkins Storm Drainage Research Project, *Tech. Rep. 3.*

Seddon, A. J. (1900). River hydraulics. *Am. Soc. Civil Engin. Trans.*, **43**, 179–243.

Sherman, L. K. (1932). Stream flow from rainfall by the unit-graph method. *Engineering News Record*, **108**, 501–505.

Singh, K. P. and Lonnquist, C. G. (1974). Two-distribution method for modelling and sequential generation of monthly streamflows. *Water Resour. Res.*, **10**, 4, 763–775.

Slack, J. R. (1973). I would if I could (self-denial by conditioned models). *Water Resour. Res.,* 9, 247–249.

Smith, R. E. (1972). The infiltration envelope: results from a theoretical infiltrometer. *J. Hydr.,* 17, 112, 1–21.

Smith, R. E. and Schreiber, H. A. (1974). Point processes of seasonal thunderstorm rainfall 2: Rainfall depth probabilities. *Water Resour. Res.,* 10, 3, 418–423.

Stoker, J. J. (1953). Numerical solution of flood prediction and river regulation problems. *Rep. 1,* New York University, Institute of Mathematical Sciences.

Stoker, J. J. (1957). *Water Waves.* Interscience, New York.

Strelkoff, T. (1970). Numerical solution of Saint Venant equations. *Journal of Hydraulic Division, ASCE,* 96, HY-1, 223–252.

Sugawara, M., Ozaki, E., Watanabe, I. and Katsuyama,Y. (1974). Tank model and its application to Bird Creek, Wollombi Brook, Bikin River, Kitsu River, Sanaga River and Nam Mune, *Res. Note II, National Research Center for Disaster Prevention, Science and Technology Agency.*

Supino, G. (1965). *Le Reti Idrauliche.* Patron, Bologna.

Swick, D. A. (1974). Letter to the Editor. *Jour. Roy. Statist. Soc.* (Series C), 23(2), 233.

Taha, H. A. (1971). *Operations Research — An Introduction.* Macmillan, New York.

Thomas, H. A. and Fiering M. B. (1962). Mathematical synthesis of streamflow sequences for the analysis of river basins by simulation. In: A. Mass *et al., Design of Water Resource Systems.* Harvard University Press, Cambridge, Mass.

Tonini, D. (1969). Formazione dei deflussi superficiali di piena. *Atti dell' Istituto Veneto di Scienze, Lettere ed Arti,* CXXVIII, 333–390.

US Army Corps of Engineers (1972) *Streamflow Synthesis and Reservoir Regulation Model,* Program 724–IT5–G0010.

Valencia, D. and Schaake, J. C. (1973). Disaggregation processes in stochastic hydrology. *Water Resour. Res.,* 9, 3, 580–585.

Wallis, J. R., and Matalas, N. C. (1971). Correlogram analysis revisited. *Water Resour. Res.,* 7, 6, 1448–1459.

Wallis, J. R. and O'Connell, P. E. (1972). The small sample estimation of ρ. *Water Resour. Res.,* 8, 3, 707–712.

Wallis, J. R. and O'Connell, P. E. (1973). Firm reservoir yield, how reliable are historic records? *Int. Symp. on Hydrology of Lakes,* Helsinki, Finland.

Wallis, J. R. and Matalas, N. C. (1970). Small sample properties of H and K — estimators of the Hurst coefficient h. *Water Resour. Res.,* 6, 6, 1583–1594.

Wallis, J. R. and Matalas, N. C. (1972). Sensitivity of reservoir design to the generating mechanism of inflows. *Water Resour. Res.,* 8, 3, 634–641.

Wallis, J. R., Matalas, N. C. and Slack, J. R. (1974a). Just a moment, *Water Resour. Res.,* 10, 2, 211–219.

Wallis, J. R. Matalas, N. C. and Slack, J. R. (1974b). Monte Carlo evaluation of the distributions of the first three moments of small samples for some well-known distributions. *COMSTAT Symposium,* Vienna.

Wallis, J. R. and Todini, E. (1975). Comments upon the residual mass curve coefficient. *J. Hydrol.,* 24, 201–205.

Watts, D. G. (1972). Discussion on 'Evaluation of seasonal time-series models: application to mid-west river flow data' by A. I. McKerchar and J. Delleur. *Proc. International Symposium on Uncertainties in Hydrologic and Water Resource Systems,* University of Arizona, Tucson, Vol. 3, pp. 1470–1490.

Weiss, G. (1973a). Shot noise models for synthetic generation of multisite daily streamflow data. *Proc. International Symposium on the Design of Water Resources Projects with Inadequate Data,* Madrid, UNESCO/WMO/IAHS, to be published.

Weiss, G. (1973b). Filtered Poisson processes as models for daily streamflow data. Ph.D. thesis, Imperial College, University of London, 138 pp.

Wilson, R. B. (1963). *A Simplicial Algorithm for Concave Programming.* Harvard University, Boston.

Wooding, R. A. (1966). A hydraulic model for the catchment-stream problem, III, Comparison with runoff observations. *J. Hydrol.,* 4, 21–37.

Woolhiser, D. A., Hanson, C. L. and Kuhlman, A. R. (1970). Overland flow on rangeland watersheds. *J. Hydrol., (N.Z.)*, **9**, 2, 336–356.

Woolhiser, D. A. and Liggett, J. A. (1967). Unsteady one-dimensional flow over a plane – The rising hydrography, *Water Resour. Res.*, **3**, 3, 753–771.

World Meteorological Organization (WMO) (1975). Intercomparison of conceptual models used in operational hydrology forecasting. *Operational hydrology Rep.* 7, WMO no. 429, Geneva.

Yakowitz, S. J. (1973). A stochastic model for dail river flows in an arid region. *Water Resour. Res.*, **9**, 5, 1271–1285.

Yevdjevich, V. M. (1964). *Bibliography and Discussion of Flood Routing Methods and Unsteady Flow in Channels.* US Govt. Printing Office, Washington, 235 pp.

Young, G. K. (1968). Discussion of 'Mathematical assessment of synthetic hydrology'. *Water Resour. Res.*, **4**, 3, 681–682.

Young, G. K. and Pisano, W. C. (1968). Operational hydrology using residuals. *Journal of the Hydraulics Division, ASCE*, **94**, HY-4, Proc. Paper 6034, 909–923.

INDEX

406

408

Date Due

Mathematical Models for Surface
Water Hydrology